Bernard JULLIEN
Yannick LUNG
Christophe MIDLER

W9-CQA-827

The Logan Epic

**New trajectories
for innovation**

Translation by
Alan Sitkin

Foreword
Carlos Ghosn

DUNOD

This work is translated from the original French edition:
L'épopée LOGAN – Nouvelles trajectoires pour l'innovation
Published © Dunod, Paris, September 2012
This work has been translated with the help of
The Ecole Polytechnique Innovation Management chair.

Couverture : © Direction du Design Industriel

© Dunod, Paris, 2013
ISBN 978-2-10-058996-8

SUMMARY

SECTION III

LESSONS AND QUESTIONS ABOUT AN EPIC ADVENTURE

FOREWORD CARLOS GHOSN
CEO of Renault-Nissan

This book tells the story of a project that has become a programme and, above all, a pillar of the strategy that the Company and the Alliance are pursuing.

The project had been launched by my predecessor at the head of Renault, Louis Schweitzer, and the success story that this book traces is rooted first and foremost in the grand idea that he was able to see through in the face of entrenched behaviour and received wisdom. It is also embedded in Renault's genes, specifically in its unusual aptitude for innovation and reinventing the automobile.

Logan is a major innovation that has often been underestimated despite having contributed greatly to Renault's success over the past decade.

Innovating does not simply mean adding more technology to a vehicle. It also involves listening to the market, knowing how to identify emerging tendencies and ensuring that customers are well served by technological or other forces of innovation. The Logan has had unprecedented success specifically because it is in sync with the big trends affecting the automobile business–and, to a certain extent, because it has anticipated them. The Logan has been able to respond to new needs, different ones depending on the country where the product was being sold. The strength of its Entry range resides precisely in this ability to respond with one and the same product offer to motorists' expectations in both emerging and mature countries.

In Europe, where our Entry range is sold under the Dacia brand name, the automobile market has been declining and its image deteriorating. 43% of young French consider that the automobile has more shortcomings than advantages. In terms of personal mobility, real needs have become more important than the projection of social status. Against this background, Dacia's modernity comes from its decision not to compete by over-equiping its car like everyone else is doing. Instead, it had the intelligence to concentrate on what was necessary. Dacia's transparent promise to customers is that they would have a bigger, more reliable, simpler and less expensive car. Its main focus has been on motorists who only bought used cars previously, with two-thirds of our customers accessing a new car for the first time ever with this purchase. Over the past eight years, Dacia has been the fastest growing automobile brand in Europe, proof that it satisfies previously unfulfilled needs.

However, there has been a very different dynamic in emerging countries where accessing personal mobility remains a major aspiration for social climbers. The Global South has an enormous need for mobility, including over short distances, due to the general mediocrity of the public transportation infrastructure. The end result has been an extremely rapid growth in automobile sales once the price matched households' greater purchasing power. The growing market for automobiles in emerging economies has been felt across all segments, including for midrange or luxury vehicles. It remains that the main growth driver has been locally manufactured affordable cars.

Thanks to its Entry models, Renault possesses a vehicle range that is perfectly adapted to this international dynamic. These are global cars assembled in seven countries across the world. They are also local cars that have evolved in response to the specific needs of the markets where they are being sold, with examples ranging from the specific design of the Sandero ph 2 sold in Brazil to the Duster's rear air conditioning system in India.

Between 1999 and 2011, the share of Renault cars sold outside of Europe rose from 11% to 47%. This would have been impossible without the Logan and its successors, with more than half of our sales outside of Europe involving this line. All in all, more than 1 million Entry range cars will have been sold within eight years after its launch.

In sum, vehicles in our Entry range are a foundation of the Group's ambitions and strategy. They reflect Renault's goal of making mobility both sustainable and accessible to all. Accessible mobility means offering products that are affordable both at purchase and also throughout their operational lifecycles. Sustainable mobility means equipping models with the latest mechanics, avoiding over-sophistication and focusing on performance. Lastly, mobility for all means responding to personal mobility needs in both developed and emerging countries.

In addition, Entry vehicles are a pillar of our growth strategy. Before the Logan, Renault profits mainly depended on the Mégane range. Today the

Entry range is the Group's most profitable line with a global reach that allows it to smooth out the effects of any regional crises.

Its contribution to the French activities of Renault and the Company's subcontractors has also been positive. Despite its international reach, the Entry still generated €630 million of value added in mainland France in 2011, notably through knock-on effects benefitting our mechanical plants and engineering operations. The profits generated by these vehicles have also made a major contribution to our investments in France and the rest of the world, helping to prepare Renault's future.

Above and beyond the initial idea of making a €5,000 car, the Entry range's performance can be explained by its rigorous and frugal implementation—and by the fact that eight years after the first Logans came on the market, the competition has not been able to reproduce our business model.

All in all, the Logan's epic adventure has been central to Renault's success. A visionary managerial decision to pilot an exemplary project based on a pragmatic lifecycle management—these mechanics are all adroitly detailed in this book, with special focus on decision-making processes, major changes in the automobile business and the people without whom none of this would have been possible—namely, the men and women of Renault who have carried this innovation to its successful conclusion.

INTRODUCTION

Lessons from an epic adventure

From the Ford Model T and Fordism to Toyotism, just-in-time methodologies, the Twingo and project management–in more than a century of history, the automotive industry has been a permanent exemplar of business theories and even of models of capitalism. Not that the sector invented everything–far from it–but it has been able to appropriate innovative concepts and give them life through emblematic cases that have helped theory to transcend obscure circles of professional academics.

The question is what characteristics a good exemplar must possess to be considered a fully-fledged school of thought. Clearly, it must be original and embody a theory or model that breaks with the past. It must also be a success. In management like other disciplines, scholars are aware that there is much to learn from failure. Yet failures are difficult to analyse and even harder to talk about with any transparency. Moreover, imitation may be criticizable but it does constitute a powerful vector for the deployment of new ideas. In addition, the new thinking must also be rooted in realities that are easy to perceive. With this in mind, what we can say is that the automobile has driven the global notoriety of the challenges that big industry faces today.

Above and beyond these management issues, it has been clear since Chandler that the main attributes characterising our economies have been at least partially developed within companies or–at the very least–that a modicum of coherency must connect organisations endowed with such attributes, the markets where they operate, the wealth that they distribute and the institutional environments within which they operate. Once again, over the course of the 20th century the automobile has willingly and frequently served as an exemplar, with some of its key topics ("Fordism", "Post-Fordism" or "Toyotism") touching on economic issues requiring much deeper analysis than is customary, and which have been more or less successfully resolved by managers working for leading carmakers. In addition to the ease with which automobile-related illustrations can be turned into rhetoric, the industry has also been crucial to employment, trade, growth and technological capabilities in many countries. This also justifies its use as an example, as does the fact that automotive spending accounts for a significant share of many household budgets and, more broadly, plays a major role in the organisation of social life.

For the authors of this text, the Logan example is worth examining both on its own merits and also because of what it represents, illustrates or suggests on a further level. This is because the Logan combines exemplary aspects of an original business problem (which some might call a model) that is interesting to analyse.

The Logan is noteworthy first and foremost because of the scale of its success. Originally launched as a particularly risky bet–because such small volumes (initially 60,000 units annually out of the Romanian factory) had been predicted, the programme has constantly upgraded its forecasts, expanding markets and production capacities until it exceeded 900,000 units in 2011, more than 15 times the original goal. It remains that the most spectacular and unexpected success of this vehicle programme–which the public is familiar with because of its exceptionally low prices–cannot be attributed to rising sales but to the fact that it has been extremely profitable for the Renault group, something that has been especially precious since a crisis broke out in the late 2000s.

Another reason for the importance of this example is its deviation from "business as usual". The changes involved have been both coherent with one another (explaining why the Logan might be equated with a "model") and covered a wide range of activities. What we are facing here is the kind of case study found in many business or economics modules, including strategic marketing classes, where the Logan perfectly embodies Christensen's "low-end disruption" strategies; project management classes, where it helps to explain why dedicated and autonomous project teams are so effective, while highlighting the efficiency of modern "design to cost" methodologies; theories of growth classes, focused on innovative firms and their management of product families, involving generations of differentiated products and the decades-long conquest of different markets (without this extension's complexity impeding the concept's coherency or the programme's profitability); corporate internationalisation classes, by resuscitating the construct of a "world car"; or management production classes, revealing the issues and problems associated with the delocalisation of manufacturing and the complexity of globalized procurement. All illustrate the originality of a kind of geographic deployment where innovation no longer spreads outwards from a firm's country of origin towards more exotic destinations but targets first and foremost distant customers before (potentially) reselling the products designed in this way in traditional Western markets.

Without trying to equate "Loganism" with Fordism or Toyotism, we consider that our case study epitomises broader industrial, economic and geopolitical issues affecting the whole of the automotive industry and, beyond this, economic organisation. Taking just one example, the constraints and opportunities that the big developed countries face as a result of the emerging economies' growing power have been wilfully tolerated for more than a decade because people believed in the manifest destiny of the knowledge economy, which was supposed to help the leading developed countries to maintain their primacy by using innovation to perpetuate a top-down division of cognitive labour. Implicitly, behind the famous "Lisbon agenda" that the European Union created for itself, there was also the idea of a division of labour that would make it possible to delegate manufacturing phases to the emerging economies without the Global North having to worry about its own leadership role. In part, the automotive industry—and the forms of sourcing and relocalised assembly that developed in the 1990s and 2000s—seems to be rooted in these hypotheses. By trying to expand local contents and share design tasks between France, Romania and (increasingly) other sites such as Brazil, Russia or India, the Logan family has evoked a more balanced form of the international division of design tasks, while possibly reversing the sources of innovative concepts.

Similarly, the demonstration made by the Logan and its family that it is possible to achieve more than satisfactory profitability at the bottom-of-the-range, breaks with the past by contradicting today's widespread belief in the industry that profitability equates to the ability to sell expensive products. This credo, shared by managers in the sector's largest companies, analysts and politicians with an ongoing interest in the automobile business, constitutes a new "one best way" that has ostensibly been confirmed by the Volkswagen group's undeniable success. The Logan questions the way that this credo affects perceptions of (and efforts to appropriate) "value" in the automotive sector. In Europe and beyond, the Logan and its family—whose successes have been surprisingly discreet—deserve special analysis to bring to light the meaning of contemporary developments and the trajectories being imposed on the industry. In turn, this makes it increasingly possible to conjure up alternatives.

Examining the Logan case study from this perspective, the book is broken down into three sections.

The first one recaps the emergence and conduct of the Logan project, which has been the seminal act in this epic adventure. The first chapter focuses on product and market strategies. It is followed by an interview with Louis Schweitzer, the project's father. The second chapter analyses product design management and the industrial developments associated with this. It is followed by an interview with Jean-Marie Hurtiger, who brought the project to completion from March 1999.

The second section analyses the expansion dynamic underlying Renault's Entry programme, involving both a broadened product range and expanded target markets globally. This story concludes in late 2011. The 2012 inauguration of a new factory in Morocco and launch of the Lodgy minivan clearly constitutes a new expansion phase that we have not wanted to discuss for reasons of confidentiality and because it is too early to have an overview of the outcomes. The second section ends with an interview with Gérard Detourbet, Entry programme Director during this entire expansion phase.

The third section is more theoretical and forward-looking, focusing on the lessons that the Company (and the automotive economy) should learn from this epic adventure. It also contains reflections on our industrial model and, more broadly, on society as a whole, ensuring an "intellectual" link-up between the perspectives opened by another ongoing Renault programme involving electric vehicles.

The book's three authors are all automotive industry experts. They have relied specifically on a 2010-2011 Renault survey that allowed them to meet all key Logan programme actors and consult relevant internal documentation.

The authors would like to thank all of the managers they met at Renault and Dacia for their kindness and availability for interviews, documentary research, site visits, etc. The book would also have been impossible without the support and confidence placed us by Gérard Detourbet, Entry Programme Director, who spent a great deal of time with the three of us, university academics seeking to conduct an in-depth study on the Logan's success, discussing his experience and providing us with unfettered insight into the specific universe that has been created within the Renault group.

As is customary in this kind of partnership, the only demand expressed by the Company was to verify that no information deemed strategic would filter out. Asides from this one constraint, the authors were given full freedom to develop their own analyses and interpretations. They remain entirely responsible for any errors or omissions in the text.

The present study was also supported by the three following institutions:

- The GERPISA international network, a scientific interest group supported by France's Ministry for Higher Education and Research, ENS Cachan, EHESS Paris, University Montesquieu-Bordeaux IV, CCFA, FIEV, CNPA, the Ministry for Industry and the Ministry for Environment, Sustainability, Transportation and Housing;
- The Ecole Polytechnique Innovation Management chair, supported by leading companies such as Air Liquide, MBDA, Renault, Safran, Seb and Valeo;
- The Maison des Sciences de l'Homme d'Aquitaine, under the aegis of its Innovation Trajectories programme, supported by the French Ministry for Higher Education and Research and the Aquitaine Regional Council.
- The authors would also like to warmly thank Alan Sitkin for his strong and talented involvement in the translation of this book.

SECTION I

FROM THE X90 PROJECT TO THE LOGAN

The epic adventure that we will be analysing here starts with a suggestion from Renault's CEO, Louis Schweitzer, regarding growth strategy scenarios. It also relates the history of the X90 project that would ultimately give shape to this idea. Like other emblematic projects, the X90 became a real challenge for the Company, as did the goal of making a profitable €5,000 car aimed at emerging economies' middle classes. At first, the challenge seemed impossible given the 50% gap between the cost of the cheapest car that Renault was producing at the time (in Turkey) and X90 project's own aims.

There are also questions about the thinking underlying this project. One is to ask how the Company shifted from its motivational but simplistic strategic intent to the concrete but complex realities of a high-performance marketable vehicle. Another question involves the resources (and processes) that helped a seeming impossibility become a reality. Answering these questions is the goal of our first section, which covers the period from 1995–when Renault's senior management first began grappling with the idea of expanding into the emerging markets–to 2005, which saw the commercial launch of the Sandero, clearly marking the transition from the initial project (the design and sale of the Logan) to the development of the diversified Entry range.

1

THE INVENTION OF A NEW MARKET

Before taking charge at Renault, Louis Schweitzer had helped the Company prepare the Skoda bid. This was ultimately unsuccessful, with the Czech government opting for VW, Renault's German competitor, in December 1992. What Schweitzer learnt from this experience was the usefulness of having a "second brand" positioned lower than Renault itself, giving the original brand an opportunity to pursue its goal of improved quality and image without losing out on commercial opportunities emanating from the emerging markets, with their focus on increasingly affordable products.

Hence Schweitzer's decision, announced to his team in 1995, that Renault would internationalise its production and sales henceforth, starting with its investments in Brazil. Renault had just spent long months working through its merger with Volvo and before this operation fell apart, company executives were all more or less fixated on the idea of a top-of-the-range brand. So it was a surprise when Schweitzer asked them to do a serious analysis of his potential scenario and help him to structure it. The executive team initially ignored this request but Schweitzer persisted, never abandoning his vision of something akin to the VW-Skoda model and seeking ways of materialising this. It was in trying to understand how Renault might take advantage of growing automobile use in Russia and Eastern Europe that Schweitzer had his eureka moment. In late 1997, he launched a plan to build a "modern, robust and affordable" car that would cost $6,000. The opportunity offered by the acquisition of Dacia, first mooted in 1998 before being finalised in 1999, became the definitive trigger for this project.

The initial commercial hypotheses already existed when Renault took over Dacia, as witnessed by the transcript of a meeting between Radu Vasile[1] and Schweitzer that took place on 3 November 1998:

---

1. Radu Vasile was Romanian Prime Minister from 1998 to 1999.

"Renault's strategic plan, in its current form, involves three major deployment phases:

Improving Dacia products (1999-2001),

Creating a range comprised of existing Renault vehicles or models in the pipelines (2001-2003),

Building a specific car for Dacia, one that is modern and affordable aimed at emerging market customers (2003 onwards)."

The trick is to be modern while remaining affordable. There is no point in building a $15,000 car that will struggle to sell. This will be a major challenge, however, given the longstanding presence of certain very inexpensive vehicles (Dacia, Maruti, Lada…) and total absence anywhere in the world of cars retailing at $6,000."[1]

The project was therefore positioned from the very outset as an "Entry" range initiative, a reference to the idea that the new vehicles would provide many people with their initial access to the automobile market and generally focus on the cheapest segments. This being the case, the Logan project largely concentrated on the emerging markets, especially Central and Eastern Europe, including Russia. Its goal was to rival existing entry-level vehicles that were past their sell-by date yet continued to dominate their markets (Lada, Dacia…). The positioning adopted aimed to achieve better value for money by offering this category of buyers an alternative. This was the initial intuition, coming after VW had acquired Skoda and preceding the acquisition of Dacia or the negotiations associated with this deal.

Even before Schweitzer, Renault had already developed in the early 1990s, under the tutelage of Raymond Lévy, a similar project called the W75.[2] The habit at the time was to deal with emerging markets by "downgrading" and marginally modifying models that were part of the existing product range. W75 started with premise that a better way of dealing with the emerging markets' cost and performance requirements would be to build a specific model integrating local market and production conditions from the outset. The model underlying this effort was supposed to be the R19, with Bursa in Turkey supposed to be Renault's anchor site. The project never materialised, however, due to the fact that Western

---

1. Cited by D. Debrosse, *La reprise de Dacia par Renault 1998-2003. Histoire d'une aventure humaine, industrielle et commerciale*, PhD in History thesis, University Evry-Val de l'Essonne, 2007.
2. J. Dieudé, J. Corviole, J.P. Reynier, "Le W75, précurseur de la Logan", *Renault Histoire*, No. 20, July 2008.

Europe was still Renault's priority in the early 1990s. This was an era when the Company was still very dependent on the French market and only help significant market share in a very few countries outside of Europe. Before "intercontinentalising", Renault's strategic objective has been to "Europeanise" and advance in commercial terms, notably in Germany.

Yet something had to be done for those emerging markets where Renault had already started selling cars. Because of the need for "true hatchback sedans" offering "maximum size" for minimal cost, the decision was made to add a boot onto the Renault Clio 1, which was Europe's leading car in the early 1990s, alongside the Volkswagen Golf. This pre-project was launched in 1995 with project itself coming online in 1996. One manufacturing contract signed in June 1997 applied to Bursa in Turkey, with another applying to Curitiba in Brazil. The actual launch occurred year-end 1999 with cars sold under the name of the Symbol in Turkey and the Sedan in Brazil. A little later, Nissan would use the same model to replace its Tsuru in Mexico (90,000 annual sales), subsequently manufacturing its Platina in the country's Aguascalientes plant. A little later, the Thalia went on offer in both Eastern Europe and France's overseas territories.

This product had a modicum of success with annual sales of around 110,000, half of which were car badged as Nissans. Yet this "European product adapted for constrained markets" was also considered quite elitist in many markets. This is because despite certain "decontenting" and "re-engineering" efforts, manufacturer return costs were at best 30% lower than rival products in the same markets. In a sense, the numbers didn't add up due to the fact that the product no longer qualified as entry-level. This explains why Renault's international presence remained so marginal, with products that had no hope of featuring at the core of its target emerging economy markets. It was the need to address this problem that would later become the Logan's key objective. Unlike W75, which can be analysed ex post facto as having failed because of a lack of clarity about Renault's international commitment (and because of its vague objectives), the people responsible for the Logan project–called the L90 at the time[1]–relied on the

---

1. The L90 corresponded more specifically to the notchback version. The project included this model as well as an estate, pickup and hatchback version, with people at Renault referring to the whole range as the X90 project. Following the planning stage (i.e. once the first model was launched and the others planned), the project became a full-blown "programme" set on an equal footing with other Renault programmes and the ranges associated with them (Twingo, Clio, Mégane…).

fact that Schweitzer had already said in 1995 that he wanted Renault to grow outside of Europe and set sales (hence manufacturing return) costs as clear and quantifiable objectives.

Internal presentations post-2003 would highlight the following strategic thinking:

- For Renault, profitable growth meant significant overseas expansion;
- In markets that were economically more constrained than Western Europe;
- Although half of the volumes involved Renault products, for the other half the Group needed a specific range of cheap adapted products;
- In bottom-of-the-range segments characterised by a range of prices and products.

In short, the commercial intent with emerging markets was never to offer the cheapest car possible but to create a product that would be positioned at the heart of its market. Schweitzer later said that it was during a trip he took in autumn 1997 accompanying President Chirac to Russia that he started thinking about the W75 again,[1] returning to "the need for a car with the same sales tag as the Lada but reliable and modern."

By so doing, he was confirming two principal considerations.

- The Logan was first and foremost a commercial innovation that consisted of inventing–in the range of local low-cost products and "imported" cars–a vehicle and category of vehicles enabling buyers in these markets to access a "modern" alternative with the same retail price or a lower one. Implicitly, Schweitzer was also offering an alternative to the used cars that were households' natural way of offsetting carmakers' inadequate product offer.[2] In emerging markets characterised by a relatively limited stock of automobiles, used cars were often imports, intimating that Schweitzer's intuition was all the more relevant in countries where used car imports were prohibited or limited.
- Initially, the innovation corresponded to a commercial "window of opportunity" that was quite narrow due to its focus on Russia and

---

1. See interview with Louis Schweitzer at the end of Chapter 1.
2. B. Jullien, "Used Cars Markets as Signs of Resistance of Consumers to the Car Manfacturers Conceptions of Demand: a Usage Analysis of Automobile Systems" in L. Fontaine, *Alternative Exchanges: Second-Hand Circulations from the Sixteenth Century to The Present*, Berghahn, Oxford, 2008.

analogous configurations (such as Romania and Iran, which seemingly offered similar opportunities). As discussed below, however, things were quite different in Brazil, India, China and (of course) France and Western Europe markets.

Later on, it would become clear that this intuition was extremely powerful and justified. Yet according to Schweitzer, it never got spontaneous support, with managers still questioning the existence of this kind of market and doubting whether cars could be made at such low prices without compromising Schweitzer's "modernity" demand. Hence the wall of scepticism that the CEO faced upon his return from Russia when he shared his plans with Renault's managers:

"I realized that the goal I was suggesting did not interest them because it went against the notion of continuous progress, of always doing more of the same thing. Moreover, Renault's economists and number crunchers all found it very easy to demonstrate that there were no profits to be had with this project."

It was at this point that the Romanian carmaker Dacia, which Renault had just acquired, became a lever that would ultimately allow Schweitzer to push through his idea. When negotiations first began, the aim of making a $6,000 car became crucial to Dacia's integration into Renault. It was this project that had been greeted so enthusiastically by the Romanian government and by Dacia's senior management. It was also with the mission of making this possible that Renault's teams bought Dacia. In fact, it was only after this acquisition that Schweitzer really launched his project, later admitting that little progress had been achieved between autumn 1997 and autumn 1999. Indeed, it was at the public announcement that Renault would be launching a €5,000 car–a step taken to force colleagues to accept the strategy–that Schweitzer really gave the green light to the X90. In March 1999, he appointed Jean-Marie Hurtiger and put together the team that would work with him at Guyancourt, along with Romanian teams helping to prepare the production and marketing of the new model.

At both levels–first upstream from the design and production phase and then in parallel to them–Renault's team tried to verify Schweitzer's intuitions while improving understanding of their target and the shape this might assume in the different countries or regions where the project was being deployed. By 2004 the project had started to mature, with the contours of what would become Renault's Entry range marketing and sales programme taking shape in the minds of the executives and teams driving these efforts. The rest of the organisation was kept informed but not involved.

It is noteworthy that the Logan's original positioning offered an alternative to other products sold at similar or lower prices, meaning that the goal was not to offer the kind of "low cost" option with which the Logan would be equated when it came to France and Western Europe. On a deeper level, the car's real purpose was to (re) position Renault as a major player in emerging markets, one with whom local politicians and distributors could and would cooperate over the long run when developing their markets and industries. The problem was that the circumstances did not always fit these hypotheses. In 2005, for instance, the decision was taken to market the product in Western Europe as well. Because the Dacia badge was unhelpful in many markets, there was a need for a more "plastic" commercial positioning. People had to accept that one and the same product might fulfil a variety of missions on Renault's behalf.

THE INITIAL TARGET AND HOW THE X90 TEAMS DEALT WITH IT

The key targets were countries where this positioning could be leveraged. Schweitzer's hypotheses had been validated even before the launch by the contexts in which the internal and external deployments were taking place. Romania was a fortuitous choice and helped the project to advance by validating it incrementally on both a political and commercial plane. Understanding the factors underlying the Entry range's commercial genesis is therefore key to understanding its later successes and failures.

The X90 only really took shape after the Dacia takeover. Upstream of (and then in parallel to) the design and production phases, Renault's teams always had this project in mind.

From Schweitzer's intuition to the Logan's different positionings

The encounter between Schweitzer's intuition and the opportunities (and constraints) associated with Dacia's acquisition would have a structuring effect at the beginning of the project's commercial life. Even though product teams started off with the idea of a global deployment, over the course of the project's lifetime, generally there was a strong focus on Eastern Europe, at least during the first few years, substantiating the product's positioning and ensuring its plausibility. It was only subsequently that the original ambition of going global would be resuscitated and attempts made to take the Logan "on the road" when an opportunity presented itself.

In the early 2000s, two teams and two logics coexisted at Renault, penetrating one another but remaining distinct. Alongside the X90 project being run by Jean-Marie Hurtiger following his March 1999 appointment, there was the "Romanian" team working on-site with responsibility for restructuring Dacia both industrially and commercially. It was the second team that prepared the Logan's arrival between 1999 and 2004. This did not happen just on paper but involved a rationalisation of the existing Dacia range's production and distribution processes.

Leading the commercial distribution operations was Jean-Frédéric Piotin, who quickly became aware of the magnitude of the task, noting in particular that it was the rationing of products and parts that had enabled Dacia to function up until that point without a distribution/repair network. Almost all of the 500 persons that he had been told upon arriving would report to him were involved in logistics rather than sales, involved in shipping the car to different regions where consumers were expecting it and where it would ultimately disappear without further ado in opaque channels run by poorly identified operatives lacking any contractual relationship with the carmaker. Piotin therefore had to recruit and build a sales and after-sales network from scratch. His big challenge was controlling prices and ensuring that products would provide after-sales services while compiling customer information so that the Dacia and Renault brands would later be able to operate in a competitive environment.

Customers were used to relatively mediocre products and doing whatever they could to find and install parts. It was therefore unsurprising that they aspired to be treated better. In other words, concepts like "customer expectations" were too simplistic to be of any real use to the product. Despite everything (and somewhat negatively), the product positioning was supposed to overcome the obstacles that Romanians associated with Dacia. It was also supposed to be sold through a professional network capable of selling the vehicle at Renault's price–and no longer through the grey market.

Clearly, the knowledge that Piotin and his teams gained of the existing situation in Romania helped them to convince the project managers that they needed specifications well below the levels to which Renault's Guyancourt engineering teams were accustomed. More specifically, Piotin–

who first considered suggesting an integrated distribution system (due to the difficulty of recruiting independent dealers)–started putting together a network before the corresponding automotive product even "existed". This is because no agents or dealers could be hired away from other networks, for the simple reason no other brand had built a network in Romania. Nor were there any independent auto repair professionals, with the country's existing automobile stock being far too under-developed to justify this kind of business. Similarly, the banking system seemed unlikely to help the former furniture salesman or butchers with whom Piotin was hoping to create a "network" to fund the property, building, garage equipment and inventory investments they would need. In light of these problems, the only thing that investors were asked to finance was the first aspect (property), with Renault and Dacia ultimately taking responsibility for inventory.

This explains why the main involvement of primary Romanian networks has always been to distribute vehicles that customers buy directly from Dacia and Renault. The natural consequence has been a need for product ranges that are both simple and short. In terms of after-sales, the recruitment of business leaders who often grew up outside the automotive market (and who themselves have had big problems finding qualified local mechanics with high-quality professional training) argued for simple choices in terms of the car's mechanics, with an emphasis, for instance, on petrol driving systems as similar as possible to what could already be found in the Romanian market.

The logic that we have just discussed in relation to product distribution, maintenance and repairs also applied to the Logan's manufacturing. The "Romanians" and the teams that Hurtiger put on the project had relatively congruent demands. The focus on Romania helped to ensure the coherency of a process that was marginal to the rest of the Renault organisation. The shape given to the future vehicle, month after month, reflected Romanian commercial realities, reinforcing the project's coherency and/or feasibililty. Even though the ambitions that X90 displayed and nourished throughout its lifetime were multi-regional and global, the project was very Romanian during key phases of its development. This became apparent to people afterwards once the X90 was supposed to be "deployed" industrially and/or commercially out of the country.

Patrick Weil–whom Rémi Deconinck (Director of Products at the time) appointed Product Manager in January 1999–later described the implicit hypothesis that had existed since the beginning as follows: "The point wasn't to imagine a car that would only target Romania, although it was clear that, given poverty levels in this country at the time, if we could make a very affordable car satisfying difficult local driving conditions, there was every chance that it might also succeed internationally."

After a time spent working in conjunction with the "Romanians", Renault's teams began to accumulate research and develop an in-depth knowledge of this market. In March/April 1999, Jean Tavarès, Head of Product Studies, launched a KYC (Know Your Customer) process in Romania to quantify Weil's impressions of this market.

The changing character of the core target

Romania was both a difficult and an "easy" battlefield, due to Renault's credible ambition from the very outset to dominate here. The country's initial importance merits discussion to apprehend the influence that this may have had on other target countries scrutinised during the same period. Indeed, some of the difficulties that were subsequently experienced in the effort to take the product "on the road" may derive from these origins. Where conditions were "Romanian", things tended to go well. Where they differed, it could be much harder.

The project's focus on Romania is easier to accept if Weil's hypothesis can be verified and supported by research. There is also the fact that the project's fundamental ambition was to change the direction of Renault group internationalisation. When the X90 first kicked, the internationalisation had been limited, meaning that there were not very many geographic locations where the project could be assessed. Responding to a host of research on the Logan, Robin Law–who served as Director of the Prospective Product unit in 2005–found himself reminded of Nissan's Z13, an entity that, based on Nissan's different global activities, structured the interface between business unit operatives and the Product Department. The latter would identify new opportunities and plan the product range, with the former mobilising their knowledge of customers and competitors. Law noted that "Nissan, whose international sales are much more evenly distributed worldwide, has a much more developed international organisation", emphasizing the fact that whereas the Z13's support team employed at least 30 staff members, Law himself only had two.

Even if Russia, Columbia, Morocco and Brazil were defined very early on as potential targets for the Logan, interactions with local teams were minimal and any studies produced occurred relatively late in the project. More specifically, according to a 2004 interview with Tavarès, the Product Department's Director for Customers Studies and Research, the dynamic following Dacia's acquisition in 1999 involved the International Department ordering a very wide range of work that consisted of drawing a "panorama of new automotive markets (with their social and economic dimensions) and customers (driving habits)." The whole of the planet was supposed to be covered in this research, including, for instance, South America and Africa. The project's slogan ("Do things simply and cheaply"), evoked by Rémi Deconinck, resulted in part from this research.

In the words of Tavarès, the objective was then to develop–above and beyond general specifications based on very generic "expectations"–a product that customers were not "demanding" per se. In turn, the gap between "expectations" and product had to be addressed creatively and innovatively. After all, "However effective a survey is, there will always be expectations that customers do not express because they consider them impossible to satisfy or believe that they only apply to more expensive cars. Our job is therefore to capture and formulate these unstated desires."[1]

As Christophe Midler would later say about the Twingo–in opposition to the advertising slogan "You dreamt it, Sony did it!" which was very fashionable at the time–an innovative project that is meant to move boundaries cannot be "called" by the marketplace but is, to the contrary, destined to shape it.[2] It must therefore identify a space of opportunity corresponding to a latent or potential demand that had not been expressed before it arrived and which should subsequently be able to impose itself on the market. If the corresponding innovation succeeds, this would then confirm the existence of a demand even as the means for satisfying the demand is only just being developed. This is the kind of process–with Romania as its central location–that was revealed in the different narratives we heard, involving the quest for solvent demand, on one hand, and the search for uncertain technical and industrial feasibility, on the other hand. These were the two poles of this dialectical process.

---

1. See interview transcripts that Renault published in 2004.
2. C. Midler, *L'Auto qui n'existait pas*, Paris, InterEditions, 1993. P. 59: "Innovations not 'market-driven', as economists often say, because customers for the cars being created do not yet know what they want... slogans like "You dreamt it, Sony did it", put the end user at the beginning of the innovation process. In reality, what we have is competition based on the supply of creativity."

Surrounding these precursors to the product (and the product itself), the "gap" in Romania between the X90's concept and the product itself began to fill in between 2000 and 2003. Tavarès has described how the first Logan prototypes were first tested in this country around 2000, followed by marketing tests from September 2003 onwards, specifically in Poland, Hungary and Turkey.

In late 2004 and with the product already on sale, Tavarès added that, "Our approach is being enhanced and will soon be extended to all of the other countries where the vehicle is assembled (Morocco, Iran, Columbia and Russia)". By so doing, he was reviving Romania's implicit benchmark role and evoking Weil's ultimately sound hypothesis.

In a June 2004 press communiqué, Renault indicated that, "The Logan combines all of the advantages that people thought impossible: unrivaled value for money given this level of habitability; reliability and robustness responding precisely to specific local uses; and a design that is modern, attractive and adds value. The Logan is polyvalent: good for city or country driving, for very different kinds of roads, for work or holidays–with its five seats and large boot space, it can be used for any kind of trip."

The reference to "specific local uses" related first and foremost to Romania, a country where income and car ownerships levels and the quality of the road network were always well below other target markets' standards. This would have the virtue of radicalising the narrative about the Logan's ability to offer, for a lower purchasing price, "more habitable space" and "lower maintenance costs" than a competition that–even in Romania–came from many other sources than Dacia alone.

In habitability terms, the main constraint was customers' tendency to be single car families focused on professional and semiprofessional uses (taxis, delivery vehicles, tools transportation, etc.). The press communiqué listed different reasons why the Logan team might be satisfied in this respect, and spoke about rival models, mainly from Korea (or American-Korean cars like Daewoo): "The new model's large size makes it very comfortable. Its length (4.250 mm, versus 4.215 for the Kia Rio Sedan), width (1.735 mm, versus 1.670 for the Hyundai Accent) and height (1.525 mm, versus 1.495 for the Chevrolet/Daewoo Kalos) are unequaled in the category of B-Entry1 segment notchback sedans and actually closer to C segment standards. Internal habitability is another advantage, with a lot of attention being focused on the back seats. Three passengers from the 95th percentile (taller than 6'3") will have no problems being comfortable, with about 25mm head clearance to spare. As for the Espace, it offers a great deal of foot room as well as 420mm wide seats. This means that customers from colder northern countries wearing big boots will have no problems settling in. The average legroom is about 185mm, versus 173 for the Chevrolet/Daewoo Kalos. The back seats are remarkably wide (1.420 mm), similar to the VelSatis and wider than the competition (1.342 mm for the Chevrolet/Daewoo Kalos). Lastly, accessibility is excellent with a 510 litre boot far exceeding the competition in this category (321 and 395 litres respectively for the Hyundai Accent and Daewoo Lanos Sedan). The general shape means that many different shapes can be loaded."

Maintenance cost and reliability parameters were justified by the underdeveloped state of the repair networks, local driving conditions, the fact that average driving distances could be high, people's habit of keeping a vehicle for a long time, and–particularly in the case of Romania–past experience with automobiles. Asides from perceptions of certain qualities such as robustness and simplicity, the key factor was the conservative technical choices that had been made. For instance, the savings achieved by replicating existing driving systems was transformed in a communiqué into a sales argument: "The 1.4 litre engine with its 1.6l 8 valve (K family) and JH gearbox have already proven themselves in the Renault range, particularly in the major export markets."

Similarly, asides from the simplicity of the technical choices, there was also an emphasis on the infrequent need for oil changes, the fact that these could be done by the owners themselves and/or the lack of any entry barriers to the repair or maintenance markets. Communications also stressed that customers would find it easy to access the headlights from the engine compartment.

Talking about the work that he and his teams had done, Robin Law affirmed that the only way of advancing from a vehicle's intention to the creation of a product targeting customers afflicted by major economic constraints was to integrate six different imperatives that should be viewed as the project's basic ingredients. These imperatives were commercial, political, economic, legislative, structural and industrial in nature.

- Commercially, everything should be structured by the tripod of customer expectations, automotive purchasing power and disposable income.
- Politically, what is important are transportation policies and specific tax and customs policies affecting new and used cars and components.
- Economically, the crux is the profitability of Renault's industrial and/or sales operations in each of the countries/regions where it operates.

- Legislatively, it is crucial that the vehicle comply with current regulations.
- Structurally, the focus is on problems such as transportation infrastructure and fuel distribution (and quality).
- Industrially, the main factors are detailed below.

Although Romania is not a particularly large market, it was the second biggest in Central and Eastern Europe[1] in population terms (22 million inhabitants). In 2003, the year preceding the Logan's launch, Romania was the fourth largest automobile market in this part of the world, behind Poland (358,000 registrations for 38 million inhabitants), Hungary (208,000 for 10 million) and the Czech Republic (150,000 for 10 million). In 2003, Dacia had a market share of about 45% and Renault less than 10%. Given the major investments that Renault had undertaken in Romania and the government's significant involvement before and after the takeover, the different political and legislative constraints might be considered as having been largely neutralised. Hence the possibility of considering that the six aforementioned imperatives could be combined in Romania. This was another driver, one that helped the project to maintain a direction that, on many different levels, broke with normal Renault standards, something hidden behind the official discourse that everyone believed in until 2003: namely that the model would be badged Dacia and under no circumstances Renault; and that it would only be sold in emerging markets.

Weil's hypothesis, when he affirmed that, "If we can make a very inexpensive car that works under the difficult conditions found in Romania, there is every chance that it will succeed internationally", was crucial to moving the programme ahead. We examine below the extent to which this view has been validated for each of Law's six registers.

Even before it was marketed in Romania[2], a certain number of changes affected the Logan. This had the effect of "re-internationalising" its sales approach.

Firstly, the product–which some people believed would have problems ever being born–actually existed. Despite ongoing scepticism, it was patently suitable, not only to its Romanian target but also to the other markets where Renault's product offer had been out of sync with the competition. This reality struck a number of international business

---

1. Which became New Member States during the period in question.
2. Planned in 2003 for September 2004.

practitioners. Luc-Alexandre Ménard, Mercosur Director from 1997 to July 2002 before being appointed Director of the International Department and Chairman of the Board at Dacia after September 2002, embodied the Logan project's second wind after 2003.

Having run Germany in the late 1980s and Southern Europe in 1993 before becoming Sales Director for France between 1994 and 1997, Ménard was aware that Schweitzer's international ambition was being undermined by the "product" policy's very French focus. He had particularly suffered from this in Brazil because of differences between Renault's product and ones offered by VW, Fiat and GM. He was therefore quick to perceive the usefulness of Renault internationalising commercially and industrially on the back of the Logan. As the man running Dacia, he was also interested in exporting out of Romania, whether vehicles or parts for subsequent assembly. For all these reasons, he turned out to be one of the most active proponents (alongside Gérard Detourbet) of getting the Logan "on the road". Towards this end, he started by eliminating two symbolic political barriers that had been erected to protect the project and ensure its viability: the idea that the product should solely carry the Dacia badge; and that it should not be sold in so-called mature markets.

Indeed, from 2003 onwards, "Romanians" such as Jean-Frédéric Piotin in the Sales Department or Gérard Detourbet, were put in charge of organising the Logan's roadshows. Piotin was supposed to replicate the work that had been done to build up networks in Romania in other countries where Renault was poorly represented, in part by persuading local teams to help out with the Logan's marketing effort. Detourbet was supposed to organise operations that had already been planned (Columbia, Morocco, Russia, Iran) and examine other possibilities (like India). Asides from Russia and the countries that Renault classified as "Euromed" (where enthusiasm was mitigated), Logan roadshows in neighbouring countries were quite arduous and contrasted with Weil's optimistic hypothesis.

Since even before the launch, country managers had expressed doubts about the tests that were to be run in 2003-2004. In 2002, Christian Estève (Dacia Managing Director from 2002 to 2004) noted at the Bucharest Trade Fair that subsidiary managers were dubious and concerned that the Logan was "dragging Renault down". Proud of having brought Renault and its traditional or adapted products to the emerging markets, they were not happy with this funny Romanian car and afraid that above and beyond its brand aspects, it did not fit the aspirations of Central European purchasers who were being constantly wooed by European and Korean manufacturers.

What happened afterwards showed the they were right to be worried and that there were significant differences between Romania and Poland, Slovakia Hungary or the Czech Republic.

Economically, in terms of GDP per capita and–above all–monthly wages, the gap between these countries was considerable (see Figure 1.1, year 2000). In 2004, the market structures and competitive situation in the big Eastern European countries created relatively unwelcoming competitive landscapes. Their upcoming accession into the European Union also reinforced their proximity to current EU economies. Markets for used cars (including imported used cars) were opening up alongside markets for new vehicles, enabling customers in these countries to access (for the price of a Logan) relatively recent and ostensibly much better quality products coming from Germany. Lastly, as a brand, Dacia, reminded customers from the former Soviet countries of a past that they wanted to forget. For all these reasons, particularly the latter, customer tests run in 2003 or 2004 were misleading and overestimated these markets' potential.

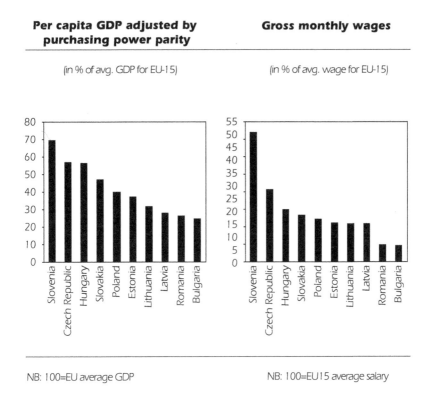

Figure 1.1–Structural indicators for Central European economies

Asked about Dacia brand perceptions in these tests, Jean Tavarès admitted: "What we established is that in some countries, the Dacia brand did not correspond to the reality of the transformation that had happened since the takeover by Renault." His worries would ultimately be justified in countries like Hungary or Poland.

The first Logan launches in its target countries

Between 2004 and 2005, the Logan was subject to a multitude of staged launches that initially involved its 1.4 L petrol engine version. It is worth examining their varying fortunes to apprehend how this caused the Logan to shift towards originally unintended destinations.

Table 1.1–Logan launches

Country	Initial sales	Logans sold in year 1	Market share in year 1
Romania	September 2004	77,837	38.5%
Croatia	October 2004	927	1.33%
Czech Republic	October 2004	2,237	1.73%
Serbia Montenegro	November 2004	4,904	13.43%
Hungary	September 2004	2,963	1.45%
Slovakia	November 2004	1,060	1.82%
Slovenia	January 2005	367	0.21%
Bulgaria	January 2006	1,615	4.43%
Columbia	September 2005	5,993	4.35%
Morocco	July 2005	9,497	14.2%
Algeria	May 2005	5,284	5.2%
Turkey	November 2004	6,645	1.6%
France	June 2005	19,084	0.93%
Germany	June 2005	3,943	0.12%
Spain	May 2005	3,822	0.24%
Poland	February 2005	1,377	0.56%
Italy	January 2006	780	0.03%
Russia	July 2005	28,172	1.86%
Brazil	May 2007	26,852	1.18%

Success in Romania

Within a few months of its launch, the Dacia Logan had already broken through to become Romania's leading car. Launched in September, by October it already accounted for nearly 38% of all new car sales in the country. The symbiosis between the project and Romania itself was very telling. As witnessed in the national press and revealed through studies undertaken by the Romanian teams, the population's relationship to the Logan looked very much like the ties that Romanians entertained with their homeland: prepared to criticise its shortcomings and tell self-deprecating jokes, they were also very proud and did not accept criticism from elsewhere. In short, the Logan became a typically Romanian projects, well adapted to what the population could do or offer itself. Moreover, given that it was infinitely superior to what Romanians had previously had with the Dacia, the car embodied progress in the country, furthering its popularity.

Table 1.2–Logan and rival entry level models in Romania

	Sept. 2004	March 2005	Sept. 2005	March 2006	Sept. 2006	March 2007	Sept. 2007	March 2008
Logan L90	33.20%	40.70%	37.90%	40.90%	38.20%	25.10%	17.40%	19.90%
Logan MCV	0.00%	0.00%	0.00%	0.00%	0.10%	6.00%	6.10%	6.40%
Gamme Entry	33.20%	40.70%	37.90%	40.90%	38.40%	31.00%	23.50%	26.30%
Thalia 1+2	2.10%	4.20%	4.60%	4.00%	2.80%	4.20%	4.00%	3.60%
Fabia	1.60%	1.20%	2.70%	2.20%	5.00%	2.70%	2.10%	2.20%
Fiesta	0.80%	0.90%	1.50%	1.70%	1.40%	3.30%	2.50%	2.40%
Corsa	0.20%	0.30%	0.90%	0.80%	0.70%	1.30%	2.00%	2.00%
206	1.60%	1.40%	1.00%	1.40%	1.00%	0.80%	0.90%	1.30%

At the same time, this was still a Dacia, not a German car. Indeed, the German automobile industry had not really shown any interest in Romania. Instead it was the French who had grabbed Dacia. The car's popularity was therefore somewhat ambiguous given the difficulty of measuring the pleasure associated with its purchase. At the same time, buyers were clearly satisfied with a vehicle that, like its network, fulfilled its promise.

Given Dacia's political and economic importance in Romania, the country's authorities tried to ensure that outlets for the Pitesti factory remained as significant as possible so that the national brand could maintain its domination. This differed from what was being observed in other new European Union member states such as Poland. Indeed, the Romanian state did everything it could to limit used car imports that might offer an alternative to the Dacia once Romania joined the European Union in 2007. This has been a bone of contention between the European Commission and Romania ever since.

To justify its policy of restricting used car imports, the Romanian government argued that the country was an automobile producing nation and that this industry sustained 1 million persons, nearly 5% of the population. Dacia's Managing Director at the time, François Fourmont, supported the government's stance by arguing that any abandonment of the "first registration tax" would lead to the market being invaded by used cars, a collapse in Logan sales and one-third of all factory workers having to be fired. Using a politically more acceptable argument in Brussels, the Romanian administration said that the country's automobile stock was comprised of 3.5 million vehicles, 60% of which were more than 10 years old. The Economics Minister concluded that "Romania needs to find solutions to rejuvenate its stock of automobiles, not make it older. A new car emits 130 g/km of CO_2, a quarter as much as cars that are 10 or more years old. Romania must not become the automobile dustbin of Europe." The authorities remembered the example of Poland, which had entered the European Union in May 2004 and was immediately submerged by used cars (75% of which were more than 10 years old), with the market for new cars falling by 35%.

The dispute remained unresolved, with the Commission almost systematically deciding that Romania was wrong and defending instead the interests of the "consumer" and the doctrine of non-discrimination. By 2008, after a few Commission successes, the number of used car import registrations had doubled. Whereas there had been a ratio of almost 3:1 between new and used cars in 2007, by September 2008 there were more used than new cars on Romania's roads. This was the direct consequence of changes in registration fees that, from 1 July 2008 onwards and in response to Brussel's's demands, had seen a sharp decline in the rates applied to used cars and a small increase in tariffs on new cars. Due to this change (and the economic crisis), in 2010 the Romanian government reintroduced a pollution tax on imported used cars, ostensibly for the same purposes. In April 2011, this was declared illegal.

The conflict surrounding imported used cars provides a relatively edifying illustration of a European policy and doctrine that was almost exclusively focused on the principle of free competition to the detriment of industrial, social or ecological policy. It also harks back to Law's six imperatives and shows the importance of being–if not a national manufacturer–then at least an economic hence political "heavyweight". In the case of Romania, Dacia, even after being modernised by Renault, remained a national brand and therefore benefited from strong political support. It was also affected by the ambiguity of Romanians' relationship with the state and their sense of being Romanian. The fact that Western European–and particularly German–consumers subsequently became big Dacia customers limited Romanians' feeling that they were being more or less forced to buy Dacias. It remains that this ambiguity still exists today, and that an audacious product policy is needed to overcome such attitudes.

Big hurdles in Central Europe

In the end, the original promise of the Central European market turned out to be a damp squib. This could be blamed on the community of automobile economists and experts more than on the Logan project teams. Note, for instance, a November 2004 article published in France's *Annales des Mines* review entitled "The renewal of the automobile industry in Central and Eastern Europe" and signed by two civil servants from the French Ministry of Economics and Finance, J.J. Boillot, a financial advisor for South Asia working out of New Delhi, and Y. Lepape, a European Union enlargement economist working out of Warsaw.

Noteworthy comments included: "Cost competitiveness will probably be less important unless we anticipate that regional automobile demand will catch up in two different ways: car ownership, which barely exceeds 50% of the EU15 average at present; and the renewal rate, with cars reaching average age of 12 or 13 years versus 8 in the EU15. New car registrations rose particularly quickly in 2003 (up 15%, versus down 1.1% in the EU15) although 2004 will be less positive at something below 10%. All in all, most specialists estimate a regional demand of 2.4 million new cars by 2010, or 15% of the EU15's projected demand, versus 6% today. Over the long run and given the importance of these countries in Europe's overall population, the region has the potential for 4 million new car registrations annually. This justifies manufacturers' commercial aggressiveness. The region offers a medium-term strategic challenge where nothing has been settled yet."

To exemplify this, note that Poland and Romania's combined populations equal France. In 2004, it was possible to imagine (as the authors explicitly did) that "Spain-like" processes would progressively shift the number of new vehicle purchases for 1,000 inhabitants towards a "European standard" that would be situated around 35/1000–a change that would over time mean more than 2 million registrations in these two countries. Before the 2007 crisis, the new member states had registered a total of 1.2 million vehicles, including 372,000 in Poland and 368,000 in Romania. By 2010, this had fallen to 937,000 passenger cars and even though Poland was still registering 387,000 units in this category (0.96%), Romanian totals had been cut by a factor three to reach 119,000 units (0.54%).

The inability to ensure that the demand emanating from the new member states matched their "promise" can be largely attributed to the European integration process, designed to create competition here instead of an integrated space of economic and social progress coordinated via integrating policies. It also reflected weak demand for the Logan outside of Romania, as illustrated by the example of Poland, featuring a highly competitive segment–called B[1]–dominated by European vehicles like the Clio, Corsa or Skoda Fabia. Asides from the Thalia and Aveo, these were mainly three or five door cars. In Poland's popularity contest, vehicles from this segment coexisted with the C segment for the same brands (Octavia, Astra, Focus, etc.). The implication is that infrequent new car buyers were being recruited in the upper middle classes, whose expectations were more aligned with Western European consumers. For less affluent households, used cars offered an alternative widely preferred to brands like Dacia, which suffered from the double disadvantage of the region's communist past and the fact that it was associated with Renault, a French (and not a German) company mainly known for the Thalia, which also seemed to come from another era.

What happened in Poland could also be verified in the Hungarian, Czech, Slovak or Slovenian markets. For instance, by yearend 2010, total sales since marketing first began in 2004 amounted to nearly 450,000 Logans (including the estate version) in Romania, but only 10,000 in

---

1. It is customary in the automotive industry to classify commercial segments by the platform used to build the corresponding model, alphabetically and by rising order of size and price: for Renault, the Twingo was an A, the Clio and Modus a B and the Mégane range a C. This categorisation coexists with older sales terminology where C was "lower midrange" noted M1 and D was "upper midrange" noted M2.

Poland, 7,000 in Hungary, 11,000 in the Czech Republic, 5,500 in Slovakia and fewer than 1,500 in Slovenia. In other words, had Eastern Europe remained the main target, the Logan would have failed. It is because the product travelled well to other destinations that had not been initially planned that it (followed by the rest of its family) became a success.

Success in Columbia, Morocco and Algeria

Without anticipating the arguments that might be made about the Entry programme's two major expansion territories (Russia and Brazil), it is worth noting that out of all the Logan launches that took place in 2005, the ones that most resembled Romania occurred in countries where there were early plans to assemble the Logan (Columbia and Morocco) and/or where Renault already had a major presence. Because production location choices were partially linked to these parameters, the successful countries were also characterised–using criteria enunciated by Robin Law–by economic characteristics (GDP per capita or average wages) or structural attributes (state of the roads, after-sales competency, etc.) that were relatively similar to Romania.

A noteworthy case is Turkey where the Logan was launched in 2006. Entry range sales were rather successful here, but Turkey was also where the Thalia was being produced, meaning that it was in Renault's interest to emphasize the marketing of this latter vehicle. Note as well the Bulgarian market that peaked at slightly more than 50,000 passenger cars in 2007 and whose configuration was very similar to Romania, with the Fabia dominating locally before the Logan broke through. Since 2005, as many Logans have been sold in Bulgaria as in Poland.

Colombia, where total volumes vary between 100,000 and 200,000 passenger cars per annum, is an interesting case testing the Logan's ability to travel far from its original design base. Because the Logan was supposed to be assembled in Columbia, it was launched very early (2Q2005) here under the Renault brand name. Conditions were relatively favourable given widespread public recognition that the product was made in Colombia and because the Renault Thalia already had a major presence in the country.

The Columbian launch was in late summer 2005. By December, the Logan had a more than 5% market share. The cohabitation with the Thalia quickly turned to the Logan's advantage, despite Renault still selling models produced in Argentina. Since Renault already knew how to get the Thalia to coexist with the rest of its Columbian range, the decision to add a similar but cheaper product did not particularly bother the brand guardians in terms of the effects on Renault's image elsewhere. The assumption from late 2005 onwards was that the Logan could also sell as a Renault in certain markets.

With its 32 million inhabitants, Morocco–where the Logan had also been launched in 2Q2005–featured a Romanian-like configuration, albeit with 2005 sales of 64,000 passenger cars and a lower market share. Here, the Logan was meant to become a tool of internationalisation and market domination, backed by powerful political support ensuring the development of local industry. Before the Sandero's launch, Dacia had a market share of about 15% in Morocco. The Logan showed that despite disappointing commercial performance in a country not too distant from its industrial birthplace and the region where it was still being designed (Eastern Europe), the product retained considerable potential beyond a certain GDP per capita threshold ($3,600 in 2005), that is, as long as car ownership rates were similar to Romania.

Table 1.3–Logan and its competitors: Entry range volumes in Morocco

	Sept. 2004	March 2005	Sept. 2005	March 2006	Sept. 2006	March 2007	Sept. 2007	March 2008
Logan L90			9.8%	19.2%	14.9%	14.9%	12.2%	15.3%
Logan MCV			0.0%	0.0%	0.0%	0.0%	0.0%	0.0%
Thalia 1+2	2.5%	4.0%	2.0%	2.5%	2.6%	3.0%	3.6%	2.7%
Picasso	1.8%	0.3%	2.2%	2.5%	4.4%	6.7%	8.9%	6.0%
206	2.8%	3.7%	2.4%	4.4%	1.5%	2.0%	1.6%	2.5%
Punto	0.1%	0.1%	0.1%	0.0%	0.4%	0.5%	2.4%	1.8%
Fiesta	0.8%	0.1%	1.1%	0.8%	0.7%	1.5%	0.8%	1.8%
Accent	0.2%	1.5%	1.6%	2.0%	1.4%	0.8%	1.3%	1.3%

With its fast-growing automobile market exceeding 100,000 passenger cars in 2005, Algeria (32 million inhabitants and per capita GDP of $3,150), confirmed this potential. Competition was very strong here–unlike Morocco–and neither the Algerians nor their government would have been happy to see the market dominated by a Renault group that had chosen to make cars next door in Morocco, Algeria's great rival. Yet despite being threatened by the Hyundai Accent, the Thalia was a bestseller in Algeria, like it had been in Columbia. Moreover, even with this cohabitation and its use of the Dacia brand, the Logan was able to achieve a market share of around 8% in 2006, with unit sales of 103, 1.000 in 2005, 112.000 in 2006, and 156.000 in 2007.

Table 1.4–Logan and its competitors: Entry range volumes in Algeria

	Sept. 2004	March 2005	Sept. 2005	March 2006	Sept. 2006	March 2007	Sept. 2007	March 2008
Logan L90			4.2%	7.3%	7.4%	9.6%	2.9%	6.5%
Logan MCV			0.0%	0.0%	0.0%	0.0%	1.4%	1.2%
Thalia 1+2	5.4%	5.1%	4.1%	5.7%	5.1%	6.2%	5.0%	8.0%
Kalos + Aveo	0.0%	0.0%	0.0%	8.5%	3.4%	11.1%	6.1%	11.3%
Accent	2.0%	8.3%	11.1%	7.4%	9.8%	0.7%	5.2%	2.6%
800	3.0%	3.6%	3.6%	2.8%	2.7%	3.8%	5.9%	9.0%
Picanto	1.6%	3.0%	2.9%	2.0%	3.8%	4.0%	5.6%	5.2%
Matiz	0.5%	0.5%	0.7%	2.3%	2.7%	1.9%	5.1%	0.7%
Alto	0.0%	0.0%	0.0%	0.0%	0.7%	2.3%	8.4%	0.0%

Thus, if we consider the Logan's "first commercial life" such as it unfolded outside of Russia and France in 2004 and 2005, we get the following table for the first year:

Table 1.5–Logan sales before its Russian and French launches

Country	First sales	2004 sales	2005 sales
Romania	September 2004	20,274	88,275
Hungary	September 2004	970	2,596
Croatia	October 2004	155	926
Czech Republic	October 2004	248	2,515
Serbia Montenegro	November 2004	433	5,488
Slovakia	November 2004	131	1,133
Slovenia	January 2005		367
Morocco	July 2005		2,499
Algeria	May 2005		2,819
Turkey	November 200	477	8,317
Poland	February 2005		2,405

One clear lesson is that before the June 2005 launch in France, Logan sales did not fully use Pitesti's existing assembly capacities. This was critical, given Romania's key role in the car's production configuration. Disappointing sales in Eastern Europe could have caused major problems if the decision had not been taken to launch the Logan in France and Western Europe.

FRANCE AND WESTERN EUROPE: THE LOGAN'S SECOND LIFE

Should the Logan have been sold in France and Western Europe?

The question of whether the product–which people already knew in 2002/2003 would be launched in Central and Western Europe–should be sold in Renault's core markets was a hot topic for a long time in the Company. Like the decision imposed to have Logan badged as a Renault in Russia (see above), marketing in France and the EU15 broke the political compromise that had, up until that point, protected the project against potential attacks from within. Indeed, it was after promising his senior managers that the two red lines would not be crossed that Schweitzer gave Hurtiger and his teams the resources to advance by minimising hostility from the guardians of the Renault temple.

The "Battle of France" began belatedly. It more or less corresponded to the period when Ménard was running the International Department before heading Dacia from late 2002 onwards. Having managed the Group's German operations before serving as Sales Director for France, he had already seen that the race to more innovation and diversification had produced certain unwanted side effects in terms of new vehicles' sales prices, forcing some customers behave opportunistically. As Dacia President, on the other hand, he was loyal to the subsidiary's ambitions and soon saw that extending the project's target to include France and Western Europe would give it a whole other dimension with positive effects for the Pitesti plant and Dacia as a whole. According to Ménard, well before the June 2004 press conference that changed Schweitzer's mind and led to his 19 September 2004 announcement, there were several opportunities to ask whether he had already finalised his decision. The possibility was already being discussed in 2003, but only within a small circle comprised of Schweitzer, the Romanians and the teams run by Jean-Marie Hurtiger. A number of people were therefore surprised by the final announcement when it was made public in 2004.

Several fears were expressed at this time, first involving Renault's image, which had been discredited at the top-of-the-range ever since the disappointment of the Avantime (launched in late 2001 and withdrawn less than two years later). Similarly, the VelSatis, which came out in late 2002, had yet to find a solid customer base two years later. German specialists' success and Audi's rapid rise meant that generalists were all dreaming of a strong presence in the high value car segment. Hence Renault's ambitions, specifically for its networks, of developing a level of quality justifying premium branding, as encapsulated in its "Network Excellence Plan". In turn, this raised concerns that a low-cost product offer, even carrying the name of Dacia, might damage Renault's image. Another fear was that the Logan and its follow-on versions–which people were already talking about–might cannibalise Renault's traditional ranges and/or the network's used car sales, including sales made by Renault's short-term rental agencies. Lastly, on a social level, manufacturing outside of France was relatively easy to defend when the product was sold in the same markets as the ones where it was made. This was harder to argue when a large proportion of sales were in Western Europe.

Despite this, preliminary studies revealed significant potential and Ménard started monthly recruitments of allies taken from the sales teams and network. In the end, the press gave the product a very positive reception in June 2004, forcing the decision. This had begun in Spain with a very traditional Modus roadshow that, according to Ménard, got a lukewarm response, despite the model's importance for Renault (especially the Valladolid plant). Then, a few days later, the Logan was presented to the press. It was an immediate hit, surprising Renault's executive to the extent that Schweitzer ended up accepting the Romanians' arguments.

In a book entitled *Mes années Renault* ("My Years at Renault"), Schweitzer wrote that, "The press reaction made this an instantaneous success, surprising everyone here. We ended up on the evening news, which we had neither planned nor hoped for. The French media saw something that we hadn't, because they were not prisoners of our internal vision of the automobile. To be truthful, no other country in Western Europe where we presented the Logan reacted in the same way. I think we benefited at home from a conjunction of several factors. On one hand, there was the fact that hard discounting is a French invention. On the other, the Company involved was, after all, Renault, and when Renault creates something, France stops to look."

Schweitzer's feeling was that like any major innovation, Logan had gone well beyond what its designers originally hoped for. Henceforth (and specifically in France), the underlying logic would have little if anything to do with what designers had imagined. The managers in charge would have an enormous amount to do to cope with the unforeseen effects of this act of industrial and commercial audacity.

Against this background, we can examine the vehicle's launch in France through the period dating from June 2005 (launch of the notchback version, for petrol engines only) to June 2008 (the Sandero's launch). The first aspect is the importance of two events: the DCI version's launch in April 2006; and above all, the estate version's launch in December 2006. These three years were when the project achieved success without having to meet any specified objectives.

Once the launch was announced on 19 September 2004 on the Grand Jury RTL radio programme, Le Monde newspaper and LCI television, the tone was set by Schweitzer who was somewhat schizophrenically alternating between his role as Renault CEO–hence guardian of the Company's unity–and his job as secret project manager. "This is something that we hadn't thought about at the beginning", he admitted. Indeed, although the 2004 Trade Fair was approaching, the Logan remained undercover because no decision had been taken by the time Renault's stand was being organised. Schweitzer acknowledged the role of improvisation and indicated that Renault was expecting to sell the Logan in countries "where customers have fewer resources than in France". He changed his opinion, however, because "it is a good car and we have no reason to be ashamed of it". Above all, "people have shown a lot of interest that we did not expect". Schweitzer added that mainly because of transport costs, the car would retail for around 7,500 instead of 5,000; it would have the same price tag everywhere; and no discounts would be negotiated. He also decided that the Logan would be sold in France's Renault dealership network as a Dacia made "by Renault".

As if feeling contrite, Renault's CEO also tried to reassure Company sceptics without raising excessive hope amongst the project's supporters. He moved quickly to say that he did not expect "massive sales in France and Western Europe" given the mediocre success of cars whose boot is separated from the back seats. Schweitzer also did not expect the Logan to cannibalise sales of Renault's other small models since it did not target the exact same customer base. At the same time, he remained enthusiastic and proud of his "dancer… an interesting experiment basically because it has no precedents. It is a total innovation, not in the high-tech sense but in terms of the ideas being implemented. It is a total innovation in the automobile market." Along similar lines, Schweitzer also said that he "did not really know" which customer base would buy the car in France and guessed that, "Used car purchasers will buy it, as will people buying much smaller cars than they really want to."

This was a way of announcing how the Logan might be managed in France over the months and years to come. Schweitzer was laying out the main lines of this move, while recognising or at least assuming that improvisation would be needed as Renault learnt more about the market for its new product; about how it might be integrated into existing networks; and about whether Dacia or Renault should include it at a more upstream level as one of the Group's Entry projects. Already as a precursor to this approach, the Group's Director of Sales at the time, François Hinfray, told the press in autumn 2004 as he was starting to work on the Logan launch that its later versions (estate, minivan) would be more adapted to Western European markets then its initial sedan version had been.

From that point onwards with the Logan, Renault came under scrutiny from the whole of its profession. This is because the product was being run by rules that were very different from what other manufacturers were doing, to the extent that its launch in France and Europe took many people by surprise, much in the same way as it surprised Renault's product or sales staff. This is because of their inclination to view customers as constantly demanding more in the hope of being able to buy vehicles enriched by increasingly sophisticated technology, an assumption that would be disproved if the Logan were successful. A May 2005 article published in the magazine *Stratégies*[1] devoted to the Logan's upcoming launch attested to this sense of being overtaken by events. The Logan soon became an "affair", raising issues that were bigger than Renault itself. The *Stratégies* article, for instance, spoke of some marketing professionals' enthusiasm for the concept and reported that Xavier Astori, Kia France's Director for Communications and Marketing, believed that "The Logan is surfing on

---

1. *Stratégies* is a weekly magazine aimed at marketing professionals from all sectors.

the wave of the *No Logo*[1] anti-consumption movement. It is also related to the trend towards house brands. After all, unlike the IT industry, the automobile is one of the rare markets where lower prices are not the rule." Similarly, Georges Lewi, brand specialist and BEC Institute Director, thought that the Logan would succeed because "whereas the quality of entry-level products continues to improve, consumers are questioning the prices for branded products." For brand strategy expert Marie-Claude Sicard, the Logan's Renault "reference is coherent with the Group's 'creator of automobiles' strapline and trends observed in the fashion world with Lagerfeld's H&M collection."

For comments on the role played by the press and its enthusiasm for the decision to market the Logan in the West, the magazine turned to Yves Del Frate, PSA budget manager at media consulting group MPG (Havas), and Christophe Decultot, Fiat's passenger car brand manager. Both replicated the tunes sung by the sceptics, saying respectively that, "Media noise is one thing but French consumers' reaction is another. I would like to know how many journalists drive a Logan. Today, the automobile market reacts to basic requirements such as novelty and innovation. This is not an area where people engage in impulse buying. From a value for money mindset, what they are now looking for is 'modernity for money'. Because a car carries both a person's family and their social image." (Yves Del Frate) "The market for simple cars is very marginal today. All of the segments, including the entry ranges, sell their models with multiple options and modern accessories." (Christophe Decultot)

The magazine went on to say that "an unexpected success would be just as problematic for Renault" given that "on the rapidly growing market for cars costing less than €10,000, the new Peugeot 107, Citroën C1, Toyota Aygo and Volkswagen Foxe–but also the Renault Twingo–can expect to have some problems." It even considered that, "In case the Logan becomes successful, with prices varying in France between €7,500 and €8,990, Mégane-type segments could also suffer"–all of which "clearly explains why Renault did not bring out its heavy artillery when launching its latest model."

Agnès Lombois, Renault's Logan Product Manager, working out of the French Sales Department, stated, "We expect to sell fewer than 10% of our Logans in the West", explaining that the French communications effort

---

1. Very successful book written by Naomi Klein and published in 2000, which launched a ferocious attack on certain mechanisms used in the world of marketing and advertising.

would be minimal, featuring a traditional launch week between 9 to 13 June, a mailshot, and an advertising campaign mainly geared towards regional dailies. It was against a background shaped (and perturbed) by this existing debate that the launch would happen in the network.

How Renault's French customers and sales organisation related to the Logan

The commercial dynamic associated with the Logan–and the success thereof–more or less justified the stance taken by those who had been in favour of launching in France (see Figures 1.2 and 1.3). Similarly, fears that Renault sales would be cannibalised by Dacia sales also abated progressively.

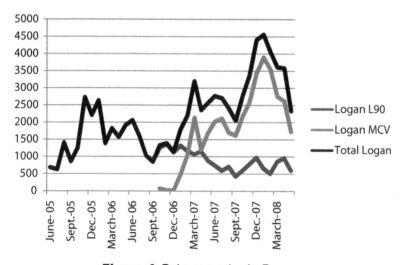

Figure 1.2–Logan sales in France

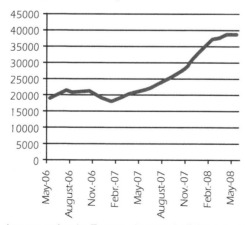

Figure 1.3–Logan sales in France (annual sliding cumulative total)

In total, the sales statistic show that even without any promotions, the Logan quickly achieved an enviable position in France's new car market, with a share of around 1% excluding the MCV estate version or ca. 2% (40,000 units sold annually) including it.

For the French Sales Department and network, this relative success was a very useful experiment due to its novelty aspect. The marketing policy post-July 2005 opted for a system where distribution became the responsibility of the Renault network working out of their normal points-of-sale, with the same salespersons receiving a small flat rate. This was instead of building a Dacia network such as it already existed elsewhere, with remuneration depending more traditionally on the number of units sold. Some viewed this as a sign of Renault's desire to prevent the product from succeeding, but in reality, it showed a clear desire to initiate a "pull" system at a time when all distribution professionals were accustomed to functioning on a "push" basis. This experiment was launched in France and over the long run the system it tested found a home here.

A combination of five elements were involved:

- Politically, it was a good idea to be commercially very aggressive while pretending to launch the product on an experimental basis, without hoping to achieve substantial volumes and so as to avoid parallel imports;
- The volumes on offer in France came on top of production capacities that had been installed to satisfy other demands;
- The distribution structures being used were justified by Renault's own sales, meaning that the fixed costs they generated were covered by the combination of Renault's sales/after-sales so there was no longer any need to push Dacia sales;
- Dacia's product offer had no direct competitor and its value for customers could mainly be judged in comparison with a used car alternative that was not even available in the network. In short, Dacia could achieve a breakthrough whether or not it was being pushed;
- Dacia's production capacities would soon turn out to be insufficient to satisfy demand. In turn, this created a situation that was the opposite of traditional experiments. With the luxury of making customers wait (and even choosing them), spending money to attract them would be a waste.

These elements would only manifest themselves little by little. Thus, over 2005/2006—one year following the launch—there were still doubts about the decision to launch the Logan in France and to pursue a "pull" approach.

During this pioneering phase, Renault's sales teams tried to analyse whether:

- The product was reaching targets above and beyond the ones touched by its usual customary product policies and marketing drives;
- The novel sales process dealing with the customers in question was adequate.

As the prospect of a steadily broader range began to materialise, different analyses paved the way for future changes both in Dacia's positioning in Western Europe and in the associated sales processes.

Verifying the absence of cannibalisation and qualifying the target

In terms of the first aspect, Agnès Lombois dissected sales between June and August 2005 to profile the customer base and measure the gap between Renault and Dacia customers. Buyers' names were used to extract (so-called AAA) grey card data from relevant available sources, including age, gender, socio-professional category, place of residence and whether the vehicle had been resold during the purchasing period. Since Logan sales through the network were done without any takeback schemes, this was the only reliable way to address what is a fundamental aspect. More specifically, the study identified the vehicles in question (brand, model, etc.) by their age and when they had been acquired, either new or used. By demonstrating, for instance, that the average profile of the car being replaced corresponded to thirteen or fourteen years, with the vehicles having been owned for six or seven years (hence acquired when they were six or seven years old), the study confirmed that Logan buyers were being recruited from populations that were not very familiar with brand networks. Salespersons or sales managers' narratives at the time confirmed these findings, and automobile blog studies enhanced understanding of how the sales processes were adjusting to the new targets.

"Logan blogs" provided further confirmation of these findings. Many of the vehicles that bloggers owned were 309s, ZXs, R19s or R21s and it was to these cars (or the used ones that they could have bought for the same price) that they compared the Logan, not the competition. Surprisingly, expressions of interest in the Logan emanating from these blogs came from individuals with a "utilitarian" relationship to the automobile, in the sense that they had already ordered a car or were planning to do so. There were a multitude of comments and questions about the vehicle's technical aspects, often featuring sharp comparisons with its predecessors. There was also a systematic examination of how much room the car had and its habitability, soundproofing and boot size. Over questions asked about acceleration, takeback schemes and road handling. The "Loganist" credo that was starting to take shape showed that the people involved did not want to "be ripped off". This was exemplified by discussions of manufacturers' inept efforts to introduce electronics and gadgets everywhere, the crass overspending on advertising or salespersons' incompetency.

Logan customers also seemed to be in the habit of squeezing maintenance costs. Many worried about this sort of expense and tried to figure out how it might be contained. Unaccustomed to dealing with dealerships, potential or actual buyers would wonder what these parties were like, while expressing concerns, for instance, about how quickly tires wear down and how much replacements cost. All in all, they clearly intended to abandon the network as soon as possible, with some even advising buyers to drop out of their primary and secondary networks without any further ado. In short, the Logan was attractive to people who refused to "be ripped off" and tried to avoid paying more than they had to. The car was appreciated because its proposition was clear and coherent, addressing people's unsatisfied expectations. Having said that, because the network did not seem to support the proposition, customers who were grateful to Renault for offering the Dacia Logan also requested greater coherency. What this revealed to the Company was a desire to be protected from networks that were perceived if not as hostile, then at least as embedded in commercial and after-sales cultures that were more or less out of touch with what customers were looking for.

How the Dacia sales process dealt with customers in France

The issues raised by Renault networks' capacity for dealing with these new "targets" relate to the originality of the distribution choices and people's sense of how hard it is to get a traditional and a Logan logic to coexist within the same networks and sales teams.

- *The originality of the Logan's distribution choices in Western Europe*

When the decision was made to market the Logan in France, the argument used by the network representatives at the beginning of this period of change was that due to a lack of organisation, they wanted to prevent their marketing effort being taken over "by gangs", leading to a situation where the Logan would end up being imported by proxy agents. In other words, theirs was a politically constrained choice and there was no question of selling the product otherwise than through the Renault network. This led to the decision to refurbish the showrooms to include little Dacia "corners" that would be identified by signage featuring the brand's colours. A kit comprised of awning and point-of-sale advertising (replete with a colour chart) was sent to the primary sites where a Dacia contract had been signed. Depending on the size of the business, group managers' wishes or Renault representatives' demands, there would be one or two demo vehicles embodying the Dacia product on offer. Clearly, the aim was to save costs while avoiding any conflict with Renault promotions or undercutting high showroom standards.

Similarly, limited remuneration was paid for Logan sales, with dealerships only receiving €350 per unit and advised to pay their sales staff no more than €45. No one wanted to see these sales included in their Renault objectives, which were the be all and end all for salespersons, sales managers, site managers and their counterparts in Renault's sales organisation. Similarly, there was intentionally very little advertising and people refused to organise takeback schemes or offer discounts.

Clearly, these choices were coherent with the low cost "concept" and defended as such, including by many customers. It remains that, implicitly, Renault executives, sales managers and above all network operatives would readily construe these choices as a message discouraging Logan sales. At the same time, the situation triggered a learning process that led to the emergence of a sales strategy which was basically founded on arguments and conclusions rooted in these initial choices, whose virtues people would start to discover and formalise over the next few months.

- *The difficulty of getting two different commercial logics to coexist*

Cannibalisation was a very topical issue at first within the network, but one that would be resolved within a short period of time. By 2006, there was a general consensus that the situation was one of "non-cannibalisation". From that point onwards, the Logan–like the product range that would soon follow–became (in the minds of the actors involved in the sales process) a tool of conquest that would bring the networks into contact with populations of households and kinds of vehicles with whom they were no or no longer familiar. Most of the time, what would happen after a few months of experimenting is that people developed the strong conviction that they had discovered a "well" of customers and "business" for the networks, hence something that it would be wrong not to exploit. Divergences would only happen downstream, when people were trying, for instance, to ascertain the size of the "well" and the best way of accessing it.

Questions about the durability of the Dacia "corners" system, with its shared sales teams, were already being asked in 2006, with everyone involved defending a panoply of solutions ranging from keeping the initial Logan system to having a Dacia showroom replete with dedicated salespersons, and including the idea of setting up an "open air Dacia tent" in a mall. Having adopted a triple product/customer identification/sales site approach, by 2005/2006 Renault's sales professionals were already engaged in a learning process that began when the Logan first started to be marketed. Whether their preconception had been negative or positive, however, everyone soon changed their mind. In the end, what evolved was a large consensus that the Logan could be a tool used to conquer new clienteles. Although some continued to hope that Renault might develop new and adapted instruments towards this end, by 2006 most everyone appreciated the experimental possibilities enabled by the product's somewhat marginal status, which allowed them to test solutions and develop their own approaches. Nor were there any real conflicts at this level since nobody had been dictated to by a manufacturer who, for once, was not acting as if it knew more than the network did.

Taking a closer look at the issue of remuneration, however, the original way in which the Logan was handled met with less positive responses. Quite the contrary, there was a real need to resolve conflict at this level. Salespersons were almost unanimous in condemning the decision not to include Logan sales in their Renault objectives. Yet this was strongly defended by the teams that the manufacturer had put in charge of Dacia. At all intermediary levels, ranging from sales managers to regional directors (and including site managers and network team managers), reactions were very different.

Almost all of the dealerships organised a sales briefing every morning. This included a chart featuring monthly or semester sales objectives that everybody had been assigned, with each participant being asked how much they had sold and/or what prospects they had. The "table" was therefore key to salespersons' incentives and control mechanisms, and managers were responsible for breaking down the objectives that the manufacturer defined for each dealership. Clearly, remuneration depended directly on this, with the value of a sale assessed by whether it met or (above all) exceeded volume objectives that the salesperson has been given. Other criteria supplementing and adjusting the incentives mechanisms included credit arrangements, maintenance contracts and window engravings. The real crux of a salesperson's professional life, however, remained the number of units sold, if only because this measure has always been so central to the profitability of the whole business.

This explains why salespersons' main complaint about the Dacia sales process was what many called "not being on the table". Much more than the relatively poor remuneration they got for each sale, this flat rate payment for sales, irrespective of their objectives, was unanimously condemned. It gave the best Logan salespersons a sense of injustice, with less effective counterparts using the same mechanism to justify their mediocre efforts. One salesperson from this latter group expressed the situation thusly: "As long as sales do not feature on the table, they won't be a priority for salespersons and Logan sales will stagnate. Organising a system this way is as if that they are telling us that they really don't care what volumes we do."

It remains that this mediocre flat rate remuneration can be easily justified through certain observations that the salespersons themselves made. Three arguments emerged at this level: firstly, these were easy sales since the product spoke for itself, customers knew what they want and no takebacks or discounts had to be discussed; secondly, the range was very narrow, meaning that options were rare and there was no real competition (i.e. sales arguments were relatively easy); lastly, the concept's coherency required an effort at all different levels.

In terms of the main argument used to justify the Logan's non-inclusion in salespersons' quotas, on the sales and business sides alike it was noted that a discount-free sales system might help to simplify and clean up the sales process but would survive neither the inclusion of Dacia sales in the Renault quotas nor the assignment of specific quotas to Dacia. On top of this, the "push" logic corresponding to these quotas could only be justified by weak demand for product and strong competition. Conversely, where demand was strong, indirect competition and production capacities that were insufficient vis-à-vis demand levels meant there was no reason to abandon the pull logic by offering to make sacrifices that the customers did not require.

Sales teams generally used two arguments to oppose these objections. The first consisted of saying that if people wanted to do big volumes and hurried to make sales before the competition arrived, there was only one solution. The second consisted of pretending that it was very possible to apply quotas without having to offer discounts. All that had to happen was for management to prohibit these kinds of practices and police this: "When you see how much time Renault spends on checking guaranteed network operations, we don't see why it can't agree to police people's behaviour and reduce temptation."

In short, the specificity of the Logan sales was that they were very high during the car's pioneering phase. This made it difficult to integrate them into a sales process that had been simple and transparent until that point. In a universe where the fiction of vertically controlling what needed to be done had become everyone's overriding paradigm, the Logan enabled and/ or required experimentation.

- *An open commercial learning process*

One of the strengths of the Logan business was to have been subjected from the very outset to a slightly ad hoc "deployment" strategy, one born out of the form of schizophrenia that surrounded the launch in France and Western Europe. Instead of being certain about things like what the product's positioning should be, its objectives or sales arguments, the process let customers take the first step themselves and only revealed the Logan's quantitative and qualitative potential later on. A long series of open debates coincided with this learning process. In the end, Renault's executive became less adamant about defining and defending principles underlying the Logan's specificity. The frontline legitimacy that they ultimately achieved (with great difficulty) came from their having given each hierarchical level room to conduct its own debate.

Over time, the pro and con sides even seem to have swapped arguments. Sceptics became the greatest fans of the Dacia corners and shared sales team solutions, considering that the potential was otherwise relatively modest and that Renault sales had to be the priority. For this reason, they did not feel it was a good idea to get to know Dacia customers or treat them any better. Conversely, those who believed in the potential revealed to them through this open experimentation quickly concluded that the methods in question needed structuring. Hence their specification of a sales approach prevent the "well" from being exploited by anyone else and/or under-used by Renault. Given that a crisis came on the heels of their success, the latter camp was vindicated in their battle against the former at the time of the Sandero's launch. Having said that, this "pull" phase lasted sufficiently long for this to take place without any of the improvements that it had driven having to be abandoned.

RUSSIA: THE LOGAN'S VICTORIOUS RETURN TO ITS REGION OF BIRTH

From Dacia to Renault

One month after France, the Logan was launched in Russia. For Schweitzer, whose seminal intuition first materialised here in 1997, this was a very important project stage. Dacia and Romania had been an opportunity to build his famous €5,000 car but, in terms of Renault's volumes and positioning in the larger emerging markets, there was a further hoop to jump through. This was due to the fact that there was no market where Renault had positions equivalent to the other major European generalists, like Fiat in Brazil or VW in Brazil and China. In the early 2000s, things were a lot more open in Russia, however, and Renault had a chance to make a big breakthrough.

For these reasons, Schweitzer asked Ménard to prioritise this business when he arrived at the International Department in 2002. Asides from industrial aspects (see Chapter 2), subsequent negotiations would relate to the product's "badge". This is because Renault's initial intent had been to sell a Dacia Logan in Russia and reserve the Renault brand that was already known there for vehicles from its traditional ranges, especially the Mégane that had been recently launched and could reasonably hope to compete with the Ford Focus, Russia's best seller at the time. It remains that the Russian partners saw things quite differently and without Schweitzer having anticipated this, Ménard would return from Moscow with a very firm *niet*. There was no way that Avtoframos' Russian managers wanted their product "to commit suicide" by associating it with the standard images of Dacia or Romania in Russia, which were deplorable. In their view, this would be tantamount to positioning the product as having intrinsic qualities that were recognisably inferior to AvtoVAZ–which, although neither better nor worse than the Dacia before the fall of communism, at least had the merit of being Russian.

In 2003, the product had yet to be launched anywhere and would continue, at Renault and elsewhere, to provoke doubt. Schweitzer knew that meeting Russian demands could make his project politically more fragile. Since 1999, he had been saying that the Logan would not be sold in France and Western Europe and that the car he had in mind here was a Dacia and not a Renault. By so doing, he was protecting the project against those who, internally, viewed it as a threat to Renault. He was also trying to gain maximum leverage from the efforts that had been carried out for years to enhance Renault's quality and brand image so that it could compete with the Germans and Peugeot-Citroën. In addition, across the industry and specifically in relation to Carlos Ghosn at Nissan, many people thought that the only way of making profits would be by developing, if not a brand, then at least a "premium" range. This was a period when Nissan was getting ready to imitate Toyota and its Lexus models by launching the Infiniti not only in Japan but also in the United States and Russia, at a time when the VelSatis' failure had become patent. The sign that it was being asked to send to Russia appeared, in this context, as something quite unwelcome.

For all these reasons, Schweitzer held back and asked Ménard to have a second go at the Russians. They maintained their stance, however, so it was Schweitzer who finally gave up. In the end, what ultimately happened in Russia in early 2004 was something that Renault had not wanted to see in Central Europe–namely the manufacturing and sale in Russia of a Renault Logan, instead of a Dacia.

Enviable positioning

Russia had many similarities with Romania but clearly differed in terms of volume (hence significance for Renault's future). The Romanian approach had more or less worked for the Logan, although the car had to constantly position itself not only in relation to imports (some of which were being assembled in Russia) but also with regards to AvtoVAZ products. Where the Logan successfully crowded out traditional products in Romania– having been conceived towards that end–in Russia it faced ongoing competition. Nor could it be considered an entry-level vehicle, unlike its rival, the VAZ. Russian buyers viewed the Logan as an "import" (with everything this means in terms of image, improved performance and reliability) that was reasonably priced.

The product therefore found itself in a kind of no man's land. On one hand, it was being compared with "imports" because it bore the Renault brand. However, it was less expensive and not as adapted to local conditions, including the income levels of the Russian middle classes to whom Putin's administration had redistributed much of the rent derived from natural gas production. On the other hand, the Logan was also viewed as an entry-level vehicle that was mainly Russian in origin. The country already had something similar with the Daewoo Nexia–an Opel Kadett from an earlier avatar, albeit slightly more expensive and much more modern and reliable.

Renault's Russian marketing teams and the consultancies they hired called the category of households whom they targeted "climbers" that wanted to escape traditional Russian products but could only do this if they were offered an alternative that cost them one and a half Zhigulis instead of two.[1] Because the local stock was largely comprised of VAZ cars and (unfortunately for the Russians) because the government blocked used car imports, the target population was very large. In 2005, the Logan was the only product meeting this demand, meaning that it again found itself in a very strong competitive position, hence with a real capacity for being sold profitably without any major commercial struggles.

Table 1.6–The Logan versus other entry-level vehicles in Russia

	Sept. 2004	March 2005	Sept. 2005	March 2006	Sept. 2006	March 2007	Sept. 2007	March 2008
Logan			0.8%	3.0%	2.9%	3.4%	2.7%	3.2%
Thalia 1+2	0.6%	0.7%	0.6%	0.3%	0.3%	0.3%	0.4%	0.3%
Samara	17.7%	16.3%	15.5%	12.1%	9.6%	7.0%	7.5%	5.8%
Lada Zhiguli	16.0%	13.7%	12.9%	9.8%	9.9%	8.4%	8.3%	6.7%
Priora							3.4%	3.5%
Kalina			1.1%	3.5%	3.0%	2.5%	3.1%	3.2%
Nexia	2.1%	3.9%	1.8%	2.9%	3.1%	1.9%	1.8%	2.1%
Accent	1.6%	2.2%	2.4%	2.6%	1.6%	2.2%	2.9%	1.9%
Matiz	0.9%	1.5%	0.6%	1.7%	1.8%	1.4%	1.9%	1.7%
Lanos				2.3%	3.1%	2.6%	2.2%	2.1%
Getz	1.1%	1.2%	0.9%	0.9%	0.1%	0.6%	1.6%	1.5%

---

1. Or the *Zhiguli*, VAZ 2104-107, a model derived from the Fiat 124 with a basic version costing less than $3,000.

Sales data show that from 2005 onwards, the Logan created a new market segment in Russia, one whose high volumes (albeit lower than the Ford Focus) enabled Renault to position itself as one of the country's brand leaders. Thus, whereas in 2007 more than 30,000 more Focuses were sold than Logans, by the next year the gap was only 19,000, with GM's Lacetti–assembled in Kalingrad–coming between the two.

Over 2006, 2007 and 2008, the Logan would contest the supremacy of VAZ's three signature products, the Kalina, 2104/5/7 and Samara. Despite being a little more expensive, by offering an alternative to Lada the Logan was helping to build the famous "climbers" group. From the perspective of the Russian authorities and in terms of their management of the AvtoVAZ situation, Renault's ability to manufacture a mass vehicle in Russia–one enabling the middle classes to access reliable modern vehicles–carried a lot of weight and added credibility to the Company's commitment to transform the Togliatti industrial complex and the range of vehicles being manufactured there. An agreement with AvtoVAZ was finally signed in 2008, a few years after the Logan first came to the market (see above).

The crushing weight of the Logan

The concerns expressed at Renault when Schweitzer agreed to use the company name in Russia seemed globally justified. In local sales managers' view, the Logan dominated the market from 2006 onwards and Renault's position in Russia was akin to its dominance in France during the 1950s when the Company's famous 4 cv was almost the only model on the market. The shadow cast by the Logan's success in Russia (ie vis-à-vis the Mégane, or the Koléos and Laguna 3 in 2008) was not nearly as long, however. Indeed, in Russia the Logan was Renault, accounting for nearly 70% of the Company's sales in this country. Before it was launched in late 2005, Renault had sold 15,000 cars in 2004 and 28,000 in 2005. In 2006, sales hit 72,000 (including 49,000 Logans). In 2007, they exceeded 100,000 (including 60,000 Logans).

Brand notoriety was therefore being built around a signature product, one generally viewed as a Russian product, particularly in the region of Moscow where it was made. At the time, Russia was being profiled as an opportunity for Renault–and the Alliance–to gain a BRICs foothold as meaningful as the one that GM, VW and Fiat had in Brazil. With this success and the hopes raised by later launches (the Sandero in March 2010 and the Duster in late 2011), Renault was able, even before signing the agreement with AvtoVAZ, to look like a big driver behind the Russian market's expansion and structuring. By so doing, the Group changed its image and not only entered the club of manufacturers with operations in Russia but also became one of a select few that was actually able to penetrate the Russian market.

Distribution

As had been the case in Romania, building a distribution network worthy of this name was an epic adventure. Renault had to adapt to a country where automakers would deliver vehicles but do little else. At the worst of times, they even had to barter with suppliers to get parts that they could not settle otherwise. The Russian automobile trade was not very transparent and the recruitment of "partners" in the early 2000s highly problematic.

During the Putin era, some very large multi-brand distribution groups learned how to stand up to the big global carmakers that had been tempted by the Russian Eldorado. With almost all of the big manufacturers making overtures to them, these groups–which often sold more vehicles in Russia than the carmakers manufactured there–were able to share and compare their respective positionings, deciding whether or not to continue working with these external partners and why they might wish to change their product or sales policies.

Distributors could not help but be attracted to a single variant product that obviously dominated its market, was positioned clearly and did not have any real competition. On the other hand, this added to their traditional ranges' handicap, specifically for less widely sold models that distributors would simply refuse to stock or even display in their showrooms. With these arguments and given the promises evoked by the prospect of future launches, the Renault network was broadly able to expand, often to the detriment of its main competitors. The Logan's launch, together with long-term work done by the Russian sales team (led by Denis Le Vot), helped the Company to develop its network and change its appearance.

This expansive and increasingly demanding approach ensured (and was itself driven by) the product's success. Because the Logan was a clear success and held great promise for the future, it would have been damaging for any large distribution group not to have Renault in its brand portfolio and/or to refuse to undertake the investments that Renault requested. This allowed

Renault's sales teams to force investors to compete with one another, both to undermine rival brands' distribution and to convince investors to abandon them.

As would happen later in Brazil, this approach–involving negotiations with very large distribution groups–was one of the main lessons that Renault, relying on the Logan as a tool, had learnt from its accelerated internationalisation phase. Although the Company did not have sufficient internal resources for the requisite investment–as Henry Ford had discovered in the 1910s in the United States[1]–this was to become a key element in its ability to develop market power and achieve a modicum of irreversibility in its positioning. In mature markets (especially in its home market) a manufacturer will do everything it can–even if this puts it in a difficult situation–to organise the distribution function so that its "partners" have as little negotiating room as possible and must accept its dictates. Back in France, for instance, Renault was very mistrustful of "mega-dealers". It was quite happy, moreover, that they had a lesser presence in Renault's Russian distribution networks than they did in other brands' networks in this country.

Russia epitomised the opposite logic, namely that the intermediation function assumed by the large distribution groups should be viewed as an expansive lever and/or as a key locus for the competition between large manufacturers. This explains why Renault, when presenting its business in Russia, depicted its counterparts as proud of standing alongside the markets' biggest players.

Featuring in a portfolio comprised of these giant companies was considered a sign of success. Renault's Russian teams–like the ones in Brazil–would communicate to headquarters distributors' demands for simplified product ranges or greater respect for local market characteristics. This tactic was used relatively frequently to counterbalance a headquarters logic perceived as being too European (and even French). Using distributors and their weight to send messages matching their own convictions became a political weapon that the "Russians" of Renault would often use.

All in all, since before the Sandero's launch in 2008–and given its close association with "the Brazilian adventure"–the Logan was the only vehicle

---

1. This refers to the decision made by Henry Ford in 1916 when he turned his back on subsidiaries and handed his entire retail distribution network to independent agents. It has been detailed in a book written by the American historian Richard Tedlow called *New and Improved: The Story of Mass Marketing in America* (1990).

that, just four years after starting its trading life, could be said to have achieved some major successes alongside the problems it had faced. The general feedback was pretty positive, with the Pitesti plant's manufacturing programmes having been multiplied by factor of four between the initial forecasts in 1999 and the actual levels in 2005.

Beyond this spectacular increase in volumes, a lot had been learned, due to the product's highly innovative nature and the associated sales approach, all of which helped to drive development. Outside of France and Western Europe where the product was the first real opportunity to experiment with a "pull" approach, the focus was on building networks enabling the Company to play major role in developing emerging markets. Because they did not seem very different to what had been initially envisaged in Central Europe, it was in Eastern Europe (especially Romania), Columbia and then Russia that the foundations for this new commercial know-how took shape.

Table 1.7–The Logan's annual sales from 2004 to 2007

Brands	Regions	2004	2005	2006	2007
Dacia	Europe	2,080	30,309	47,396	80,042
	France		9,800	18,791	32,684
	Germany		2,043	6,292	17,312
	Euromed	20,751	102,272	127,284	136,433
	Romania	20,274	88,275	96,037	101,799
	Morocco		2,499	12,723	12,638
	Algeria		2,819	8,560	9,090
	Turkey		8,317	7,352	8,951
	Eurasia		1,029	6,423	10,189
	Asia-Africa	2	1,574	3,362	3,613
	Americas			7	0
Total Dacia		22,833	135,184	184,472	230,277
Renault	**Eurasia** = Russia		7,057	49,323	67,844
	Asia-Africa		0	0	28,432
	India				17,771
	Iran				10,656
	Americas		2,858	13,811	40,466
	Columbia		1,894	7,219	9,450
	Brazil				14,604
Total Renault		0	9,915	63,134	136,742
TOTAL LOGAN		22,833	145,099	247,606	367,019

Against this backdrop, and whether or not the product were being badged as Dacia or Renault, by 2007 they had started to account for big volumes and were helping Renault to become a less marginal player in markets such as Russia.

In addition, although European and "Euromed" sales were being served out of the Romanian production site (which struggled to respond to this demand), the same applied neither in Russia nor in Brazil, where–as we will see below–production capacities were customised so that from 2008 onwards new ambitions could be nourished affecting the future of the "Entry" range.

Interview with Louis Schweitzer

How did the Logan project emerge? What was the context at the time at Renault? And how did you come up with this idea?

Louis Schweitzer: The idea was born in stages. In autumn 1995, there was a meeting between Group executives where I announced Renault's further internationalisation. Until this time, people had always talked about its European destiny but now we were looking at development further afield, on an unprecedented scale.

The reaction was enthusiastic, especially since we were also announcing the Brazilian market's opening. One audience member suggested that it would be useful for Renault to acquire a second brand. He was thinking about Delage, a top-of-the-range product. The scars we carried from the Volvo era were still very present. I think I answered that I wasn't opposed to the idea of a second brand but if we had one, it should be below Renault, meaning that we would be developing something at the entry level. This reflected my own experiences when I negotiated with Skoda and became convinced that, like VW with Seat firstly and Skoda later, any second brand would have to help us offer cheaper vehicles targeting lower income customers who could not afford the Renault brand otherwise.

Were you already thinking about countries with lower average incomes or did you have the developed world in mind?

L. S.: Clearly we were looking at countries with lower per capita income. I was thinking about emerging markets like Brazil or Eastern Europe. Renault's major focus was improving its image and quality, avoiding any compromises in performance terms. The power of our brand did not allow us, however, to penetrate these emerging markets using this strategy. Hence the idea of a second entry-level brand associated with Renault's internationalisation.

In 1996, we were also having to deal with closure of the Vilvorde site. These problems were more urgent. We always kept this brand idea in the back of our minds, however.

In your mind or your teams'?

L. S.: Mainly mine at this point. I found it hard communicating my vision to my teams. This was not really something that came to them naturally.

A new stage was reached in autumn 1997 when I went on an official trip to Russia with President Chirac and Prime Minister Jospin. We were thinking about establishing Renault in Russia and I was there to accompany the delegation and negotiate a deal. I used the opportunity to visit a dealership, actually a vast hangar where they were selling Ladas retailing about $6,000 at the time. I came back with the notion that this was a good price level for a "modern, robust and affordable" car. This then became the three specifications that I established for our project

From that point onwards, discussions started with our Product, Engineering and Marketing departments. We ran seminars called "Corporate rendezvous", with each focusing on a major obstacle presented in the form of an apparently unsolvable dilemma. Either we had to make the cheapest possible components, requiring major investments and adding to the risk of a project whose ultimate success was very uncertain; or else we would have to use existing components and run the risk that these would be too expensive and keep us from building the car. We played hide and go seek with Jacques Lacambre, our Director for Advanced Studies. We also had a series of meetings that I chaired at the Department for Research and Pre-Projects without anything ever really materialising.

Renault executives and design teams also put their heads together alongside of this. The design people were interested because they were always trying out new projects and thought it might be fun to do something out of the box. The specifications people saw this as a German sort of project, meaning that its image had to be robust. From the outset, the consensus was that it would be a notchback, because this is the most economic form to produce and does not have the same soundproofing problems as a hatchback.

What I remember from this stage was people's lack of belief in the project. We then chose a project manager who was not a star at Renault but later showed what he was really worth.[1] Having said that, he could never have been a star since the project did not attract any stars.

Are you the one who thought of this person and appointed him?

L. S.: Yes. There was a lot of scepticism even on the Executive Committee, so I announced on Europe 1 radio that we were going to make a $6,000 car, as if the decision had been approved by everyone. In reality, this was far from the truth. Of course, my idea was to make waves and challenge the Company.

From that point onwards, things built up around the Project Director, with the design being stabilised shortly thereafter. Actually, we were surprised at how well the project went. The vehicle engineering team was able to build a synthetic car, what the English call a "Frankenstein", assembled from existing parts. Thus, we did not use the Mégane platform since that would cost too much. Instead, we took items from various cars that provided very good value for money because we could then include them in our cost specifications.

Then came the Dacia takeover. Was this operation closely linked to the Logan project?

L. S.: The negotiations were led by our Director for International Operations at the time. If I remember correctly, they took two long and very hard years. Ultimately, we bought the factory for almost nothing, around $50 million for a 50% stake, a laughable sum in the automotive industry. But this was crucial to kick-starting our low-cost business (wages were €1 an hour versus €20 at Renault) and also because we need to put pressure on the system. After all, once you have the factory, you must use it.

Did the Romanian government force you into the Logan to qualify as a buyer? This is how some people analyse the episode...

L. S.: No, and to be honest, they would have sold the plant in any event. However, the opposite is also true, since it would have been idiotic to acquire Dacia if we did not have the Logan project. I didn't buy the factory only because of our plans, which had mutated in the mean time into a €5,000 car. Euro and dollar exchange rates were extremely volatile at the time and all of our costs tended to be in euros.

---

1. Jean-Marie Hurtiger, see interview at the end of Chapter 2.

From the Romanian government's perspective, Renault was the only buyer. I think Dacia was a problem for them so they were happy to get rid of it and let Renault take it over. What we were offering was pretty good anyway. Dacia had 20,000 staff members manufacturing 80 to 90,000 cars, which was 4 cars a head, or 10 times lower than the standards of a good French factory. If we hadn't taken it over, they would have closed.

Was that the real trigger for people supporting the project?
L. S.: Not really. Some people were really committed, mainly the project and design teams. We also had the support of Jacques Lacambre, who somewhat belatedly expressed the thought "that we have found a solution". The normal delay for developing a car is around four years. This project was launched in 1997 but hit the market in 2004. The pregnancy was therefore very long, as was the pre-pregnancy, meaning the time between when we first addressed the problem and when we found a solution later on.

To answer your question, I was very isolated with this project. I remember, for instance, that there were decisions to be made alongside the launch, including figuring out where we would run our press releases and roadshows.

For these releases, it quickly became apparent to the Communications Department that Turkey was the right place, based on three very revealing ideas that our people had developed regarding this operation:

We needed an attractive place to attract journalists;

We did not want to locate the car in the environment where it would sit alongside more modern vehicles. This attitude tells you a lot about how neurotic the car made us feel;

We wanted difficult driving conditions to highlight its qualities. We also wanted a road network where it would be hard to drive 100 miles an hour because the Logan makes more noise at this speed than other cars, putting it at a disadvantage.

Communications and I had a debate about the roadshow. They were against doing a presentation at the Technocentre because they thought that the contrast between the location's modernity and the nature of the car would have a negative effect. I wanted to do it here because it was important to show that the car was based on Renault technology, and that it was modern, robust and affordable. I won in the end but have to admit that the roadshow's media success was as much a surprise to me as it was to them.

That was in 2004. Weren't people already on board?

L. S.: Not many. I remember receiving 2005 global sales forecasts of 80,000 Logans and getting really angry, saying that I would accept nothing below six figures, and that it was silly of them to provoke me like this. 80,000 would have meant a failure. It was in mid-2004 that Luc-Alexandre Ménard, our Director for International Operations, sent me photos of the moment when we first began showing the Logan in Romania. There were long lines in front of the dealerships. No one on the Executive Committee had expected that.

We want to take a deeper look at the changes made to this project and the directions that it took, whether you were in favour or simply agreed to them. The first was the decision to sell the Logan in Russia under Renault's name.

L. S.: That was something that I had originally opposed since I only wanted to sell the Logan as a Dacia product. But I soon realised this wouldn't work. The Russians didn't want it and we couldn't force them. We then figured out that it could be sold with a Dacia brand in those places where Renault already had a solid presence, and that we would put a Renault badge on the product where this was not the case. This enabled us ex post facto to give some "legal" coherence to decisions that did not completely depend on us. It was, however, a decision that I probably would not have taken before seeing the car. When I viewed it for the first time in 2003, I understood how good it was. Before that we hadn't been sure. Our cost structure made sense and the design was what wanted but the baby could always be stillborn. Thankfully, it turned out to be comfortable, big, really healthy. We were relieved and felt that there was no reason not to sell it under the Renault brand name.

The other big decision we took involved marketing the car in Western Europe. I announced this on radio one Sunday during the Paris Trade Fair in autumn 2004. It is a decision that I was happy to take because it was a sign of success. Moreover, we didn't really have a choice because we were not in a position to prevent parallel imports.

How did the French Sales Department react?

L. S.: The professionals came on board quickly, since they were very worried about parallel imports at the time. Moreover, they sensed how enthusiastic the press was.

At the top of French Sales Department, people accepted the idea of marketing a product characterised by much reduced network margins. Our launch was very different from what we usually did since we didn't spend a red penny on advertising nor did we beef up the networks. It was unprecedented, but our networks soon found it to their liking. Because it sold like hotcakes and that created a lot of traffic.

We should also mention the important role that the press played in this launch. I believed strongly in the project but for rational reasons. The press, on the other hand, had realised before us how big an event this was. Unlike us, it successfully drew a contrast between house brands' success and low cost goods. In our view, the point was to offer less affluent people a good car. We hadn't taken into account the fact that the low-cost trend had reached the wealthier nations. Moreover, we hadn't done any marketing studies in Western Europe before the launch.

This is indeed one of the most noteworthy aspects of the whole Logan story, since it shows that a market considered saturated was not being analysed accurately because it was still possible to find customers whose only previous recourse had been to buy used cars. Was this factor quickly integrated into the equation?

L. S.: It is clear that the fact that we were able to say very quickly, "Dacia is a competitor for used and not new cars" greatly facilitated its acceptance in France. There wasn't any cannibalisation, something reinforced by the car's notchback shape. If we had started with the Sandero, people would have been dismayed.

You mean that the Sandero went off in another direction…

L. S.: No, not another direction, which is what happened to Renault in Russia, where we deviated from our original idea, or in France, where the sales opportunity was something that we hadn't expected.

On the other hand, it was entirely logical that we transformed the Logan into a family. The first major family that we ever put together was the first generation Mégane in 1996/1997, the first car for which I was specifically responsible. We had a minivan, hatchback, notchback, SUV, estate and convertible coupé. Aside from the latter, the idea of breaking the Logan down into different variants came to us quickly and quite naturally. Once something works, there is no reason not to do it again.

But it is worth noting that during this entire development phase, our economic studies had always predicted disasters and argued systematically that we shouldn't continue. The more innovative a product, the less reliable its forecasts. With the Scenic, for instance, our marketing forecasters expected 300 cars a day whereas we ended up with 1,800. Conversely, the Avantime and the current version of the Espace sold much less well than we expected. Ultimately, I think it's dangerous believing in forecasts. Clearly you have to do this but you should never rely on them.

In terms of changing directions, there was also the geography of the Logan's market. In all of the provisional studies undertaken in 2002/2003, people were predicting major sales in Eastern Europe. In the end, this didn't happen, except in Romania.

L. S.: Internationally, some countries worked well but not others. Russia was a success. Colombia and Brazil also. I'm not sure about what happened with Mexico but there were also some clear disappointments, such as China, India or Iran.

The problem in Iran was political. We had designed a "minimum risk" strategy in this country where we were not prepared to invest directly due to a lack of confidence. The election of Mr. *Ahmadinejad* was followed by the Iranian government firing everyone with whom we had negotiated. This strongly affect the speed that we entered this market. The problem in Iran had to do with the technical incompetency of our local partners and the complete disorganisation of the economy. India, on the other hand, was a commercial failure resulting from a politically targeted fiscal policy sanctioning the Logan. This is despite the fact that we had a majority local partner, Mahindra, who was remarkably competent.

Iran and China were failures for reasons that had nothing to do with the product. The Logan's only real commercial disappointment was India.

In Brazil and Russia, the Entry was marketed under the Renault brand name. What is Renault's image in these countries given the kinds of Renault being sold nowadays in Russia? Is the Company associated with the Logan in Brazil or with the Sandero?

LS: When we looked at Renault's sales prospects at the time the Logan was launched, this would have meant extra volumes on top of the stable or slight higher numbers that Renault had achieved. Policy changes following the arrival of Carlos Ghosn, given his focus on margins instead of volumes, meant that unit sales tended to decrease. As such, even though Dacia had not grown as quickly as I had expected due to certain problems in India, Iran and China, Dacia's share of total sales remained much higher than I had expected, because "real" Renault sales had dropped so much.

But weren't things different in the emerging countries?

L. S.: Yes, because these were markets that Renault tried to enter from the top, a strategy that did not produce the expected results. It explains why we relied on the Logan more than I had anticipated.

In other words, the original plan was not for the Entry programme to become Renault's international development driver?

L. S.: To repeat, my initial emphasis was complementarity, in line with the Skoda-VW model. It is obvious that both are useful everywhere, with one being the "noble" brand and the other being slightly off-centre. I always considered the Entry as a complementary but not main focus. It should only lead in Central European and very poor countries, meaning ones that had not yet become major automobile markets.

But the thing helping us not to feel bad about this was that we were selling a good product, one achieving satisfaction rates exceeding Renault's usual standards. Logan buyers understood that it didn't come with wood panels, that its dashboard was monoblock and that it did not have any leather. But they were happy with the car, it was worth the money that they had spent and therefore in brand image terms we had kept our promise. Because I consider that the key point in any sale or image is to "keep your promise".

Maybe one of the problems was that Renault didn't really know how to communicate positively about a bottom-of-the-range automobile?

L. S.: That's not true. Sloan, who ran General Motors for 30 years, invented automobile marketing. The most popular brands in the United States are Chevrolet and Ford. Both used to be the world's cheapest cars. Value for money is an extraordinarily strong commercial theme, probably the most convincing of all.

Even today, your strategic reasoning remains relatively original. The traditional strategic discourse argues in favour of entering a market towards the top-of-the-range before going downscale. It is surprising that despite your success, you haven't had any imitators.

L. S.: Historically, the Japanese started by selling relatively cheap products, but not as cheap as the Logan was in the developing countries. Having said that, I was not surprised that we didn't have any imitators, unlike the Scenic. For several years now, people have been saying that the Logan offers better margins than other Renault cars, something that should have whetted people's appetite. I was really surprised, for instance, that PSA did not follow in our footsteps. It is true that our whole approach had been heavily criticised and debated before it succeeded, with people probably finding themselves prisoners of their own critiques. We still hear that this is an irresponsible business killing used cars' market value but that is nonsense. The question remains, however, whether the Logan is a good car. Because the Lada, for instance, is still selling well yet is a really horrible car.

My strategic vision for Renault was more or less complete back as 1988. There was nothing really original about it since it derived from the model that VW and General Motors had put together. Volvo was supposed to be our Audi, Renault was VW and Dacia the Skoda of the group. For GM's models, the biggest volumes were towards the bottom, whereas at Renault and VW, they were in the middle. But there was always an overlap, and we had to learn, if not to eliminate this, then how to limit its effects. VW, for instance, let Skoda go upscale but I don't think that we should allow the Logan (or Dacia) to go too high. Otherwise you create a lot of confusion. Renault's brand image should not be the same as the Logan's. That would be a mistake.

Interview by Bernard Jullien and Christophe Midler.

2

ACHIEVING THE IMPOSSIBLE €5,000 CAR

The previous chapter showed how judicious the Logan's commercial intuition turned out to be. Yet even if the goal of building a simple, habitable, reliable and durable car costing €5,000 made sense from a marketing perspective, questions remained about its feasibility. For Renault at the time, the challenge associated with this project involved building a profitable growth model based on the development of a new global commercial segment. In the automotive industry, which is very capital-intensive, profitability reflects the interlinage between design investments and new products, and between industrial investment and manufacturing costs, whether internal or external.

A few orders of magnitude can provide an idea of the challenge that the Logan faced.[1] In 2003 when the project was supposed to come online, Renault's least expensive product in terms of manufacturing cost was the Clio, which was being made in Turkey. To achieve sufficient profitability, the Logan aimed to cost 50% less–a goal that, astonishingly, it ultimately achieve. In investment terms, the most relevant comparator was the Twingo, whose launch in 1992 had been impeded by severe economic constraints. After adjusting for inflation, the Logan's development and industrial investment expenditures were in fact similar, having achieved savings of 35% on the former and 44% on the latter.

The present chapter will try to specify the conditions enabling Renault to meet a challenge that had first seemed unlikely or impossible to most professionals and observers, namely to develop a quality new car retailing at €5,000. Our analysis will focus on the three areas that structured its efforts to achieve this improbable dream: the product and process design, with Renault's engineering teams mobilising to define the characteristics of the product and its underlying manufacturing processes; industrial

1. L. Baudino, M. Chahbi, *Les problématiques et les enjeux du développement à l'international : Le projet Logan (Masters in Project Innovation Design Dissertation)*, M.A. thesis in Project Innovation Design, Supervisor C. Midler, Ecole Polytechnique, 2006.

rationalisation; and procurement, a key aspect of modern automotive systems. Clearly, significant changes were made in all three of these areas.

In design terms, engineering professionals' normal continuous improvement plans turned out to be inadequate to the scale of the challenge. Instead, there needed to be a sea change in standards of automobile design excellence, such as they had been conceptualised previously at companies like Renault. Moreover, as discussed in the previous chapter, this would have to happen in a context defined by the scepticism of Renault's Technocentre experts when Schweitzer first presented the project to them.

The Logan adventure was also unprecedented at the industrial level, based as it was on the reconversion of an old Eastern European manufacturing complex, namely Dacia's Pitesti works. The question here is to what extent the site would be compatible with the particularly tough productivity and quality constraints that the Logan faced. Once again, the ambient theme here was radical innovation. Successful industrial operations–for instance, cases where Japanese manufacturers have shone– have often involved starting from scratch in a particular environment (so-called "greenfield" strategy) by "cloning" the latest processes and managerial practices found in factories in the company's country of origin. For the Logan, this reconversion would have to be achieved in a framework shaped by agreements signed with the Romanian government back when Dacia was being privatised, but without "transplanting" processes and practices from French factories, given widespread agreement that these would have prevented the project from reaching its cost targets.

An analogous rupture occurred at the level of the supplier ecosystem. It was unclear whether any local suppliers would be capable of the requisite quality and productivity performance, or if the group's customary partners would want to take part in an adventure that, from the very outset, seemed uncertain and barely if at all profitable.

Lastly, Renault was not fully mobilised to help the Logan project team overcome these three challenges. The size of the original project (180,000 to 200,000 units mainly targeting Central and Eastern European markets), together with its risks and identity problems, meant it was often deemed marginal. It was also happening at a time in the history of Renault when people were focusing their attention and energy on another operation considered altogether more important, to wit, the Alliance with Nissan.

What we will demonstrate is that Renault was able to mobilise a certain number of elements that seemingly began as constraints or risks before being turned into ruptures with the past. This led to the birth of what would ultimately be known as the "Entry" line. Financial constraints forced the Company to find novel solutions deviating from its normal standards and requiring a mobilisation of local competencies. Lastly, the project's marginal status gave its management team of experienced marauders free rein to transgress normal company rules.

HOW ENGINEERING DEALT WITH "DESIGN TO COST"

From the outset, there was a consensus that meeting the challenge of making a €5,000 car would require radically a new approach to traditional automobile design processes. With this in mind, the Logan was able to rely on an emblematic precedent: the Twingo project that, in the early 1990s, had formalised and implemented an original design to cost approach.[1] The importance of this successful benchmark clearly helped to legitimise the new initiative. It remains that the X90 project would somewhat reinvent this predecessor and go even further in scale and scope. In part, this is because Renault's strategy since the Twingo had been to focus on other performance criteria, such as becoming European leader in safety and quality. Additionally, the scale of the Logan challenge was such that even greater changes were needed.

We gotta do something!

Figure 2.1–The Twingo and its "design to cost" approach

Source: Dubreil, 2009.

---

1. C. Midler, *L'Auto qui n'existait pas, Management de projet et transformation de l'entreprise*, Paris, Dunod, 1996.

Targeting precising without compromising on performance

The general principle of "design to cost" is simple. Traditional design approaches seek technical solutions that prioritise functional performance before the cost is even quantified ('cost to design'). With 'design to cost', the cost is part of the original design problem, much in the same way as other performance criteria found in the automotive industry. Many projects claim to pursue this goal but the implementation can deviate, often because they are clawed back by various business functions that prefer to repeat tried and tested solutions instead of taking new risks. By setting a maximum target return price for the vehicle and its components–a goal that Renault's organisation might achieve by marginalising projects like the X90–there was an incentive to come up with new solutions meeting this objective. Project managers would constantly remind everybody of this goal and show zero tolerance for failures to achieve it.

Thus, the specific starting point for the Logan was customer value. In marketing jargon, this was its "unique selling point" (USP), being the aspect that journalists immediately identified as the model's strength compared to rivals. For the purposes of the present text, USPs are those elements that salespersons use to substantiate their arguments and convey them with passion. They therefore become the most significant aspects that customers associate over the long run with the product's identity.

The Logan's three USPs were sales price, habitability and reliability/durability. With this product, "design to cost" was not an all-encompassing cost-cutting exercise but the idea that the car should be designed in such a way as to minimise items that do not contribute directly to these three objectives. Instead, resources should be concentrated on the car's goals. In the end, some aspects of the Logan would outclass more traditional products, one example being its robust suspension system, which was superior to many cars sold into a European market characterised by its high standard road networks.

One of the more intelligent ideas underlying the Logan's target "product" was that–as pointed out by Programme Engineering Manager Dominique Bellot–some design principles seemed to operate in synergy with all three of these initial objectives. "Habitability is not expensive since you can make more room inside the car and increase the boot space with just a few more kilos of steel. It is certainly less expensive than introducing sophisticated gadgets. It also creates a lot of value, particularly in emerging markets where mobility is much less extensive than in affluent highly urban environments, where the car boot is often key to soundproofing, which can be expensive in hatchbacks. Product simplification is another cost reduction lever that goes along with reliability and durability, since quality problems are often associated with sophisticated performance and technology. This makes it possible to get rid of parts (the Logan has three times fewer than a traditional car in its range) and means that we get a car that is lighter and performs better than others with the same engine size."

The X90's approach deviated from the "decontenting" trend that had characterised the automotive industry in previous years, based on the idea that a car could be stripped down to the bare minimum by getting rid of anything superfluous and going downscale in terms of pricing. Indeed, the opposite effect was at work here, with design starting from a lower base that could be enriched later to move the car upscale.

Following the project's strategic clarification, six cost-cutting levers were deployed to reduce investment and manufacturing outlays: product certification; carryover; digital validation and design productivity; manual processes; reuse of equipment; supplier involvement and local integration; and the logistic gains associated with a compact site. Each of these levers will be reviewed and illustrated below.

Product simplification: starting afresh with new technical specifications

This principle was key to the actions propelling the Logan project and, more generally, to any and all "low-end disruption" strategies. It involved returning to the essential aspects of a product's value proposal, through a radical orientation of its compromise around key values considered important to target customers. The question then became why this kind of strategy might be classified as a radical break with the past, given that design technique optimisation can be considered the basis for all new product development. The answer lay in design competencies' technical capitalisation logic. Engineers' decisions were based on "business rules" that took corporate history into account. Such capitalisation was crucial in reducing quality risk since it eliminated solutions that could cause defects. At the same time, the logic was inflationary, insofar as it only advocated solutions capable of satisfying the most demanding criteria.

Starting with a new hierarchy of criteria meant testing the business rules' relevancy, an operation requiring highly competent engineers assessing the justification for whatever exceptions were being made, on one hand, and possessing decision-making capabilities, on the other, insofar as any problems arising would become their responsibility. New product projects all involve arbitrages of this kind, but they are generally infrequent and limited to a few vehicle elements, ones where designers will try to introduce a threshold effect. The originality of the Logan project resided in its systematic and diffuse nature, its application to all constituent aspects, thus the way its implementation affected all designers. In short, it attested to the importance of having a powerful project structure to drive and sustain these kinds of initiatives in design centres that are subject to the pressures associated with rapid development (i.e. quality concerns), all of which creates an incentive to apply the most tried and tested solutions.

For example, the dashboard is generally a particularly complex and costly component comprised of several subsections including visors and surface vents coming in different textures and colours. In the case of the Logan project, the designers and engineers opted for a single block solution that would allow them to cut the cost of tools, decorative parts and, to a lesser degree, logistics and assembly operations. Similarly, they made the other unusual choice of having a single piece monoblock shield featuring an integrated grille. Here too, there were gains in terms of tooling and process costs although design costs remained relatively high. To diversify models, designers opted for a painted solution, even if this meant that unpainted models needed other masking devices.

In terms of materials, the decision was made to use traditional steel, since this was well suited to the production methods in place on the expected manufacturing sites, which stood out for their less robotised processes. Such steel could also be sourced locally.

From the outset, stamping constraints were accounted for via a design that limited vehicle body edges to facilitate manufacturing tools' design. This also had the effect of making stamping and bodywork processes more reliable while cutting costs.

Other significant gains included brake lines moulded in the factory and protected using one-piece longerons, as well as an integrated piped fuel tank with removable outside filters for use in countries dominated by "non-stabilised" fuels.

Another key element in the Logan's ability to meet its economic challenge was the choice made to adopt a front axle similar to the Clio but without its anti-roll bar, as well as a rear axle from the Renault-Nissan Alliance's B platform.

In addition, to reduce tooling investments and simplify assembly operations, rearview mirrors and protection strips were designed so they could be assembled indifferently on the vehicle's left or right hand sides. Lastly, by reducing window curvature (notably in the back), designers achieved further savings in tooling costs, while limiting trimming costs through the use of single section window panes on the back doors.

Like other levers described below, product simplification not only had an effect on manufacturing costs but also on design investments.

General support for tighter deadlines

One of the main factors explaining the success of the Logan project was the Design function's ability to convert the abstract concept of a €5,000 car into an attractive enough vehicle. This need for convergence between attractiveness and mobility is one of the biggest problems that people face in the car business, particularly towards the cheaper end. It is a leading explanation for the recurring failure of successors to the Renault 4L, before the Twingo at least.[1]

In the case of the X90, designers willingly mobilised from the very outset around what they quickly began to view as an atypical project. This was somewhat surprising, given the general assimilation of a stylist's talent with the kind of purity and sophistication characterising luxury vehicles. In reality, automobile designers had been abandoning this "style" preconception for decades, seeking to expand their mission by giving a concrete and ostensibly coherent and adapted form to the concept of automobile mobility. Under these circumstances, the brief of a €5,000 car that would be "modern, robust and affordable" seemed an interesting challenge, an epic saga requiring a whole bag of tricks to ensure that the product could be inexpensive while offering a modicum of "Germanic" robustness.

The styles that became part of the Logan converged remarkably quickly. Decision-makers took little time before agreeing on the original model. The crucial moment was the presentation of the scale one model, when several high level executives became convinced of the project's credibility,

---

1. Cf. C. Midler, op. cit.

overcoming their earlier scepticism as to the feasibility of translating its particular constraining specifications into an attractive object. Clearly, everything was not perfect. For instance, the styling on the vehicle's rear section disappointed the Project Director at the time, Jean-Marie Hurtiger, who bemoaned, "The compromise between boot size and the look of the car's rear section (…). Too many sacrifices were made to help the former to the detriment of the latter." All in all, however the press and customers responded very favourably to the new product, demonstrating that its rapid internal convergence had been based on qualities intrinsic to the object and were not a mere organisational artifice.

Carryover, or the success of a "Frankenstein" creation

Initial studies on the Logan stumbled over the traditional design dilemma facing all low-cost cars. On one hand, simply reusing existing model platforms would not enable the hoped for 50% reduction in return costs vis-à-vis the Clio export model being produced in Turkey. On the other hand, significant investment in specific new subsystems could not guarantee that the books could be balanced given the low margins characterising the project. This dilemma, which the Company had already faced on multiple occasions with other bottom-of-the-range projects,[1] was avoided here by resorting to a "carryover" process that was systematically geared towards lowering return costs.

Carryover consists of reusing components shared by several vehicles. For consumers, this is a guarantee of reliability. For the brand, it means savings, on design investments (designing and validating new parts) and often on inhouse manufacturing or supplier charges (thanks to the reutilisation of tools and extension of production series).[2] This approach, which had already been put to the test by top-performing Asian manufacturers, was applied at every stage of the Logan's development. Nearly 30% of the car's parts, accounting for nearly 50% of its value, came involved carryover.

Examples included the reuse of elements from two existing projects: the Alliance Renault/Nissan B platform; and the Clio (Nissan Micra, Renault Modus and Clio III). Unsurprisingly, they turned out to be quite effective in terms of the Logan's specific structure, with its chassis taken from the B

---

1. Cf. C. Midler, op. cit.
2. These gains should be compared with the benefits of designing a new component, notably according to 'design to cost' standards integrating the latest technologies.

platform, a decision that lowered wheel base development costs as well as design and tool manufacturing outlays. Regarding accessories, the car's electronic functions were combined into a central enclosed unit derived from the Clio and Twingo. The heating module was also the same as on Renault's segment B vehicles. The car's seamless design (simple ducts, short circuits) enhanced the reliability of installations and enabled design savings without undercutting thermal performance, which was top-in-class. Similarly, instruments, inside and outside door handles, steering wheels and column switches also came from the B platform. Having said that, where other solutions seemed more appropriate, the Logan was also capable of "creating a market". Its colour-free vents were the same as the ones used on the Espace IV; the gear shift came from the Espace III; and the rear window electric switches came from the Mégane I. In terms of mechanical systems, the Logan recycled the Clio's engine case, which was designed suing the same interfaces to keep an assembly process that the Company already mastered. Similarly, the front axle, the guidance system and the rear brakes came from the Clio II phase I.

The strategy did raise a number of questions about assembly system coherency. After all, system effects are crucial in automobiles. However, any fears about overall incoherency (caricatured in the image of a "Frankenstein design") remained unrealised. The Logan was both aesthetically and functionally coherent.

Digital design and the rise of productivity studies

The X90 project piloted digital product and manufacturing tool design simulations. It also offered an opportunity to fine-tune a new production process.

Digital vibration and auditory calculations enabled noise forecasts without the need for a physical model. The advantages of this digital approach, specifically its ability to define and develop the body frame through digital calculations, avoided the need for costly prototypes and meant Renault could dispense with many physical stages that would have otherwise been necessary, notably having to make prototypes.

This was yet another example of how the product's simplicity became a significant strength that the Company could leverage. The Logan's relatively simple design surfaces were easier to model than the sophisticated curves found on traditional models. All in all, around €20 million was saved on design costs. Even more significantly, the project finished much earlier than expected (lasting 27 instead of 32 months).

A return to manual production

The sites' low labour costs unsurprisingly drew the process designers into labour-intensive assembly operations that took advantage of simple locally available technologies and the lower level of automation. Renault's engineers decided to install largely manual processes that optimised their use of materials. This meant that they would no longer be able to engage in large bodyworks. They also abandoned laser welded metalwork, a high-tech but expensive and very complex process enabling an optimal compromise between a structure's weight and resistance.

The predominance of manual processes at the Pitesti bodyworks plant contrasted with the automated factories that the global automotive industry had opened in recent years. Whereas managers from these other factories would delight in the number of robots and other automated tools at their disposal, the Logan's Pitesti production lines had fewer than one dozen robots. Yet they churned out nearly 350,000 unit in 2010!

The first explanation for this reliance on manual processes was that wages in Romania were lower than in other central European countries like Hungary or Poland, where some of Renault's competitors were working. At the time of the 1999 Dacia privatisation agreement, average wages in the Romanian automotive industry were 25% of what they were in Poland and one-thirteenth of French levels.

Table 2.1–Comparison of 1999 automotive industry wage costs[1]

France	Romania	Hungary	Poland
€1,484	€110	€387	€434

Source: International Labour Organisation.

Global automakers had progressively lost their competency in manual processes following a 40 year expansion in automation. In the Logan's case, Romanian engineering was still operating at a seemingly obsolete technological level, but the competencies it did possess could be widely mobilised to install manual processes that would produce sufficiently high

---

1. Average monthly remuneration as per NACE sector 34.

quality vehicles to satisfy market standards. Renault sent a team of up to as many as 70 expatriates to Romania including many experienced employees. Rather than recent graduates from top French universities, these were professionals who had been trained on-the-job by Renault before progressively rising through the ranks. Christian Estève described Renault's expatriates as "Nuts who worked all the time–a small group of French people dedicated to advancing this business…We were late middle aged managers who had never given as much in their entire careers. We weren't young hotshots wearing three-piece suits coming from fancy universities but guys who had generally learned the business at the coalface and subsequently been promoted. We were soldiers fighting in the trenches and had a lot of experience, which was really useful. I would often tell the HRM people and President Schweitzer to be thankful that nobody really wanted to help us, since this actually facilitated exchanges between the Renault and Dacia teams."

Viewed at first as external to the group organisation, the project's famous "Romanian" team devised their own procedures without always having to worry about fitting in with what was already being done at Renault– especially since no one was trying to supervise the things happening here on the other side of Europe. This marginal position allowed the team to come up with original solutions that were very different from Renault's standard norms and procedures.

A second major justification for minimising automation was the project's small budget, reflecting its marginal position in a Renault Group strategy focused on the Nissan alliance. The X90 was seen as relatively minor project whose production scale of around 200,000 vehicles per annum was supposed to self-fund at first. With little prospect of amortising the fixed costs that would have been associated with significant process automation– and given the limited budget–automated equipment purchases were few and far between. They were almost entirely absent in the bodyworks unit, which relied on ad hoc solutions where necessary, notably involving mechanical operations. Indeed, Renault Group transferred its range of engine and gearbox production activities to Romania, due to the fact that quality constraints were greater here for mechanical operations than they would have been for assembly work.

Hence the need to find suitable equipment while respecting the Logan's small budget. The solution involved being clever, for instance, by scouting unused equipment in the Renault Group's different mechanical plants worldwide, assessing and then transferring it to Romania where it could be upgraded and adapted to produce petrol and diesel engines or gearboxes. This is how Renault's Cleon plant came to provide several segments of the gearbox machining lines. It was a pragmatic approach where many operations were still done manually, a modus operandi that was very different from the standards of today's highly mechanised mechanical factories. One example was the suspension system, outsourced for a while to ACI (Auto Chassis International) in line with the general policy of handing production operations to suppliers. It would later be brought back into Dacia's workload after the Renault Group bought ACI.

SUPPLIERS' CENTRAL ROLE IN MEETING THE LOGAN CHALLENGE

The success of the X90 project can also be explained by suppliers' involvement and a rigorous management of procurement. There were two challenges at this level: outsourcing a big share of component design and production; while encouraging local integration to meet return cost aims. The idea was to take maximum advantage of local suppliers' potential–characterised by low prices but limited competencies–by involving them in Renault's normal supplier shortlist, comprised of automotive equipment multinationals. This difficult and variable balancing act was something the Renault Group sought to achieve in Romania and all international locations.

Suppliers' involvement in "design to cost"

Compared to Renault's other projects, the Logan was characterised by suppliers' greater involvement in vehicle production and design, accounting for 80% of vehicle value. This was near the archetype that seemed to dominate the automotive industry (and a few others), one where manufacturers would only be involved in core businesses, including:

- designing the vehicle's overall architecture and driving system while delegating component and subsystem design to Tier 1 suppliers;
- manufacturing the mechanical systems and assembling the vehicle using components made and assembled by suppliers;
- product marketing.

In a context where this representation tended to dominate industrial thinking, several specific factors justified suppliers' substantial involvement in the Logan project. Firstly, given the financial goal of reducing the entry ticket for a project that was initially only supposed to cover a limited volume of vehicles on the emerging markets, project managers had very small budgets.[1] Asides from carryover or reused second-hand equipment recovered from different group factories, suppliers were now being asked to make big investments in the new model's production, enabling Renault to meet the budget it had set itself. Secondly, there was no guarantee at first that the industrial challenge of making a 5,000 car could be met, with many sceptics (both in the industry and amongst sector analysts) forecasting that failure. Earlier attempts to make low-cost cars had fallen short and Fiat's recent problems with an emerging country car (the 178 Palio/Sienna project) reinforced most observers' belief that this was impossible. In this situation, characterised by the uncertainty accompanying any breakthrough innovation, suppliers' involvement facilitates risk sharing amongst different companies. Similarly, under the privatisation agreement that Renault signed with the Romanian authorities in late 1999, Dacia's reconversion was supposed to involve the reallocation of some staff members to the Logan's supplier companies. A suppliers park was therefore created within Dacia's Mioveni complex in the suburbs of the city of Pitesti, the purpose being to take advantage of the space and workforce that the ongoing restructuring was freeing up. Valeo (wirings), Johnson Controls (seats), Piroux (containers), IRI (machine tools) and ACI (chassis, cradles and axle gears) were the first such outsourcing operations, leading to the transfer of 1,592 jobs in 2002, two years before the Logan's launch.

Dacia had been an integrated industrial combine before its takeover by Renault and this major outsourcing drive, which was very new in Romania, was a sea change. Asides from significant vertical integration on the Mioveni industrial site near Pitesti, 57% of all purchasing (in value) had been within the Dacia group, with 35% coming from other Romanian suppliers. Only 8% of all purchases were imports, basically involving parts that were unavailable in Romania (like Bosch injectors).[2] Suppliers had to be brought

---

1. Renault's goal was for the Dacia takeover to self-fund "via resources taken from the Romanian automotive market itself, plus protections and exemptions obtained from the Romanian authorities" (Internal document, cited in D. Debrosse, *La reprise de Dacia par Renault 1998-2003. Histoire d'une aventure humaine, industrielle et commerciale*, PhD in History thesis, University Evry-Val de l'Essonne, 2007, p.88-89).

2. Source: D. Debrosse, op. cit.

up to speed since outsourcing was supposed to be accompanied by the local integration of components production to ensure that the project met its cost objectives.

Local integration

By keeping costs down, the local integration of component production and assembly operations made a great contribution to the goal of making a €5,000 car. On one hand, to cut logistics costs, a large proportion of components had to be made on-site, starting with the most voluminous. Moreover, producing in Romania meant the Logan would benefit from the country's low wage levels, notably during labour-intensive stages like the assembly of subsystems. Lastly, in terms of currency risks, the euro's rise and/or devaluation of the Romanian currency (the leu) would have raised the cost of components sourced from the eurozone. Generating small margins was already hard enough and unexpected euro/leu exchange rate variations might easily have destroyed these efforts.

With this kind of arbitrage being applied to each component, the general paradigm was to always opt for the least costly solution satisfying the manufacturing return cost objectives. Cost targets would only be revised downwards, never upwards.

Searching for local suppliers

To benefit from these cost advantages, there was a systematic search for local suppliers, in part because their prices were lower than the multinationals dominating the global automotive industry. From the outset, Renault was always trying to help suppliers meet international quality and competitiveness standards. Know-how would be transferred, notably relating to quality management, through a host of actions that included annual contracts, the foundation of the Dacia Institute for Quality and Management, the seconding of dedicated teams and many similar initiatives. In a Romanian automotive sector that had long been isolated from the rest of the world and ignored the purchasing function despite its growing importance throughout the 1990s, this was a big step.

Romanian suppliers' level of technological competency meant they only accounted for 10% to 20% of total purchasing. Whereas Dacia pickup trucks had had 128 Romanian suppliers, the Logan only had two.[1] Despite these limitations (which would ultimately move the focus to foreign imports), there were also several successful examples of local suppliers receiving assistance and rapidly improving their levels of competency. One was plastics specialist Delta Invest. Founded in 1994 and located ca. 10 km from the Mioveni site, Delta used its few machine tools to make parts for the electrotechnical industry. As part of its systematic exploration of the fabric of Romanian companies after taking over Dacia, Renault asked Delta to join its supplier shortlist in 1999. Thanks to considerable assistance from Renault technicians, the company got stronger, not only through the acquisition of new plastic injection presses but also by building a design centre that would bolster its engineering competencies. The result was that it now offered an integrated package of component designs (interacting with customers via shared CFAO tools) as well as moulds capable of preparing prototypes and series production. With around 200 employees in 2010, today this Tier 2 supplier produces more than 200 references. More than half of its turnover depends on the Mioveni industrial site (supplying Dacia and certain Tier 1 suppliers), but its output is also shipped to other Renault Group sites or actors in the automotive supply sector.

This learning process took around 10 years. Renault, unable to find a local industrial fabric matching international standards of competitiveness, had been forced to turn to its customary supplier shortlist, comprised of multinationals, to source its new assembly lines at Pitesti. These suppliers were involved, for instance, in designing the Solenza, a new Dacia model that prepared the Mioveni site for the requirements of the Logan, which started being produced there starting in late 2004 (see above)

Table 2.2–Supplier contract inventory on 24 June 2003

Supplier	Activity	1st contract	Staff
Metalimpex *Groupe Boone Comenor*	Recyclage de matériaux	26/07/01 (z)	30
Valeo Electronice si Sisteme de Conectare Romania[70] *Groupe Valeo*	Câblage automobile	30/09/02 (z)	302
Piroux Industrie Romania Groupe Piroux	Conditionnements métalliques	30/09/02 (z)	85
Johnson Controls	Sièges	30/09/02 (z)	377

---

1. Source: D. Debrosse, op. cit., p. 406.

Euro Auto Plastik Systems *Groupe Faurecia*	Planches de bord et pièces plastiques d'intérieur	4/12/02 (z)	205
Ingénierie et Réalisations Industrielles Romania *Groupe ABB*	Équipements de carrosserie	30/09/02 (z)	227
Auto Châssis International (ACI) Groupe Renault	Trains et berceaux moteurs Mécano-soudure	21/10/02 (z)	598
MCI Inginerie	Menuiserie, constructions métalliques	1/04/03 (z)	40
Johnson Control	Coupe Couture	1/04/03	25
Cowel Société Bozal/Cortubi	Lignes d'échappement	16/03/03 (z)	40
Valeo Thermique habitacle	Chauffage climatisation	1/05/03 (z)	25
Eurest Rom Groupe Compass	Restauration d'entreprise	1/04/03 (f)	83

Source : Yann Burnel, *"Contrats signés entre Dacia et ses Fournisseurs"*, 24 juin 2003.
(z) contrat ZIF : bail ou prestations de services ou location-gérance
ou détachement de personnel
(f) contrat de fourniture
Source : Debrosse D., p. 387

Multinationals' involvement in the supplier industry

Against this backdrop, it was always possible that some people would be very reluctant to see Renault engaging in what they might consider a dangerous undertaking. The profitability of its new investment was far from guaranteed when planned production was expected to be 200,000 units per annum, with a vehicle sold at bargain basement prices that would hit margins hard. On certain highly labour-intensive products such as wiring, the risk did not seem excessive, given this activity's relatively cheap entry ticket and the possibility of sufficient flexibility to redeploy the investment if necessary. Elsewhere, however, there was the daunting fact that Renault had to design new components and construct a new production base. The Company therefore put a lot of pressure on suppliers to move to Romania. As one supplier group executive said, "As one of Renault's main suppliers, we had no choice but to follow." Most of this follow sourcing was done cautiously. Companies would analyse what was needed to make the parts in question and negotiate a payment for their studies with Renault, in contrast to the automotive industry's custom of having the design function remunerated through production contracts. Suppliers would then ally with other partners, either through joint venture arrangements or technology transfers. Responsibility for investment funding and components production would then be left to other actors.

One example was French supplier Faurecia, an important partner in developing not only several plastic components (dashboards, bumpers, door parts) but also other elements like carpets or sun visors that could be at odds its core business. Having collaborated with Renault from the Solenza project, Faurecia was happy at first to commission design studies and help medium-sized suppliers during their production phases, working out of the Mioveni suppliers park. Thus, two European SMEs (AD Plastik Croatia and Simoldes Portugal) founded a joint venture called Euro Auto Plastic Systems (EAPS) Romania in 2002 without Faurecia having to assume any industrial risk. The Logan's success translated into higher volumes in Romania. The internationalisation of the X90's production process persuaded Faurecia to get more involved. By 2007, it had acquired the Portuguese company's stake in EAPS and was now helping Renault to evolve its product and decline it into different variants, which meant developing new engineering competencies in Romania. In the end, Faurecia was itself producing on-site everything relating to the life of the series, adapting the product over its lifecycle thanks to a Romanian platform that was specifically dedicated to the Logan. By 2010, the company was employing nearly 700 persons on the Mioveni site.

Another big French supplier, Valeo, also joined on Renault's epic journey, notably by building a presence on the suppliers park, where it had 350 employees making "heating and air conditioning" equipment as part of its climate control business. The Valeo Group also had a division busy on the Logan, building headlights in collaboration with ELBA, a Romanian lighting specialist that had been Dacia's historic supplier. Technology was transferred via licensing agreements covering a lighting system that was half as expensive as on equivalent vehicles, thanks to product simplification and low wages in Romania. From the very outset, Valeo had also been in charge of developing and industrialising the wiring that Dacia used, before selling all these activities to Leoni in 2007. As was the case for Faurecia, higher volumes and range upgrades caused it to become more involved in Logan assembly sites in Romania and elsewhere. Lastly, some of the other parts supplied by Valeo, including radiators, condensers, top column modules, switchers, alternators and clutches came from its other European sites.

The example of Johnson Control International is also interesting because it demonstrates the limits of this kind of involvement. Working out of the suppliers park to make Logan seats, this American company cut its operations down to two front and back seat assembly lines, moving the production of other seat inputs to a different site a few kilometres from Mioveni. It did this for two reasons: JCI had won a contract to make seats for the Ford factory in Craiova; and the move helped it to contain wage hikes. This is because the collective agreements signed with local trade unions applied across the whole of the Moveni site, with one consequence of the Logan's success being a steady but significant rise in wages at Dacia, spreading to other companies on the suppliers park. By only leaving module assembly operations on-site and transferring components production elsewhere, JCI was keeping a lid on wage costs.

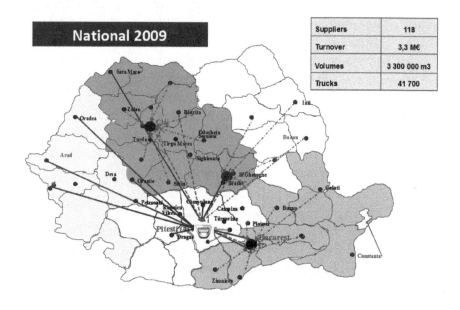

Source : Dacia

Figure 2.2–Location of Logan's Romanian suppliers

Source : Dacia

Figure 2.3–Logan component imports

This local integration drive was successful since ultimately "95% of the Logan's packaged volumes and 65% of the parts it sourced were made in Romania. Out of the 14m³ of packaged Logan parts, 11.5 m³ were products produced either in its plant or in the suppliers park", according to the Company.[1] Because of the "compactness" of this procurement process, the Logan's upstream logistics costs were half as high as those on a traditional vehicle made in a top performance plant in Western Europe.

Local integration at the heart of the internationalisation strategy

Initially envisioned for the Pitesti plant alone, the Logan would assume a strong international dimension very quickly. Indeed, the product seemed to open doors in emerging markets where Renault did not yet run a portfolio of adapted products. Thus, Russia and Brazil soon became part of its agenda, with Colombia and Morocco being targeted for low volume

---

1. Source: Renault, *R&D La Route de l'innovation*, No. 34, October 2004, p. 28.

assembly operations (15 to 20,000 units annually). The question became how to support suppliers and achieve local integration within very different contexts, offering pragmatic responses without preconceptions asides from the necessity of having at least 30 to 40% of the mass of components localised to reduce logistics costs. Local integration almost systematically involved dashboards, seat assembly operations, shields, fuel tanks and wiring, not to mention generic tires and batteries. In Brazil, the supplier fabric was sufficiently dense for all the necessary partners to exist locally. This was not the case in Russia, however, where a substantial part of all components awaiting assembly had to be imported. The same distinction existed between Colombia, with its dense industrial fabric, and Morocco, despite the latter country's being closer to Romania, which was the heart of the Entry line.

Elsewhere, Renault founded an Iranian joint venture called Renault Pars in May 2004, working in partnership with IDRO (Industrial Development & Renovation Organisation), an Iranian public body responsible for the national automotive industry. Renault Pars was supposed to link up with Iran Khodro and Saipa, Iran's two main automakers. It had a very ambitious goal of producing 300,000 Logans annually, renaming the car the Tondar 90. Project volumes were ultimately triple initial forecasts. This led to strong profits, with the project satisfying return cost objectives that had been established in light of an expected annual output of 200,000 vehicles.

Asides from logistics costs, the extent of local integration could also be adjusted on a case-by-case basis depending on factors such as taxes on imported components (low tariffs in Morocco versus higher taxes in Colombia or Brazil) or local integration rate targets negotiated with the national government in exchange for market access (notably in Iran, where state intervention is significant). Naturally, suppliers could not follow each of Renault's global moves and local solutions would be negotiated depending on the circumstances, leading at times to product reconfiguration (i.e. fuel tanks made out of metal or plastic).

The internationalisation of the X90's production paved the way for an International Logistics Platform (ILN) in 2005. Located less than 1 km from the Mioveni-Pitesti site, the ILN was used to prepare shipments of kits. The ILN centralised all components, engines and spare parts that Dacia or its suppliers made on-site (Cortubi for exhaust pipes, EAPS for plastic parts, JC for seat frameworks and metal parts, etc.). It also received imported parts before forwarding them to overseas assembly units. In 2005, 292 persons were employed on the ILN, shipping a total of nearly 31,000 Logans.

RECONVERTING A "BROWN FIELD": EMERGENCE OF AN ORIGINAL PRODUCTION MODEL AT ODDS WITH CUSTOMARY RENAULT STANDARDS

The Logan project was the interface between two approaches that Renault followed under Schweitzer's guidance: the acquisition of the Romanian automobile company Dacia; and the plan to build a $6,000/€5,000 car. In his memoirs,[1] Renault's former CEO indicated that the two projects were related in his mind, with the production of a 5,000 car necessarily involving industrial operations in a low-cost country, a condition fulfilled opportunistically through the acquisition of Dacia: "My idea in taking over Dacia, which had no intrinsic value, was to use it for the $6,000 car project that we would been unable to do in Renault's name."[2] Had it not built a new plant, the industrial complex that Renault bought in 1999 would have been from another age and eventually required upgrading so as to be able to produce the X90 five years later. In short, the two projects were run in parallel within the Renault Group: modernisation of the Romanian industrial site, achieved via an explicit collective learning strategy; and designing a €5,000 car while creating the conditions for its production in Romania.

To manufacture a vehicle of this sort, Renault decided not to build a new plant and instead make the car at Dacia's Mioveni site, less than 1 km from the Pitesti city (170 km west of Bucharest). This was a typically integrated combine plant requiring a complete restructuring even as it offered a number of competencies and types of know-how that could be mobilised to develop original solutions. We will specify the conditions in which this production model materialised in 1999-2005[3] before presenting how it was organised at the Mioveni industrial complex.

---

1. Also see interview above in Chapter. 1.
2. L. Schweitzer, *Mes années Renault. Entre Billancourt et le marché mondial*, Paris, Gallimard, 2007, p. 82.
3. Much information on these negotiations and the Dacia plant's upgrading comes from Daniel Debrosse, a Renault executive who took part in this adventure: *La reprise de Dacia par Renault 1998-2003. Histoire d'une aventure humaine, industrielle et commerciale*, PhD in History thesis, University Evry-Val de l'Essonne, 2007. Another useful source is Georgiana Angelescu, *Une analyse du processus d'apprentissage organisationnel dans un contexte spécifique : la gestion de projet (étude de cas sur l'entreprise Dacia – groupe Renault)*, PhD in Management thesis, Universite Paris 1 Pantheon-Sorbonne, 2007.

Pitesti, a decrepit automobile plant

Renault took a 51% equity stake in Dacia on 29 September 1999 as part of the Romanian company's privatisation process. The French carmaker had already tried to gain a foothold in Eastern Europe by buying Skoda in the Czech Republic but was beaten to the punch by Volkswagen. Dacia's privatisation was a second chance. Renault had historical connections to Dacia since long before the Logan. The first car to have ever been produced in Romania was a Renault: the R12. In 1990, Dacia's main product was the 1300, a vehicle derived from the R12 under the aegis of a technological cooperation between Renault and Dacia that had started in 1968 and ended in 1980, largely because of the confusion provoked by the Ceausescu regime. Following the Skoda bid, Renault was regularly solicited by the Romanian authorities, notably by Constantin Stroe, Dacia's Managing Director (and still Vice President in 2011) and asked to explore the hypothesis of another investment in Romania in the 1990s. Stroe was convinced that Dacia's future would require a link-up with a major automaker. After 1997, Renault really started to push this direction by sending research delegations and initiating negotiations. The sessions were quite anarchic at first, with the Romanians bringing Korean manufacturer Hyundai to the table, signing two contracts with this firm to twist Renault's arm.

Renault was hesitant about investing in a firm whose organisation had been badly affected by many years of bureaucratic functioning and whose inhouse technologies were completely obsolete. Production volumes were acceptable with something above 100,000 vehicles being assembled in 1997 (450 vehicles daily, including 60 Romanian designed Novas, mainly derived from the R12). Quality was not up to scratch, however, with each Dacia 1310 typically having five defects and each Nova up to 15. "Every vehicle needed an average of eight hours a day being spruced up."[1]

The Pitesti industrial complex was characteristic both of a big combine using technology that is more than 20 or 30 years old, and of a typically integrated model of state socialism. Standards were well below what was found elsewhere in the automotive industry in the last 20th century, and Renault engineers' visits to the Pitesti industrial site quickly revealed the extreme obsolescence of its production methods, increasing doubts about how useful it would be for the French manufacturer to invest there.

---

1. D. Debrosse, op. cit., p.56.

After Schweitzer's 1998 announcement of plans for $6,000 vehicle, Dacia began to be seen as a more credible acquisition opportunity, specifically because it gave Renault a second brand plus a new industrial tool. There was no way that the car could have been made in France, Spain or Belgium. After difficult negotiations marked by more or less fraught episodes until the day the contract was finally signed on 2 July 1999–and once the final bureaucratic obstacles had been surmounted–Schweitzer started to make certain commitments, in the belief that he had finally acquired the industrial base he needed to achieve the big challenge he had set. The 1999 agreement stated that from 2004 onwards, a New Dacia Car (NDC), costing less than $6,000 would be produced "for sale in emerging countries only". For 2008/10, plans were that "out of 200,000 vehicles, 120,000 will be sold in Romania and 80,000 exported to emerging countries."[1] Christian Estève would later modify this link between plans for a $6,000 car and the Dacia operation: "During the privatisation process, we spent lots of time working on the famous phrase announcing the development of a "modern, robust and reliable" vehicle. But it was merely to express the idea that there more to come."[2]

Restructuring the Dacia industrial site

The goal of making a €5,000 vehicle in Romania implied an in-depth restructuring of the site by rationalising and upgrading it through the introduction of Group methods. Rationalisation meant matching international competitive standards by means of deep cuts in the very high number of staff members. The privatisation contract between Renault and the Romanian government clearly indicated a staff adjustment programme, with the number of employees going from 27,560 at Dacia in July 1999 to 14,823 in June 2003, as per commitments made under the privatisation contract (on top of which came 2,000 employees and suppliers working out of the suppliers park). Specific laws were voted to carry out this programme. Rationalisation would continue due to the collapse in Dacia sales, which had fallen by half since the start of the decade. A new redundancy programme targeting 4000 people was negotiated in 2004, with staff numbers falling to barely 11,300 employees by yearend. All in all,

1. Source: December 1998 Renault. Reproduced in D. Debrosse, op. cit., Appendix 6, p. A6/3.
2. Interview with Christian Estève, 12 November 2008.

more than 5,500 people left Dacia in 2004, but with nearly 3,000 being hired, around 25% of all staff was renewed during the course of the year. Declining sales compromised the project's expected cash flow. A new funding source was found with a rights issues than allowed Renault to take almost full control of Dacia (its equity stake reaching 92.7% in 2001).

Beyond these redundancies, there was also an effort to introduce production methods that the French manufacturer developed to upgrade Dacia's organisation, notably by introducing 'elementary work units' in the plant's workshops. This was accompanied by the "Renault Production System", largely inspired by Nissan, with whom Renault was building an alliance at this very same time. The Renault Production System stipulated specifications for each workstation, seeking standardised tasks to enhance quality by emphasizing worker training. Each workshop at the Mioveni plant began offering dexterity lessons to help operatives perform their line tasks. Site modernisation quickly increased production. Productivity rose more slowly, however, in part because Dacia sales fell more quickly than planned staffing numbers.

Throughout this modernisation process, the relationship between Dacia's management and local unions played an important role, alternating between cooperation when unions would support the manufacturer's new industrial ambitions—with the lengthy mandates accorded union leaders, mostly ones working at the lead body (the Dacia Automobile Union), creating a climate conducive to this strategic vision—and conflicts concerning the distribution of the fruits of growth. The union framework was atypical for Renault. Firstly, union rates were as high as 80-90%, with membership fees being taken directly from Dacia workers' wage packages. In addition, collective bargaining was done annually, as per a predefined procedure. Lastly, the agreement covered the Mioveni industrial complex (including suppliers) but not Renault-Dacia's other operations in Romania.

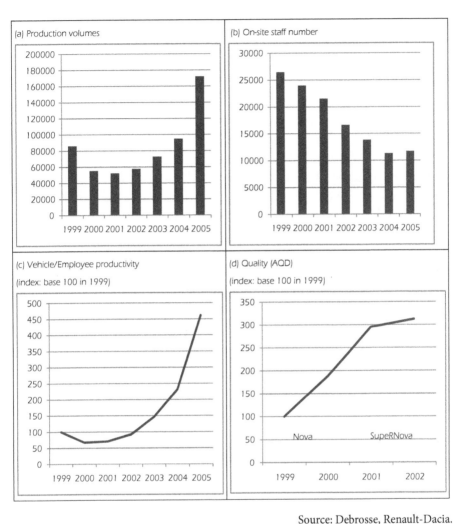

Source: Debrosse, Renault-Dacia.

Figure 2.4–Dacia's changing output, 1999-2005

Negotiations first focused on redundancies, working conditions and staff training, in a context that was not particularly conducive to people demanding higher wages. This is because the main Romanian market began to shrink after 1999, with Dacia's market share plummeting from 73% in 1999 to 50% in 2002. The business plan had expected sales of 85,000 units annually but actual volumes fell to around 55,000 units in 2000-02. This meant that staffing levels were excessive, causing temporary layoffs (averaging 82 days in 2000, or one-third of the normal workload[1]) followed by the decision in 2001 to implement a "survival plan". Wage hikes at Dacia matched the national average until early 2002 but rose faster afterwards. This is because the economic recovery that started around then focused unions' attention on wages once new products began to roll out and the Company regained market share. The first industrial action came a few months after the Logan's December 2003 launch, with unions demanding a 20% wage hike and management offering 13%. Dacia got the Romanian judiciary to declare the strike illegal and production was only interrupted for three days before both sides reached a compromise. On 31 January 2003, internal assessments by Renault found that Mioveni factory team wages were one-third what their colleagues received in Turkey and one-eleventh what they got in Spain.[2] In other words, immediately prior to the Logan's launch, the Romanian plant still had an advantage in terms of wage costs even as quality had improved (especially following the Solenza). The introduction of a new vehicle would sustain the progress in terms of productivity and quality.

SupeRNova and Solenza, textbook projects paving the way for the Logan

To prepare for the Logan, Renault relied on two new Dacia vehicle launches, the SupeRNova in 2000 and above all the Solenza in 2003. The SupeRNova was scrabbled together quickly because Renault wanted a product that would help Dacia continue dominating the Romanian market while approximating international automotive industry standards. With its new driving system and other technical modifications (like completely refurbished electric wiring), the product had been jointly developed in Romania and France, enabling an initial experience of cooperation between the Dacia design centre, with its more than 600 persons, and the Renault Technocentre, where Renault engineers would coach their Dacia engineers counterparts in head-to-head tutorials. Local resources were also mobilised to develop a diesel version of the pick-up truck, equipped with a Renault F8Q engine. Very popular in emerging countries, this affordable €5,100 vehicle had been part of the Dacia range for years and offered the brand a way to consolidate its presence.

---

1. D. Debrosse, p. 131.
2. D. Debrosse, p. 302.

Solenza was even more ambitious, being a textbook project "that helped the whole industrial system to prepare for the X90 (Logan)."[1] Indeed, the Logan's unexpected success translated into the Solenza being withdrawn just 18 months after launching. Fewer than 10,000 units were produced in 2003-2005, despite initial expectations that it would last until 2007. The organisational structure was the same as the Renault system, with a single executive working as Project Director (code X41), a project team comprised of 51 persons (including 41 Romanians) and elementary function groups (featuring 34 Romanian pilots) working out of a project office. Initiated in 2000, the scheme ran for 34 months, going through all the different phases that Renault vehicles experience during their development phases. Based on the Nova, the idea was to introduce major modifications improving product quality, design (with help from IDEA) and safety, while keeping the retail sticker at €3,800 (less than the SupeRNova). The Solenza also counted on the involvement of suppliers working on the ensuing Logan project: Faurecia (with EAPS), Johnson Control (seats) and Valeo/Elba (lighting).

Learning came from the Renault Group transferring its most up-to-date organisational methods, but also from adaptation to conditions (local competencies, cost constraints). This was a hybridisation that necessarily transgressed certain Renault rules and culminated, after a period of trial and error, in an original production model.

Organising the Miovesti industrial complex

The Miovesti complex hosted a number of different units. Asides from its two large body shops (UVD Dacia Assembly Plant) and mechanical units (UMD Dacia Mechanical Plant) that we briefly describe below, there was also the industrial suppliers park, a zone combining contemporary RTR-related engineering activities (see Section 2) with logistics activities such as the reception of components, organisation of internal flows or preparations for the shipment of vehicles in either fully assembled or kit form. By 2010, nearly 300 trucks were using the site on a daily basis to supply various departments (upstream flows), with the transport of fully assembled vehicles or spare part kits (downstream flows) mobilising around 100 trucks a day. On top of this, the site hosted 16 train loads a week. All in all, having

---

1. François Fourmont, Dacia Managing Director, *Global* (Corporate newsletter), No. 31, 4 June 2004, p.6, cited in D. Debrosse, p. 260.

shipped the equivalent of 30,000 vehicles in 2005, the ILN platform ran more than 300,000 in 2010, employing the same number of staff members.

The vehicle assembly unit was the biggest of all, employing half of all personnel on-site and accounting in May 2010 for 8,500 employees split between 328 elementary work units. Six years after the Logan's launch, the participative approach associated with this kind of work organisation had yet to be widely assimilated, with management considering that a great deal of progress was still needed to overcome a very hierarchical structure reflecting operatives' lack of initiative. It is true that the Renault Production System had already been adopted, but this seemed to be more of a formal move than a real one. RPS rules were ostensibly being followed but there had been no real appropriation of the tool itself.

The stamping section was probably one of the most difficult units to reorganise. It had second hand presses and semi-automatic cutting processes but no robots, grippers or trolleys. Presses could be reorganised down the line but items were still being transferred by hand from one machine to the next. Thus, if one machine was stamping two small parts, two operatives would have to grab the metal sheet from behind and position it manually, working together with two other operatives stationed across from them. All four would then put both hands on the items' safe points before starting the first stamping operation. The item would then be turned around and slipped into the next matrix, following which the operatives would again grab its safe points before the second stamping. The operation would then be repeated a third time before the stamped item was removed by the latter two operatives while the first two grabbed the next piece of sheet metal. Parts were stored next to the press. A little further down the line, another flow involved four presses working on door parts. Once again, there would be no robots here, just human handlers, with two operatives taking the items out of the presses, turning them over and transferring them to their neighbours working on the next machine. This carried on until the end of the line where the last operatives brushed the parts before checking and storing them on shelves awaiting transportation.

This was a very different world than ultramodern factories where humans mainly fulfil equipment supervision functions. The unit was always operating with three eight-hour shifts. Cycles were extremely rapid (the time it took to put a part in the right place, operate the press and turn it over or remove it for transfer to the next machine). Although noise levels were no higher than 90 dB, they were deafening compared to modern factories. Yet a great deal of progress had been achieved compared to what Renault teams had discovered upon arriving in 1999, when one expatriate manager participating in the site's upgrading (J.N. Deteix) described the stamping processes as "18th-century" whereas another (Christian Estève) remarked, "Yes, it was a complete disaster, starting the stamping unit where the machines harked back to Renault's golden age. As a joke, I would always say that 'This is extraordinary, better than Rolls Royce–each part is different so we never make the same car twice!' And we did have enormous problems with stamping, which took a long time to resolve. After that we had a lot of work to do in the body shop, where assembly workers had been banging away like crazy, mainly using hammers and mallets."

With more than 1,500 employees by the 2010, however, the plant was responsible for 70% of the global production of body frames used on the Group's Entry range (with a smaller percentage additionally being shipped via the ILN platform to other plant assembly lines in Morocco or Columbia). The bodyworks unit had a few crimping robots, plus automats handling parts that had been positioned manually before teams of experienced welders would solder the 15 to 21 points they had been assigned. The same configuration was found in the painting unit, with the few existing robots also requiring modernisation. A few sub-sections here were automated, notably the unit applying varnish to outside surfaces (with inside surfaces being masked and painted later by hand). Lastly, the assembly line workstations were all manual. Having said that, this allowed for greater flexibility, which was useful insofar as the declination of the Entry range into different variants led to the production of body models that were very different from one another yet all made on one and the same line, with time cycles of less than one minute for each workstation.

Technical requirements meant that the mechanical plant had higher automation levels. It made two of the engine types fit onto the Renault range: the K7x petrol engine; and the F8Q diesel engine. It was also responsible for transmissions (JH gearboxes). The aluminum foundry was completely modernised to make gear cover castings. Much of the equipment recovered from various Renault Group plants for resuscitation were found in this unit, although each workshop still hosted many manual operations (i.e. foundry finishings of castings). After consolidation, ACI was transformed into the Dacia Mechanical and Chassis Plant (UMCD), employing 3,700 people in July 2010.

Although various plant departments mainly churned out Logan components, they also diversified their outlets by supplying other factories, for Renault but also for other manufacturers (i.e. axles sold to Nissan or PSA-Toyota's European plants). The rise of the Entry line bolstered the Mioveni complex considerably, helping it to become the Renault Group's largest shipment centre in 2010 and the leading producer of axles (beating the historical Le Mans plant). Similarly, Mioveni's aluminum foundry was third in the Group in terms of transmissions output and sixth in manufacturing engines. Having started as an obsolete industrial combine in 1999, the modernisation drive, combined with the Entry range's commercial success, turned Mioveni-Pitesti into the Renault-Dacia-Samsung Group's biggest industrial complex.

SUMMARY: LESSONS FROM SUCCESS IN THE FACE OF AN IMPOSSIBLE CHALLENGE

A spectacular reduction in manufacturing and investment costs ...

The end effect of these actions was that the X90 met its manufacturing return cost target. The chart below recaps the main breakthroughs explaining this success. Four items seem paramount: local integration; product certification; carryover; and productivity gains. All in all, manufacturing costs were one-half what they were on the benchmark vehicle. This is why Renault could make a basic version of its €5,000 car.

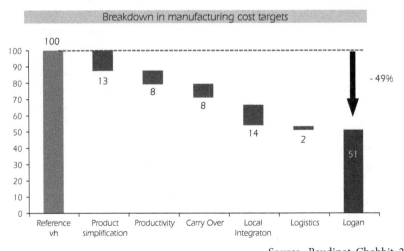

Source : Baudinot, Chahbit, 2006

Figure 2.5–Breakdown in manufacturing cost targets

The objective of reduced engineering and process investment costs was also met. Significant leverage was achieved through product simplification, supplier involvement in design, use of manual processes and carryover. Although there were few gains at the mechanical level (the Logan's mechanical systems were identical to other Renault vehicles), significant progress was made in relation to bodywork.

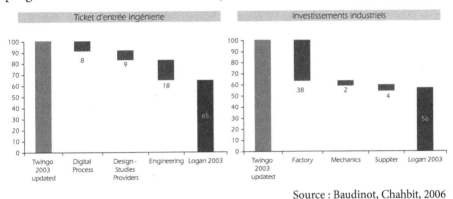

Source : Baudinot, Chahbit, 2006

Figure 2.6–Compared design and industrial investments

Whereas the €5,000 car project had once seemed destined to fail, the Logan's industrial success at the design and production levels paved the way for an unexpected deployment of the Entry line, one that could then be broken down into a real product range and converted into the next phase in the Renault Group's internationalisation trajectory.

... and frugal performance requiring a wide variety of competencies

Observers tend to associate excellence in technical competency with the kinds of exceptional performances found, for instance, in motorsports. It is clear that the full-blown frugality drive shaping the design of the Logan was also particularly demanding in terms of all kinds of technical aptitude. By systematically testing the rules of business in light of the project's singular objectives and context–and by prohibiting systematic "copying-pasting" of ready-made solutions while prioritising new compromises–the Logan's design turned out to be particularly greedy for high-level expertise. Refining understanding of customers who had once been ignored and refusing "top-down" non-choices; dissecting technical options to understand what might be eliminated or saved; understanding the cost structures that aggregate manufacturing, logistics and exchange risks–all these decisions required "professionalism" in each area where their effects were felt. The conclusion to this section will show that the Logan project was able to count on the involvement of experienced professionals, a condition that is rarely associated with radical innovation, despite constituting a key factor of success.

Managing risks and meeting deadlines: anticipation and concurrent engineering

It is easy to imagine that this challenge evoked some fairly serious risks. The question then became how feasible it was to achieve such ambitious cost-cutting objectives; what the new production site's industrial capacities would be; how suppliers operating outside of Renault's traditional perimeter would fare; and how these risks could be reconciled with the increasingly crucial goal of lowering new products' time-to-market.

Renault's approach was inspired from modern concurrent engineering methodologies that stress maximising the anticipation of problems and implementation of processes dealing with them upstream "on the spot". The chart below represents new product development as a kind of dual process[1] comprised of decisions that progressively block different project variables, and of a kind of learning that lends itself to the acquisition of the knowledge needed to make decisions. The two processes may have been independent in this case but defining components depended on factors such as sourcing and industrial operations. A sequential approach successively addressing different project parameters might generally have raised certain issues, albeit belatedly and at a cost. Learning inertia tended to draw people's sense of possible choices back to existing solutions. Innovative scenarios would be eliminated due to a lack of time, forcing the adoption of ready-made solutions.

---

1. C. Midler, "L'apprentissage de la gestion par projet dans l'industrie automobile», *Les Annales des Mines, série Réalités Industrielles,* Special Issue on Automotive Industry, October 1991.

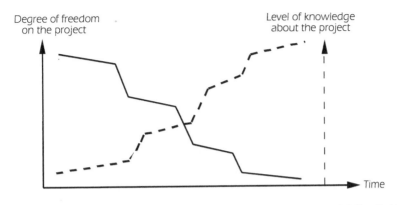

Source : Midler C., 1991

Figure 2.7–Project convergence: piloting decisional irreversibility and learning to achieve creation within a context defined by uncertainty

In short, one major challenge for an innovative project like the X90 involved anticipating and accelerating this learning curve.

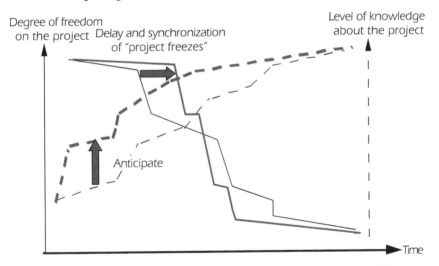

Source : Midler C., 1993

Figure 2.8–Anticipation as key to project acceleration and robustness

This approach deepened the projects' upstream phases by forcing design work to seek a level of precision going well beyond the kinds of upstream milestones that had been traditionally required, where people would only reason in terms of the overall framework and simply quantify different orders of magnitude. The problem was that certain irreversible commitments associated with the project were often made without the protagonists having a proper vision of different scenarios' reliability. Over-estimating the objective assigned to a particular component made it hard to explore other technical scenarios downstream, if only because of deadline constraints. In turn, this could cause delay, cost or performance problems. Conversely, choosing a suboptimal option within the initial framework meant that more ambitious scenarios would be automatically eliminated.

The X90 was the perfect illustration of an approach aimed at enhancing a project's upstream phases. The chart below represents its actual progress versus initial plans derived from more traditional projects. At the upstream level, protagonists gave themselves time to explore the feasibility of this "impossible project", validating options affected by major uncertainties (in particular Dacia's industrialisation, based on an exploration of economic scenarios coherent with the objectives). The downstream level saw ultra-rapid execution, driven by rich learning coming out of the upstream phases and unambiguous decisions taken within each of the freeze stages.

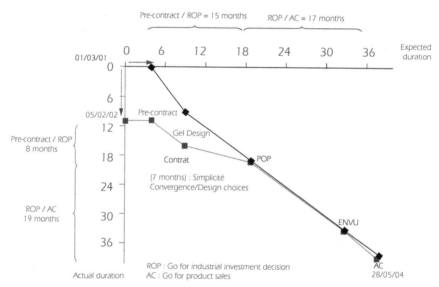

Figure 2.9–Running the X 90 project

In the end, the project did better than expected (27 months instead of 32). For a while at least, it was the quickest project that the Company had ever implemented.

Section 3 below demonstrates that at least part of the Logan project learning came from the introduction of an anticipation logic, one based on changes in Renault's development process entailing greater involvement by the Design departments and by suppliers during the pre-contract phases, a crucial moment for freezing the decisions that would frame the project.

The organisational conditions enabling a clear break with the past

Overt approval and solid support from the CEO

One proposition that has been validated on many occasions in the field of innovation management is that achieving a clear break with the past requires high-level support. The Logan project was no exception to this rule. As aforementioned, it enjoyed clear support from Schweitzer in the face of prevailing opposition across the Company. Much in the way that the Twingo project "wasn't stopped" at the time of Raymond Lévy despite its disappointing figures, and similar to the way that the 2008 electric vehicle project was pushed by Carlos Ghosn and Patrick Pelata, it is clear that the Logan owed its emergence and subsequent survival to Schweitzer's vision.

On one hand, the growth scenario that the President had envisioned following the failure of Renault's alliance with Volvo–a further conquest of emerging markets via vehicles aimed at the masses of customers found in these countries–was far from unanimously supported by executive. It should be remembered that at the time (and even today), the consensus was that Western manufacturers' competitive advantage when attacking these markets lay in more sophisticated products and the brand image associated with them. Hence the idea that they should be attacked towards the top-of-the-range, by selling luxury goods to fast developing countries' most affluent classes.

Having said that, few people believed at the outset in a project defined by a "modern, robust and affordable" car. The risk of creating a "sub-car" or one afflicted by this image was a major obstacle to people getting on board, particularly technicians.

This scepticism could be seen in the forecasts put together by the committees charged with deciding about the project, which was being called Renault's "rendez-vous" with history. The chart below shows that expected production volumes at the Pitesti plant were four times lower than what the plant was already producing two years after being taken over. In our interview, Schweitzer remembered how angry he became in the early 2000s when forecasts never seemed to exceed 80,000 units, which would have prevented the programme from becoming profitable and made it unviable.

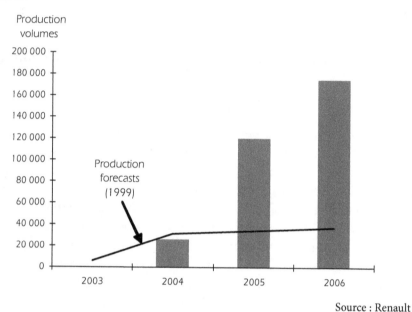

Source : Renault

Figure 2.10–Forecast comparisons, 1999 vs. 2006

This is redolent of a constant difficulty encountered in innovation management–the use of unreliable quantification methods.[1] Calculations extrapolate from current realities. If an innovation involves new thinking, however, these might deviate from tradition. When specific studies are trying to account for this, they are often treated with suspicion because they are based on ad hoc hypotheses that the company has not validated yet through other programmes.

As Berry has pointed out, quantitative management tools have long had a major effect on the decision-making processes of big companies in the

---

1. At present, there is one important research orientation that specifically seeks to develop more suitable evaluation methodologies. Cf. C. Midler, R. Maniak, R. Beaume, *Réenchanter l'industrie par l'innovation : stratégie et management de l'innovation dans l'industrie automobile*, Paris, Dunod, 2012.

automotive business.[1] It is therefore easy to understand why, without executives' personal, direct and devoted involvement, so-called "deviant" scenarios find it impossible to emerge.

When this kind of condition is fulfilled and the innovation progressively affirms its credibility,[2] a network of allies (to recycle a concept that innovation sociologists often use) will start to expand.[3] For instance, the general scepticism felt by Renault executives steadily dissipated as design model started to materialise in a way befitting the concept of a €5,000 car; when the first prototypes showed that the "Frankenstein car" was something real that handled well and could be comfortable; and when return costs came in at levels enabling the programme to generate real margins.

Managing "heavyweight" projects

It remains that the wishes of senior management, even when expressed powerfully and tenaciously, would not have been enough to drive the project to fruition. These wishes had to be relayed and deployed throughout the organisation, reaching the hundreds of parties within the different business areas who would be responsible for their concretisation. These were the people who would embody the global and abstract concept of a €5,000 car through concrete and precise local decisions about things like window shapes, bodyshop tools and suppliers' seat frames.

Product development professionals would be responsible for upstream marketing; design; product and process engineering; and procurement. These businesses constituted (and leveraged) the firm's generic competencies, enacting them through successful projects. The ensuing "business rules" would protect the specificity of the brand identity, so that customers would realise they are driving a Renault and not some other manufacturer's car.

1. M. Berry, *Une technologie invisible ? Le rôle des instruments de gestion dans l'évolution des systèmes humains*, Paris, C.R.G., June 1983.
2. Although clearly this has not always been the case. The Avantime and VelSatis are innovations that demonstrated, if need be, that a clear break with the past does not always rhyme with success.
3. M. Akrich, M. Callon, B. Latour, "A quoi tient le succès des innovations ?", *Gérer et Comprendre*, Vol. 97, June and September 1988, pp. 4-17, 14-29.

Yet although it was absolutely crucial that traditional development engineering approach[1] drive the rapid and economic development of a good quality new product, by itself this was not enough to correctly pilot the decision-making process involved in the new product's design.

Since the early 1990s, this role had been devolved to project functions, a significant organisational reform for which Renault was the historical trailblazer with its Twingo project[2] that inaugurated a "heavyweight project manager" function[3]. The approach included delegating senior management across the whole scope of the project; finding experienced people with sufficient status both to imbue the project with the internal legitimacy it needed and to exercise substantial influence; as well as a mission horizon coherent with other vehicle programmes' key milestones. In the case of the Logan, team definition was complicated by the duality of the two projects at hand: designing the car; and the acquisition and modernisation of Dacia. Regarding the first point, Jean-Marie Hurtiger was appointed director of the W90 pre-project on 1 March 1999 before becoming director of the X90. Regarding the second, the first Dacia team was comprised of a triumvirate comprised of Constantin Stroe as Managing Director and his two deputies, Manuel Roldan (Industrialisation) and Christian Estève (Trade, Finance, External Relations). Gérard Detourbet got to Romania in May 2001, serving as Assistant Director for Industrial Development, with a focus on the new Dacia vehicle programme. He would later become Dacia's Assistant Managing Director and X90 Programme Director. The convergence between the two projects would lead to overlapping responsibilities. The Logan project very much appears to have been the operation at the heart of Dacia's development. A compromise was reached by the two project managers involving a breakdown between products and processes, encapsulated in the constant interactions analysed throughout the present chapter. Things changed in 2006, when Jean-Marie Hurtiger took over Renault's Korean subsidiary, with Gérard Detourbet being appointed Programme Director for the whole of the initiative, expanding his project function to include commercial aspects that had been excluded

1. P. Le Masson, B. Weil, A. Hatchuel, *Les processus d'innovation – Conception innovante et croissance des entreprises*, Hermès, Paris, 2006.
2. C. Midler, *L'Auto qui n'existait pas Management des projets et transformation de l'entreprise*, Dunod, 1996. Midler C., 'Projectification of the Firm: the Renault case', *Scandinavian Management Journal*, Vol. 11, No. 4, pp 363-375, 1995.
3. K.B. Clark et T. Fujimoto, *Product Development Performance: Strategy, Organization and Management in the World Auto Industry*, Boston: Harvard Business School Press, 1991.

until this point, as well as the management of all products derived from the platform. His function will be analysed in Chapter 5.

Beyond the project management aspect, Renault projects were always based on a dual track approach. On one hand, there was the linkage between the constituents of the overall project, broken down into "elementary function groups" (technical division), truly autonomous and multidisciplinary sub-projects responsible for aspects such as the technical design of the product's sub-assemblies (dashboard, seats, etc.) or processes (bodywork, painting). The goal at this level was to obtain the requisite balance between quality, cost and deadlines. Given the huge scale of an automobile project (between 600 and 1,000 persons involved during the development phase), this decentralised organisation was necessary to ensure that compromises needed for the project's overall equilibrium are integrated rapidly and efficiently into its basic technical decisions. On the other hand, there was also a connection between the Company's different business areas. The Project Director's team was comprised of various project managers responsible for coordinating, across the whole of the project, as well as all of the specialists working on its development: product; design; engineering; performance; purchasing; industrialisation; logistics; marketing; sales; and after-sales.

One major indicator attesting to the team's collective competency was the stability of staff during the development phase. This helped to build and stabilise a deep understanding of the "meaning" of the programme, forging a shared collective strategy that could be leveraged and implemented from the project's beginning to the end. On average, the parties involved during this first phase of the initial project spent more than five years on mission, a period of time matching the project's total duration.

The Logan project: typifying a form of "heavy" project management organisation

Project management involves a kind of matrix structure, with literature in this area characterising four forms depending on the level of responsibility or capacity for action at the disposal of project managers compared to representatives from the functional groups.

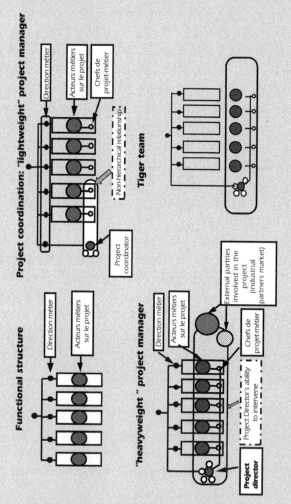

Source: Clark, Hayes, Wheelright, 1988.

Figure 2.11–Different project structures

Strong functions are particularly important in the case of original projects such as the Logan or, from 1989 to 1992, the Twingo. These were "impossible projects" that could not have happened without the firm implementing automatic processes. Through the decision-making powers at their disposal and their connection to different professions (via "project businesses heads"), programme teams were there to focus people's energy and steer compromises around the specific project objectives for which individuals were responsible. This stimulated a search for unusual solutions deviating in one or the other sector from the norms of excellence that experts had generally favoured in that line of business. In turn, this encouraged actors to agree original compromises.

The virtues of marginality

It is in this way that senior management gave an impetus to the Logan project, embodied in its formal project management structure. The two conditions were surely necessary but also insufficient. In the balance between risky and customary solutions, between transgressing or applying normal business rules, the question was on what basis the project might affirm its radical identity. At first glance, the answer seems paradoxical–the project's greatest strength lay in its precarious and marginal nature.

A situation where "doing the ordinary" is likely to end in failure gives the individuals facing this dilemma the advantage of being able to risk displeasing others by transgressing norms and agreed rules. Yet such transgressions can pass under the radar in marginal contexts where energies and resources are being mobilised around other priorities. Under other circumstances, arguments might be raised about a project's "core business" but such opposition was not really worth it in our situation, because there was little chance that it would have been successful or that the transgressions would have ultimately been institutionalised. Management literature describes this as a "skunk project" situation developed quasi-secretly by small highly autonomous groups operating under the protection of a very senior sponsor.

This description fit the Logan project to a tee. On one hand, the challenge set by Renault's CEO was far from representing executives' consensus about the project's feasibility. On the other, the Company was embarked upon another adventure at the time of the Logan project, namely the Alliance with Nissan, considered much more important by employees at all levels and in all business areas. In the words of Christian Estève, "We were really lucky that no one believed in Dacia. Guys used to say to me, and are still saying, that I was taking unbelievable personal and professional risks, but I thought this was silly and didn't worry about it. Very few people helped us because they had other things to do. It was the time of the alliance with Nissan. Planes leaving for Tokyo were full be we were heading off to Bucharest… and Pitesti…".

These circumstances inevitably affected the profile of the actors who embarked upon this adventure. Most Renault managers who joined the X90 were considered adventurers going down a road that was destined to turn sour. Most of their colleagues advised them to refuse the offer of joining Dacia and/or the X90 project. According to Jean-Noël Deteix, who was appointed to the project in 1999 and put in charge of the Entry range at the Painted Assembled Body Department (part of Renault's Engineering Department), "Upon being appointed to the Logan project, the first thing you'd wonder is what you'd done wrong. People would try to reassure you but you'd still be tortured by doubt."

Interview with Jean-Marie Hurtiger

Could you tell us about your trajectory at Renault before Logan?
My time at Renault was fairly unusual. I joined the company relatively late, in 1988, after an early career in the oil business. This set me on a path to do something different, in part because I was in a better position to envision major changes than if I had spent the whole of my career in the Company. Moreover, I've always been an independent spirit and sought jobs that I found interesting and where I would enjoy some autonomy, instead of something that merely helped my short-term career prospects.

I started in the Methods Department under Georges Douin, who was Technical Director at the time. They had noticed me during some negotiations with the Administration in Brussels, where I sorted out one of the Company's problems. I then joined the Delta group think tank which was at the origin of many conceptual innovations at Renault. Later I broadened my spectrum of activities to include the International Department, where I was notably responsible for Russia. In late 1996, Manuel Gomez asked me to run Colombia.

How and why do you think that you were chosen for this project?
Remember the context. Renault had just missed out on Volvo, mainly for public policy reasons. At the time I was working on China because Renault

was trying to expand internationallly. This was Schweitzer's 2010 plan, with its target of 4 million units, mainly in emerging markets benefiting from Asian growth. We realised that we did not have any products to carry our strategy forward in these markets. In 1998, we started thinking about a low-cost car, back then for India.

The Dacia opportunity came by accident. It's striking that whereas the emerging market growth strategy and deployment to Asia had clearly been premeditated, the concrete opportunities offered by Dacia, Renault Samsung Motors and Nissan were totally unexpected. Georges Douin suggested that Schweitzer use Dacia to make a radically new vehicle.

Why me? I had organised a meeting between Schweitzer and a Russian minister in April 96. When they started looking for a boss for the X90 project, Douin and Schweitzer remembered me. I was called in and Schweitzer asked whether I thought we would be able to make a robust, reliable and modern car retailing at $6,000. I said yes, in part because you don't contradict your boss. Above and beyond the sales tag, I asked him what the goal was in terms of manufacturing return costs. He said that was up to me as long as the programme made money.

I also saw Carlos Ghosn at the time. He was about to leave for Nissan and had doubts about the programme. He didn't see how we would be able to make money at the bottom-of-the-range and theorised that the top-of-the-range was the place to be. He did wish me good luck ... Pierre-Alain de Smedt[1] didn't believe in the project either, he had the VW model in mind and reasoned that we couldn't make a quality car under these constraints.

How did you build your team?

I met people from different lines of business. Everything went great except for Engineering. The Director at the time, Jacques Lacambre, did not believe in the project. Neither did the appointed Chief Engineer for the project. His role was to adhere to certain engineering standards. Instead of changing specifications, he was a fan of carryover. Obviously that became a big problem. Things were really hard for a year and I asked to replace him. That's when Odile Pantiatici came in. Her attitude to the mission was very positive and she attacked it with great rigour, unlike what had come before. She stayed in the box but showed a lot of willpower and was highly effective.

---

1. Who became Renault's Assistant Managing in 1999, replacing Carlos Ghosn when he took over at Nissan.

What key tools did you need to face this challenge?

The first was building a compact and unified project team, with everyone working together at the St Quentin office, thus outside of the Technocentre. Our office hosted all of the different business areas as well as the project management teams and engineering subcontractors. This was a golden age for the X90's project management. Things have gone downhill since. Our organisation saw projects differently, we had a global objective and a contract and would make our decisions within this framework. My job was to manage the manufacturing return price and entry ticket aspects and I was free to do this as I saw fit, without ever having to ask the CEO for a judgement call. Actually, Schweitzer gave us a lot of support. It's true that in a convergence scenario, rapid decision-making is key to achieving a clear break with the past. So for example, whenever Engineering didn't believe in something, they would give us a long list of risks associated with the changes being mooted. As time passed, the only solutions that remained possible were the old standards because we wouldn't have enough time to address the other risks.

The second important aspect was having a subcontracting contract with outside engineering companies such as IDA (for the body) and UTS (subsidiary of Fiat and a metalwork specialist). This gave us a lot of autonomy. At first, Michel Faivre Dubosq, who ran Engineering, wanted this aspect to be totally done outside of Renault. Actually he didn't want to hear about the project. We soon realised that this was impossible, with Engineering responding to each subcontractor proposal by saying that it did not comply with Renault standards. This meant that we also had to get the Renault Engineering people involved. The X90 office therefore housed both external engineering interests and our own business areas. Of course, this had the advantage of ensuring coherency with our internal standards, one example being the pavement kerb that exists at Renault but not at Nissan. The wheelhouse is different at Renault than at Fiat, where the subcontractors had come from... All of these decisions affected the vehicle design and had to be negotiated. Having everybody working on the same site and integrating the project team was key to dealing with these issues quickly and getting a team consensus for the compromises.

The third point is that we were under a lot of pressure to reach our goal without this ever really being imposed on anyone. The project aims (modern, reliable, quality car costing €5,000) had been "top down" but tasks were distributed from the "bottom up". From 1999 to 2001, we spent two years trying to ensure the credibility of each business area's performance objectives, line by line. We really got into the details of Pitesti's cost structure and saw that things were not as good as we had first expected but could be improved. The same applied to local suppliers.

Another factor of efficiency was the way that we started to control modifications. We didn't delegate this. All the changes were put into the system and would be informed in real-time. There wasn't any paper, meaning, for instance, that in meetings we would project up-to-date information taken directly from the database. From that point onwards, our periodic official reports were mere formalities since everybody had the same data.

The last good thing we had going for us was that we never compromised on quality. Each milestone was preceded by a pre-milestone one month before, we always kept to schedule and manufacturer return cost variances were a few euros at most.

I also got pretty involved in the commercial activities. Before 2006, we were the ones marketing Dacia. We started by working on its brand image until we got something that was both simple and strong, which remains the case today. Where products were concerned, we acted like sales representatives securing minimum commitment from our networks and giving them sales arguments they could use. In terms of dedicated networks and pricing policies, we applied the programme's general orientations. Schweitzer supported us in all of these choices, which ultimately worked really well. Ultimately, it was more the press that sold the car than our network…

So what was the main challenge you faced at the time?

No project is easy, but clearly with the X90 it was the beginning of the project that was going to be hard. So we had to build relationships with Engineering to get them to deviate from standard in-house specifications. Some other issues were also very difficult, like braking systems, assisted driving modules (electric or hydraulic), etc.

As the project progressed, things got easier. Actually, once the models came out, the overall credibility skyrocketed, with early opponents beginning to see that we were being reasonable and professional. The general corporate buy-in increased. One of our first big allies was Michel Faivre-Dubosq,[1] who thought the project could be a great lever for engineering learning. Then there was Carlos Ghosn, who had not been a big fan at first but started to support us about this time.

---

1. Vehicle Engineering Director at the time.

Looking back, do you have any regrets?

In a project as complex as this one was, there will always be some aspects that were more problematic. I can think of two. The compromise between boot size and the look of the rear section. We went too far sacrificing the latter to help the former. Otherwise, there were the anticorrosion solutions that we chose, using protected steel that cost a lot, bringing in sealants and wax to protect vulnerable areas. The project didn't have a particular doctrine in this area, asides from finding solutions that were economic. It was Engineering that opted for waxes and sealants. In fact, during the trials, we saw that certain areas could be flooded by water, sharply increasing the risk of corrosion in a way that had not been anticipated. In the end this forced us to use protected sheet metals. Behind this, there was the fact that engineering designs that had seemed so great on paper, were actually not the best given the realities of our industrial processes. From this perspective, Japanese engineering would have been more practical and effective.

Why did you leave the programme in 2006?

I had been with it since 1999. The Logan came out in 2006 and after the launch of the MCV estate version and the Sandero, I came to the conclusion that there wasn't enough room for two people at the head of project. So I asked to leave. They offered me Brazil or Korea and I chose the latter.

What did you learn from your experience with the Logan that helped you most later on?

Three things above all.

Firstly, there was a management lesson. A project works because people get enthusiastic about it. Contracts have to be signed with the right players, who must really believe in its success. For instance, I never tolerated a manager viewing an objective as coming with a 50-50 risk. This means that they did not really believe in what they were doing. People have to incorporate risk into their calculations but then move on.

A second lesson relates to the car business. Regardless of the price, quality is crucial. This explains the success of the Logan as well as its long-term prospects. "Quality is never a waste of money."

Lastly, I developed the personal conviction that the identity of a product or brand resides in the culture of the organisation that designed it. Design know-how is clearly important but identity actually reflects the designers' culture. If you want different products, you need teams working separately and autonomously to create an identity reflecting the product and brand.

In Korea, I again came into conflict with Renault engineering standards but the other way around this time. They didn't understand that a top-of-the-range facility in France is midrange in Korea. The Korean market is full of status-oriented vehicles because Asians like sophisticated cars and spend relatively more on driving. It is a market that demands more sophisticated and better equipped products. The Logan project only succeeded because our team knew what level of autonomy it had in relation to the dominant culture at Renault Engineering. With the operations we had in place since 2005, it would have been impossible to construct a different identity since engineers would always have gone back to solutions they controlled. When Toyota tried to create a premium brand, they came up with a dedicated engineering group that would copy codes from companies like Mercedes. In other words, they deviated from Toyota standards. Similarly, VW and Audi also have different personalities, because the organisations have different histories. You'll understood why, from this perspective, I did not agree with the reforms that happened in early 2005, which went back to the future with projects being run the way they were in the 1990s.

How would you analyse Renault's relationship with the Logan family?

To some extent, we were victims of our products' commercial success, something that was particularly unexpected in Europe. The lesson was that it is possible to succeed in the car business even if you offer small or zero discounts. This was a real game changer. Otherwise, there was the success of the Dacia brand.

Renault's weakness, on the other hand, is that it was unable to take full advantage of these successes. We took fright when Russia and Iran forced us to operate under the Renault brand name. This caused confusion both internally and in customers' minds. With our diversification towards the top-of-the-range and our strong products (led by the Duster), there was a risk that the Dacia range would swallow Renault. Even as Dacia was building up its range and developing a brand identity, it lacked strong products, design, innovative concepts, all the different signs of innovation and performance that it needed to match Renault's other brands.

It is important that this change in the years to come, with the two brands offering strong but differentiated products. In which case, we should be able to take full advantage of the progress we have made (in terms of networks and industrial bases) without running the risk of confusion between (and cannibalisation of) our brands.

Interview with Christophe Midler.

SECTION II

A BIGGER WORLD FOR THE ENTRY FAMILY

Following upon its surprising early successes, the Logan entered a second phase that can best be described as a time of expansion, played out on three different levels: markets expanding well beyond their initial targets; a product range expanding beyond this one product alone; and a production system expanding from a single site to a polycentric network deployed across three continents. It would be wrong, however, to deduce that this was a naturally occurring process, and that all Renault had to do was "surf" on a wave of success. Above and beyond the initial breakthrough, the Logan's long-term survival was just as (if not more) difficult to manage because of two obstacles:

- A lack of descendance. The Logan project's exceptional success had made it into a "milk cow" that was tempting to exploit for as long as possible without changing anything for fear of betraying a winning formula or, conversely, of wasteful investment in something that had already given the best of itself. The history of the automobile is full of successes that, having failed to renew themselves, ultimately lost leadership of concepts that they had inaugurated.
- The search for market opportunities can create situations where products over the medium-term lose their identify in customers' eyes, or their dynamism and strategic coherency from the company's perspective.

Between these two options and starting with the Logan project, the Entry programme was progressively deployed across eight countries, with six (and soon eight) models being marketed in both mature and emerging economies. Questions at this level include how this impressive metamorphosis happened; how dynamics at odds with the Logan project's initial DNA could be managed; how the new coherencies were progressively redefined, ostensibly by transgressing the initial concept; and how the "Logan spirit" could be preserved yet reincarnated in products, markets and production systems that were very different from what had been originally imagined.

Chapter 3 will analyse the Entry line's deployment in product and market terms. Chapter 4 will then assess the design and industrialisation strategies that were implemented to enact this mutation.

EXPANSION AND METAMORPHOSES OF A COMMERCIAL SUCCESS: THE ENTRY RANGE

As demonstrated above, the decision to deploy the Entry programme commercially in France and Western Europe was a real test for the concepts and tools forged during its first phase. This bifurcation in the initial trajectory would strengthen the project and the teams involved in sustaining it or altering its course. It explains why certain decisions were underplayed at first, to avoid destabilising the fragile equilibrium that had nurtured the Logan's seminal compromise. The launch had focused narrowly on a single model (the Logan) and its target countries, plus France. On the positive side, this approach helped to accumulate the kind of learning that later facilitated key launches in Brazil and Russia. More negatively, it failed to avoid subsequent defeats in Iran and India. It is true that the commercial dimension was marginal in the latter two countries—but they are still worth examining in this light.

After 2007, the Entry programme went off in several directions. The first consisted of increasing the number of spaces where the Logan alone, followed by the Logan and the Sandero together, were produced and marketed. The second consisted of diversifying the range by launching MCV estate cars and small vans, first by altering the initial model to facilitate sales, then by introducing a new model, the Sandero. Last came an in-depth learning phase structuring the different lessons that could be learnt from this whole experience, first by launching Duster, and then by designing the product extensions that the Group decided to add to the programme.

THE SANDERO: A NEW MODEL FOR NEW HORIZONS

The MCV estate version had demonstrated that design is important but people can have variable reactions. The project that later became the Sandero gave birth to the concept of an "Entry range". As had happened with the MCV estate (but on a much larger scale), this product would alter the range's industrial and commercial shape. In turn, this change featured different aspects.

In internationalisation terms, the Sandero was a first attempt to move the project away from its previous focus on low-cost vehicles. Where Romania had been crucial to the birth of the Logan and even though this helped to concretise Louis Schweitzer's original intuition (see above), the Sandero resulted from a Brazilian "demand" that was largely conveyed by the European teams. In this sense, more than any other previous product, the Sandero embodied Renault's internationalisation or "intercontinentalisation" trajectory and prefigured subsequent commercial design schemes and radically new "product" policies. The Logan broke with the past because of the way it freed itself from domestic references to develop a product offer that was adapted from the very outset to different commercial contexts. Observers saw how the product resulting from this journey unveiled very high latent demand in certain contexts (especially in France) and from then on in began organising deviations from projects' design phase onwards.

In terms of its commercial methods, the Sandero (and Renault's ambitions for this car, particularly in Brazil and France) helped transcend the creative improvisation that had marked the Logan's launch to develop and apply a veritable Entry "method" that varied depending on whether Dacia or Renault products were involved. The commercial learning acquired in the wake of the 2004/2006 launches was transferred into procedures applied and improved by men and women who had not necessarily worked on the Logan and would soon leave the Entry programme to return to more standard projects or products. In other words, the Sandero was a first attempt by Renault to "normalise" its Entry line, in the narrow sense of this term.

As discussed below, **Gérard** Detourbet and his teams conceptualised and managed this normalisation to stop the Entry programme from being banalised and/or drawn back into Renault's ranks. The Sandero's prospects were intimately linked to the resolution of this issue and to the attempt to leverage the competencies used to make the Logan to transform its clever ad hoc system into real procedures, without abandoning a marginal status generally viewed as being crucial to the family's commercial development.

This second aspect was particularly important given that, in both cumulative sales and monthly sales terms, the orders of magnitude associated with the Entry programme changed with the Sandero. The Dacia brand and the volumes handled through its networks changed the consensus view on distribution issues. Renault's market share would rise significantly in Brazil in a context defined by strong growth in "all brand markets". Although volumes continued to be restrained by production capacities that, despite growing (see chapter 4) remained below potential demand, these changes–largely accelerated by the crisis–helped the Sandero give the Entry a more central role in the Renault Group strategy.

Having overcome internal obstacles experienced during the Logan's launch, the Entry line's volumes and (above all) margins meant that the Director for this range assumed a greater profile within the organisation after the Sandero was launched. This third aspect of the metamorphosis coincided with the problems that Renault and its executives had satisfying plan 2009 targets even before the crisis erupted.

It is worth remembering that Carlos Ghosn replaced Schweitzer in 2006 and quickly devised a very ambitious plan for significant growth in volumes and margins. This was supposed to involve a complete reshaping of product policy and Renault's return to the top-of-the-range. It was a 180 degree change from Schweitzer and translated Ghosn's desire to publicise Renault's conceptual innovations, particularly involving its minivans. The new CEO was said to prefer "car to sell" over "car to live in"[1]. After the Modus, Avantime and VelSatis had all failed, he had several arguments to justify requiring project teams to show less audacity than they had previously and focus on quality, reliability and performance, in the much more traditional register that Ghosn overseen at Nissan. It was against this backdrop that the Twingo II and Laguna III projects were born. Although volume growth objectives largely concerned Entry vehicles, the new management team had relatively little time for the Logan, neither appreciating its design nor the image it offered of Renault. In countries like Russia or Brazil, where the Logan carried the Renault badge and accounted for a big share of brand sales, this legacy from the Schweitzer era understandably did not fit the new team's vision.

Even before the crisis, the Laguna III's launch had already failed to meet the assigned volume and unit value (thus margin) objectives, in contrast to the Logan, which went from success to success, with the Sandero–once Carlos Ghosn announced this new vehicle in Frankfurt in 2007–promising

---

1. Branch slogan during the Schweitzer years.

to amplify the movement. This was a period when it seemed that the Entry line had earned top management's affection. The fact that the product was much more "presentable" (according to Western dogma) certainly affected the situation. But then came the crisis, coinciding exactly with the Sandero's launch in June 2008, shaping its commercial prospects and confirming, for at least three reasons, the Entry range's changing status within the Group strategy.

Firstly, Romania was hit hard by the crisis and only bought 50,000 from the 120,000 Logans that the Pitesti plant made between summer 2007 and summer 2008. This freed up significant capacities that, following the notchback's modest success in other countries, could then be justifiably allocated to the Sandero. Subsequent measures taken in the European markets to combat sharp falls in new vehicle sales following the late 2008 world crisis largely consisted–particularly in France and Germany–of wreckage bonuses. Combined in France with a bonus/penalty system based on a car's ecological performance, the scheme lowered new car prices by several thousand euros and caused significant downscaling. Lastly, the big mature markets were slower to exit the crisis than their emerging counterparts. This led to some restructuring in large global manufacturers' strategic priorities, which in turn made the Entry and Sandero appear the symbols Renault's advance in this key area.

The Sandero: a Brazilian project

The Sandero's history is closely related to the desire to exploit the Entry range's potential in South America, a region that Renault entered early but where it lost ground both to its European challengers (VW and Fiat) and American rivals (GM and Ford). Yet, as shown by what happened in Columbia or the success of Fiat and VW in Brazil–not to mention GM and Ford with products originating from Europe–South America was clearly going to imitate South Europe and became part of Renault's international ambitions. More specifically, the fact that Fiat had tried a few years earlier to develop its Palio in Brazil made this a good place for the Logan to get "on the road".

Problems facing Renault in Brazil and the Logan's relative inadequacy

Christian Pouillaude, who managed Renault's business in Brazil from September 2005 until late 2010, had a front row seat during this journey, having arrived in the country just after the decision to launch the Logan there had been taken, and with work already being done on the Sandero. The Brazilian teams had opposed this launch decision, worrying that the product did not suit their market (due to its price and customers' dislike of notchbacks). They also had problems figuring out how to integrate the rest of the Renault range. During the 1990s, the Company had used its new Curitiba plant to make the Scenic I. Even with the Clio (made in Argentina) supplementing its core range in Brazil, the Curitiba decision positioned Renault's brand in this country as something equivalent to Saab in Europe, appealing to relatively affluent customers with above-average knowledge that they were happy to show off. It was relatively easy for Renault to ask for top dollar but, at the same time, the Company found itself imprisoned in a niche characterised by very low volumes and an underused plant.

On paper, the Logan was capable of being a gamechanger. Early tests, however, had seemed disastrous. At least one-third of the market was already cheaper than the Logan, meaning that the challenge in Brazil was not launching an "Entry" model but a core model. In addition, the product was not particularly sexy in a Brazilian context. All in all, there were three levels (Renault teams, networks, and customers) that needed persuading. This became the first mission for Renault's trade teams in Brazil. They were able to "tropicalise" the car by changing its wheels and adding certain elements to the dashboard. They also opted for communications highlighting how modern it was in comparison to rivals like the Gol, Ka, Centa, Uno, Palio, built using very old platforms and positioned as cheaper. Other sales arguments included how roomy it was inside and its reliability compared, for instance, with the Corolla notchback. From the Renault management perspective, the Logan's 2007 launch was equivalent to launching the Solenza in Romania in 2002: a trial paving the way for the arrival of the Sandero, which was supposed to be much more attractive to the Brazilian market.

Entry volumes de facto repositioning the Renault brand

Working together, Christian Pouillaude (who ended up in 2011 managing Renault's brand) and Jérôme Stroll (President of Renault do Brasil and once head of Renault's Mercosur operations) quickly identified that the main problem was how to reposition their brand. Launching the Logan in Brazil implied that Renault change its customer base. Henceforth, it would target a less intellectual and more popular lower middle class audience for whom a new car purchase was a lifetime experience.

According to Pouillaude, "We had no idea what we were doing when we launched the product but discovered that by changing its image and targeting, we would avoid being seen as an import. At the same time, we now had to take customers from the Gol or other cars like that. We needed to break through brand entry barriers so that we would no longer be fighting on Honda's battleground (sophisticated but relatively expensive and hard to repair products) but instead against the four majors. It was at this level the Brazilian brand strategy really broke with the past."

When Carlos Ghosn visited Brazil in December 2005, he allegedly asked local teams whether they wanted the Renault brand to resemble Honda or Ford in the future. For Ghosn and his counterparts, the answer lay in the question. The Logan's launch signified that Renault would henceforth "take on the four majors" in Brazil.

Globally, Renault had been positioned up until that point as a small "importer" who could neither rival the local Big 3 (in order, Fiat, VW and GM) nor Ford, which had a 10% market share. Its intermediate position included two Japanese automakers (Honda and Toyota) as well as PSA, all of whom emphasized technology and style and defended their 2% or 3% market share with vehicles that were relatively expensive and elitist in light of Brazilian conditions. Note that Citroën had also had recent success in this segment with its C3 and C4–more than Peugeot with its 206, called the 207 in Brazil.

Thanks to the promise of Sandero and the Duster–and thanks to its policy of local design and manufacturing–Renault was able to add its name to the four other carmakers operating in Brazil's top division. Henceforth, it would assume the identity of a local manufacturer instead of a mere importer. Local distributors started to believe that Renault had at long last understood their market and its requirements, and would consolidate its status in the years to come with products that were sufficiently convincing to ensure rapid stock turnover. The assortment would also be relatively narrow because the Company finally knew what consumers wanted, namely cars with high residual values to facilitate resale. This was the future "landscape" whose contours had to be shared with distributors to convince them to accept lower unit margins. In the end, the biggest distributors fell in line. But in order to be credible when painting this glorious picture of the Logan's future, Renault first had to unveil the Sandero.

In the end, the Logan's launch did much better than the first test had intimated. "We are generally less expensive and we are better" was the argument, one intentionally focused on the rational nature of this purchase, based on the idea of TCO (Total Cost of Ownership) with its emphasis on low maintenance costs and the probability of high residual value. All of this was very important in Brazil, where people change cars every three years and want to be reassured that the resale can help fund a new purchase. Underlying the sales argument was the TCO-based slogan "One Real a day", linked to an advertising campaign that stressed habitability, first highlighting the Logan and later the Sandero.

Table 3.1–The transformation of Renault's Brazilian mix

Years	2005	2006	2007	2008	2009	2010	2011
Clio	18,910	19,892	19,638	11,397	13,889	30,097	27,063
Thalia	15,846	16,273	12,573	4,031	7,393	8,398	6,160
Mégane	12,573	5,945	5,798	3,534			
Mégane 2		5,811	15,744	13,615	8,547	5,921	9,827
Logan			14,604	36,603	30,133	36,734	39,088
Sandero			279	39,634	49,391	68,843	81,788
Misc.	199	3,761	4,978	6,339	8,171	10,304	20,374
Renault	47,528	51,682	73,614	115,153	117,524	160,297	194,300

The Logan may have been launched in July 2007 but Renault's Brazilian teams were already preparing the Sandero, which was meant to have much greater potential nationally. Launch publicity had not been planned this early, with the Sandero only meant to come to market in February 2008 (after the Carnival). But Ghosn let the cat out of the bag in Frankfurt in autumn 2007, accelerating the process. Before this, nothing had filtered through, although some people sensed the possibility, explaining the slogan "the Renault that you didn't expect". Subsequently, Christian Pouillaude and his teams only had six months to prepare, display and extol the Sandero, scarcely six months after the Logan came out.

Within a relatively short period of time, Logan sales were overtaken by the Sandero, although less than some people had expected in Brazil and witnessed elsewhere. For instance, the ratio of Sandero versus Logan sales in Brazil in 2009 and 2010 was not 2:1 but only 1.8 or 1.6:1. As regards the rest of the range, unlike the Clio the Thalia was clearly crowded out (since, despite the Thalia 2's arrival in 2009, sales had halved in five years in an otherwise fast-growing market). Otherwise, Mégane (Scenic) sales fell by a factor of four between 2007 and 2010, indicating that the 150,000 rise between 2005 and 2011 in the number of units that Renault sold in Brazil corresponded exactly to Logan and Sandero sales (131,000 units in 2011 plus nearly 10,000 Dusters). In other words, Renault's image in Brazil would henceforth be the image of its Entry range, particularly the Sandero. In exchange for this, the Company had to accept the loss of its earlier Saab-like image.

Brazilian motives and inspirations: global ambitions

The goal was to enable Renault to change its dimensions in Brazil with a car designed in Barcelona with Brazil in mind, in collaboration with local teams. Similarly to what happened with the Logan in Romania between 2000 and 2004, there was a constant reference to Brazil, with everyone aware of which products customers would compare to the Sandero: the VW Fox, the GM-Opel Agila or the Ford Fiesta (the model that had helped Ford to get back on its feet after its problems with VW). Designed thusly, the product was attractive, helping to reposition Renault.

Sandero became Renault's core product in Brazil, with locals not realising that it was a Dacia yet aware that it had been made at Renault's Curitiba plant, something they approved of. It is worth noting that journalists had used the Logan's launch to widely publicise the fact that this was a Dacia, hence a Romanian car. With the Sandero, however, they could not say this: the Sandero was a Brazilian Renault.

For Christian Pouillaude, this changed the relationship between Renault Brazilian teams and distributors. "It was clear to the larger distributors that something had happened at Renault. The biggest, for instance, was carrying almost every brand and had sold around 100,000 new and used cars. He could have criticised our sales policy, saying it didn't suit the Brazilian market, something bad and aggressive. Or at least, this is what I was afraid of what we showed him the Logan. Plus I was taking two or three points off the margin. But he told me that I'd got everything right. I asked him about the margin points but he said, 'Who cares, we can sell this thing, that's all that counts'."

This dimension was crucial during an expansion phase requiring real commitment from distributors, who would be the parties ensuring the product's greater or lesser presence. They would anticipate market share and use the forecast to inform their showroom and sales staff investments. Plus, as was the case in Russia, getting big Brazilian distributors managing broad brand portfolios to praising product policies for their suitability to local market conditions would very much help to convince smaller operatives and become a kind of self-fulfilling prophecy–the more people believed in the vehicle's success, the better it would work. This was particularly important in Brazil due to the crisis in local networks, with Renault was struggling to stabilise a situation in which it had 70 investors for 170 points-of-sale. Against this backdrop, the Company could not afford to be choosy about its counterparts. Brazilian operatives had modelled themselves after American distribution networks and enjoyed, for instance, attending the NADA, National Association of Dealers in America conference. Typically, they would manage five to six brands working out of the major provincial capitals. Being aware of their strength, they would bargain hard with manufacturers, making demands that they justified on the basis of the constant requirement that they benchmark everything.

On many occasions, "Country Management" teams would implicitly side with the distributors, whose inevitable presence was often invoked to justify "local interests" being given a louder voice in disputes with headquarters. It may seem logical that product managers back in France wanted the range to be present everywhere and in everyone's showroom, but as Pouillaude said, "I prefer few products but large volumes. Instead of having a huge range like others want, I'd rather stick to eight or nine models, it's more than enough. The network sees things the same way, if only because it makes inventory easier to manage, suits customers and enables real marketing. Marketing isn't laying everything out and telling customers they can choose whatever they want. It means making choices."

This was a crucial insight, highlighting the growing gap between emerging markets, which manufacturers were increasingly treating as a serious possibility, and another vision of them as mere supplements amenable to the older saturated markets' policy requirements and practices. The emerging markets also offered a chance to clarify commercial proposals, in contrast to the allegedly saturated mature markets where companies would do a commercial belly dance simply because they were convinced that customers were extremely demanding and, just as problematically, unstable. With its huge volumes, Brazil could afford to adopt idiosyncratic practices, and even suggest that they might be applied elsewhere one day.

The commercial importance of local engineering

Having influenced Renault's operational dimensions, countries like Brazil (and more broadly, South America) could no longer be treated as mere export targets. This put them in a better position to impose their dictates. The crux was obviously the fact that products were being manufactured locally. Another consideration was the freedom that the centre gave country managers to develop their own original specifications.

According to Pouillaude, "Everything here has been made in Brazil and Argentina. In principle, we empowered the local engineering teams to develop adaptations, giving them a greater voice in the future. One day we should be able to develop our own body frames here, ones that could then be sold in other markets, like what happened with the Stepway. Rivals like Fiat or VW all have local engineering teams that are totally autonomous. They are Brazilian and have a good feeling for the market and how it changes. They are creative."

Implicitly, this is an allusion to the kinds of the vicious circle that prevailed in the past, when the absence of local engineering restricted the Company's ability to offer products in sync with local demand. Once volumes and market share began to rise, assembly units and engineering capabilities had to be localised. Sales managers started to have input before and after product launches, if only because they now had a sufficiently strong argument to convince distribution group executives of the credibility of Renault's commitment to the country and, behind this, their "importer" rivals' weaknesses.

The Sandero is what helped to change Renault's status in Brazil. Unlike the VW Gol, however, the product was not meant for this one country alone but also supposed to succeed elsewhere, notably Western Europe. As such, it overcame the hurdle that many big carmakers face with a strategy of trying to appear local in the large emerging economies. This then led to the rise of a "state within the state", one whose learning and know-how would be integrated throughout the rest of the organisation. The "Entry" organisation's recipe was to recentralize by ensuring that the individual running the Entry programme have the final word and make decision based on Brazil's wishes and on the imperatives of any other contexts in which the product would be deployed.

By bringing Renault products into line with the market's needs, this approach revealed the shortcomings of the old arrangement. It had been impossible to integrate other Renault products, given how hard it was to get Brazilian teams to dialogue with managers from programmes other than the Entry. The kind of debate witnessed in Russia, as aforementioned, also arose in Brazil, but unlike what happened wherever the Entry had borne Dacia colours, the battle was fiercer in Brazil because it involved defining Renault's strategy and brand identity, and no longer just "adding another string to the bow" of the France Sales Department or the national subsidiary management teams. Clearly, these strategic dilemmas were embodied in the conflicts between the people running the Entry line and Renault's other programme managers, who had no intention of limiting the commercial deployment of products that they had originally designed for stagnant mature markets alone but now hoped to sell in emerging markets, taking advantage of their extremely rapid expansion. Between these two visions, there was nothing for Europe to arbitrate, especially given the possibility of a seamless coexistence between the two product types on offer, including in Eastern Europe or nearby North Africa. The same did not apply in Brazil, however, where issues relating to the Entry's integration into the organisation–or to Renault and the Alliance's strategic vision–were more contentious than elsewhere, once the Sandero's success was to see.

The Sandero in France and Europe: the Entry range reaches maturity for the first time

The Sandero was launched in France in June 2008, three years after the Logan. Compared to the relative schizophrenia that surrounded the Logan's coming out party, the, Sandero's launch seemed low cost but firmly under control. Formalising the lessons drawn from marketing the Logan and the Logan MCV estate, it seemed with this new product as if the Entry range had reached maturity for the first time. Of course, its commercial trajectory was also affected by the economic crisis that–due to the wreckage bonuses governments were paying to support demand–caused in Europe in general (and France and Germany in particular) a general downscaling that was very good for the Sandero. As a result, demand constantly exceeded the Romanian site's output. It was on this occasion that the network started giving Dacia specific showroom space and sales teams, without abandoning its original "pull" approach.

The Sandero in Western Europe: the Entry product as a conquering hero

When Schweitzer announced in 2004 that the Logan would be sold in France and Western Europe, several managers (including Patrick Weil) thought that marketing a hatchback model would enhance Dacia's future commercial prospects. Moreover, despite Brazil's leading role in the Sandero project, Europe was omnipresent in defining its specifications and range. This reflected people's sense of its great potential and awareness that the "aesthetic" measures taken with the MCV estate, in comparison with the notchback version, could not be repeated with the new model.

The volumes and margins generated by the Sandero in 2008 were all the more crucial to Renault given the relative fragility of the rest of its range. The Twingo II was barely surviving; the Clio III (launched in 2006) was ageing and having to compete with a younger rival, the Peugeot 207; the Mégane and Scenic needed renewal, which was supposed to happen in November; and the Laguna III, which had stirred much hope two years earlier, was underperforming. In this context, the Sandero could be construed as a symbolic failure of Renault's return to the top-of-the-range (the famous vehicles "costing more than €27,000"), as Carlos Ghosn had outlined in his plan 2009.

Without the battle of France being as epic as in 2004, the Sandero rekindled hostilities, but this time in a managerial and organisational context that was much less fraught. Arguments and methods had stabilised in the mean time and teams were in place to develop the product. The Logan programme's leader had used its success to build his own teams. He brought in a young manager named Karsten Crapf who, after working on the Kangoo, had been involved in the Entry range for several years. It is Crapf who took responsibility for pricing and developed studies demonstrating that the cannibalisation that people had been feared was not going to happen in France or elsewhere.

He based this insight on the "Logan's progress" and designed original methods that essentially consisted of positioning the product in terms of target customers' used vehicle benchmarks instead of the new vehicles that competitors were offering. This was because studies done for the Logan had confirmed the initial findings that 80% of all Dacias were first new car purchases replacing used cars bought when they were at least five years old. The Sandero therefore had to remain within this space of commercial opportunity, in both performance and price positioning terms.

This was a vast field of opportunity characterised by huge volumes. In France, for instance, out of the 5 million used cars sold every year, half involved vehicles between five and ten years old. In terms of target products, the Logan and Logan MCV estate had also shown that the vehicles being replaced were too diverse to be properly marketed. Back in 2005, Logan purchasers had been owners of cars such as the AX, 309, R19 or Clio 1. This was because the Dacias' positioning in terms of habitability and loading capacity meant that they were comparable with vehicles built using higher-level platforms (M1). This lessened the relevance of traditional new vehicle marketing methods, which had consisted of comparing them with rivals from the same segment. What was now needed were more open-ended exercises anticipating potential surprises in customer reactions to the product positioning that was now on offer.

Similarly, the performance reference could no longer be to a segment "standard" expected to improve constantly until overkill ensued. The constant desire to offer something "more" than the competition or the preceding generation of brands within a model segment could make it very difficult to sell new cars. Of course, there were other constraints as well, including manufacturing return cost, reliability and maintenance cost objectives. Also, the cars would be compared with what used cars over the age of five might offer, these being the products that customers could consider buying instead of a Dacia. The end result was that many standards from the 2000s were still around in 2008, including air-conditioning systems, assisted driving, ABS, airbags, electric front windows and centralised locking systems. All these features tended to be found if not at the first level finishing then at least on the second. What was still absent, however, were ESP, GPS, speed regulators or self-initiating headlights or windscreen wipers.

Table 3.2–Comparing prices for the Sandero and similar cars
(April 2008)

B90	Prix d'accroche B90 (€)		Prix d'accroche concurrent principal (€)		
France	1.4 75ch	7,800	Skoda Fabia	Classic 1.2 60	10,690
Germany	1.4 75ch	7,500	Skoda Fabia	1.2	10,140
Romania	1.4 75ch	6,900	Skoda Fabia	Classic 1.2 60	9,550

Clio III	Prix d'accroche Clio III 5 P (€)		Prix d'accroche Clio III Estate (€)	
France	1.2 75ch Authentique	12,450	1.2 75ch Authentique	13,450
Germany	1.2 75ch Expression	11,750	1.2 75ch Expression	13,400
Romania	1.2 75ch Extreme	10,250	1.2 75ch Extreme	10,800

The new vehicle category ostensibly asked customers to consider prices and position themselves around this. In actual fact, the real choice was via-a-vis used vehicle prices. To compensate for having fewer options, the new vehicles were roomier and had more loading space. Hence the big price gap (30 to 40%) with comparable "traditional" entry range vehicles that, in the case of the Sandero, came from the B2 segment (Clio, 207, C3, Polo, Corsa, Fiesta, etc.). As indicated in the tables below, this price positioning meant that the Sandero (B90) was almost €3,000 cheaper than the Skoda Fabia in France and €2,650 in Romania. The gap vs. the Clio was €3,750 in France and €3,350 in Romania.

Compared with used cars–and considering that (as had been witnessed with the Logan) being able to access new vehicles justified that buyers make an "effort" of around €2,000–the reference would henceforth be the values communicated through three to four years of transactions for equivalent or slightly superior vehicles. Hence the price catalogue for the E0/ENTRY version, with its basic options and inexpensive driving system. What remained was the need to price higher quality finishings and/or options for people who were clearly ready to pay more than the vehicle's manufacturing cost.

Based on these studies, at launch the Sandero was offered at a price that was very similar to the Logan, or below €8,000 for a 1.2 L petrol engine. The first range included a 1.5 Dci diesel variant whose basic version retailed at just above €10,000. The application of Dacia pricing rules positioned the Sandero a little higher in the "less than €10,000" category. The product broke through in France in September, selling 1,500 units. The crisis and the major backing given to the GPL version with the €2,000 government bonus let the Sandero rack up, between its release and the Duster's launch in April 2010, total sales of 79,263 units. Over the same period, 62,964 Sanderos would be sold in Germany.

The Sandero paving the way towards a Dacia network

After the Sandero's launch, Bernard Cambier, Director of Sales for France, described Dacia's conduct in France as similar to a "cuckoo bird". Much like a cuckoo is reputed to lay its eggs in other birds' nests, the Dacia started out–and probably still remained in 2011–a free rider in the Renault network that slowly began to set aside showroom space and staff for it. As aforementioned, this policy was not only eminently defendable but also the only one possible at first, when there was a single notchback model and great uncertainty about the possibility of a second brand below the Renault umbrella in France and Europe. Shortly thereafter, however, questions started to be asked.

Dacia's low marketing costs owed much to the "cuckoo bird policy" in the sense that it was basically an "accounting illusion", with Renault paying for all overheads, allocating them to Renault sales and offering cover by Renault's after-sales service. The real problem was implementing changes in the system without forgetting the lessons learnt from the Logan, particularly the Dacia distribution network's "pull and low-cost" aspect.

In traditional retail automobile distribution structures, problems selling new cars and "pushing" recalcitrant customers towards an expanding product offer always led to networks being asked to increase showroom space; tighten standards; and carry more inventory. This hit profits on new car sales, because of land costs plus the costs of upgrading and carrying extra stock. Against this background, networks only survived due to after-sales (repairs and spare parts sales) whose function was to cover overheads (mainly attributable to conditions underlying new car sales). This practice of sales and after-sales subsidising one another was quite explicit, with a key indicator for evaluating and monitoring a "business" being " after-sales' rate of overhead coverage".

It was easy for the people running the Entry programme to show that their range had escaped this trap. Not only did Dacia not have to build its own network or worry about land prices but there weren't enough Dacia cars on the road to generate significant spare part sales or repair activity. Nor was there any real prospect of this happening.

On the other hand, from the point where Dacia's annual sales prospects started to exceed 50,000 units in France, meaning a market share of around 2.5% (rising towards 5%), it became possible to demand–at least from Renault's biggest distributors–that they dedicate showroom space and specific sales teams to Dacia.

This kicked off in 2009, which saw the promotion and progressive "deployment" of the "Dacia box" concept. Based on a Dacia sales threshold of around 300 units per annum, the idea was to ask networks to buy showroom space or, usually, to arrange room for Dacia "corners", where customers would see the range displayed, replete with its two models (excluding the MCV estate). This rose after April 2010 to three models, serviced by one or two dedicated salespersons. Given Renault's ca. 20% market share in France, this threshold of 300 units corresponded to a point-of-sales "contract" of around 2,000 Renault units sold per annum. With a French network of around 400 businesses accounting for Renault's 20% market share (of ca. 400,000 units, minus "direct sales" to rental agencies, big companies and administration), the average contract was around 1,000 units. Hence the impossibility of forcing the "box" on everyone. It remains that the direction had been given and, as Bernard Cambier still says, "The Dacia basically follows the same model as Audi". Step-by-step, year after year, launch after launch, something that started out as a Renault sub-brand had become autonomous and would be managed with quite distinct contracts and standards.

Vincent Carré, a guardian of the "Entry" temple, clearly saw things differently, stressing the efforts made to avoid these changes banalising Dacia distribution practices. Although businesses would henceforth be remunerated for Dacia sales– something that would quite logically impact on the management of Dacia sales teams–a "pull" logic continued to reign with the constant reaffirmation of the "no exchange and no discount" principle that had characterised Logan sales. Similarly, the boxes may have affected the definition of showroom space or total cost standards, but these were far below what had customarily been demanded not only by Renault but also by a number of importers in France (like Nissan), ones whose sales volumes were comparable to Dacia. Inasmuch as the mechanism established implied that distributors who tried to set up a specific structure would temporarily see their sales slightly better remunerated to offset the extra costs they incurred, the consensus view became that everything should be done to advance Dacia and the network's common interest and minimise this cost. A distinct "Dacia maintenance" department was envisioned, but this was never mandatory and the "cuckoo bird policy" continued to apply in most workshops.

Viewed in this light, deployment was largely based on voluntary input, meaning that group bosses had all the time in the world to acclimatise standards to the specific contexts where their activity was being deployed.

Dealers working in rural areas characterised by cheap land prices and strong Dacia sales were unsurprisingly more amenable to the idea of a Dacia Box, especially if their annual Renault sales had been no more than 1,000 units. Other dealers, whose contracts specified 3,000 units, were much more hesitant about making the change, if only because there were already being squeezed by high land prices. Similarly, on a commercial level this trend bolstered Dacia's identity amongst sales staff and confirmed group managers' support for the idea of developing the Entry range, still by following a "pull" approach. Without making any predictions about the future, the Sandero experiment can be deemed a success from this perspective. The ease with which Dacia objectives were met did not create a situation in which intra-brand competition necessarily caused the kinds of discount practices where sales were routinely made to undercut the dealer next door and "hit the quota". In other words, the adoption of the "Audi model" did not undermine the original distribution scheme's integrity or affect the minimal sales costs associated with this. Of course, the Entry programme's under-capacities since 2004 were a key factor at this level as well.

Under-capacities, choice of targets, allocation of volumes

A chronicle of Dacia sales in France, Germany and Romania between the launch of the Sandero and the Duster reveals the particular circumstances in which some sales policies were deployed. It is clear that difficulties faced in Romania in the wake of the global crisis were more than offset by dynamic sales in Western Europe. This led to most capacities being allocated (even as they were being expanded) to the Sandero, with a preference for markets characterised by the biggest margins and where there was the greatest chance of being able to build a strong position in the future.

Table 3.3–Logan, Sandero and Duster sales volumes from 2004 to 2011

		2004	2005	2006	2007	2008	2009	2010	2011
	Duster							19.694	51.676
France	Logan		9,758	18,742	32,637	34,148	26,667	22,288	10,067
	Sandero					9,419	39,787	68,089	27,325
Total		0	9,758	18,742	32,637	43,567	66,454	110,071	89,068
Europe/Euromed Part		0.0%	7.4%	10.7%	15.1%	18.3%	21.9%	32.0%	26.4%
	Duster							14,128	23,832
Germany	Logan	6	2,043	6,292	17,312	18,688	33,542	9,329	8,774

	Sandero					6,375	51,310	16,844	11,630
Total		6	2,043	6,292	17,312	25,063	84,852	40,301	44,236
Europe/Euromed Part		0.0%	1.5%	3.6%	8.0%	10.5%	28.0%	11.7%	13.1%
	Duster							4,822	7,549
Roumania	Logan	20,274	88,275	96,037	101,799	75,792	35,097	28,890	18,569
	Sandero					8,917	6,765	3,018	2,519
Total		20,274	88,275	96,037	101,799	84,709	41,862	36,730	28,637
Europe/Euromed Part		88.8%	66.6%	55.0%	47.0%	35.6%	13.8%	10.7%	8.5%
Total sales Europe + Euromed		22,831	132,581	174,680	216,475	238,117	303,569	343,437	337,757

Table 3.3 shows the context in which the Sandero grew. The 2009 loss of 43,000 unit sales in Romania was more than compensated by an extra 20,000 in France and 60,000 in Germany. What followed was a lesser output of Logans, with productive capacities now free to cope (albeit with difficulty) with demand for the Sandero. Germany would be a priority, with many French customers having to wait until 2010, when Sandero jumped by another 35,000 more units before the Duster took over from its predecessor.

Since the Pitesti plant had generally had more of a problem producing vehicles than finding outlets, it was fairly logical that this situation had a knock-on effect on distribution choices. As French carmakers had done during the postwar period, the tendency at Renault was to choose customers for Dacia who would be as profitable as possible. Along these lines, the €2,500 German wreckage bonus opened a window of opportunity. This was only temporary, however, and by 2010 Logan and Sandero sales were back to their 2008 levels, having already more than offset 2009's disappointing sales in Romania. When the wreckage bonus was suddenly dropped in Germany, making French customers wait seemed clever in hindsight, since the equivalent scheme in France was dismantled much more slowly. The end result was that in 1Q 2010 French customers took over from their German counterparts, until such time as Renault had freed up sufficient capacity to cope with the demand for the Duster.

This partially explains the relatively favourable mix of Sandero sales, dominated by better equipped models compared to the E0/M0 version (minimal options and cheaper engine). The basic version accounted for fewer than 10% of all sales in 2008-2011, with "upmarket" versions (Lauréate or Prestige) representing more than 50%. Without going as far as to say that Dacia's sales teams refused to entertain demand from less solvent buyers, it is clear that the vehicles being stocked–thus, which became available rapidly–systematically corresponded to the versions generating the highest margins. Everything was also done to avoid losing sales due to the basic models' longer delivery times. In addition, buying a cheaper car due to the "state's gift" of more than €2,000 (corresponding to the wreckage plus GPL bonus in France, or the GPL bonus alone in Germany) automatically induced customers to "have a little fun". This made it easy for salespersons to attract them towards the better equipped versions and/or sing the praises of the Stepway, retailing at €4,000 more than the basic version.

In appearance, the Sandero embodied the Entry line's renewed focus on Europe, as illustrated by the figures for 2009 and 2010 when German and French Logan-Sandero sales were close to 150,000 even as Romanian sales were dropping below 40,000. Dacia quickly threw in the towel for the Logan in Eastern European markets that turned out to be harder than expected to penetrate with a product bearing a Romanian stamp. With the Sandero, Pitesti could work at full capacity covering French and German needs, on top of which came sales from other important markets for Renault, like Italy, Spain and Benelux. Even those markets that did not want the Logan were very attracted to the Sandero and would soon, and predictably, like the Duster as well.

One example was Spain, a market that had just overcome the subprime crisis and bought three times as many Dacias in 2010 as in 2007. In Belgium and Luxembourg, where the MCV estate version's launch had made everyone aware of the Logan, volumes doubled with the arrival of the Sandero. In Italy, which had a large supply of vehicles costing less than €10,000 (especially cars sold by domestic manufacturers), more than 15,000 Sanderos were sold in 2009 and 2010.

Table 3.4–Entry range volumes in Belgium, Luxembourg, Spain and Italy

		2007	2008	2009	2010	2011	Total 5 years
Belgium and Luxembourg	Logan	2,117	3,100	2,755	3,743	1,953	13,668
	Sandero		590	2,118	4,502	4,189	11,399
	Duster				68,089	27,325	11,660
	Total	2,117	3,690	4,873	11,400	14,647	36,727

Spain	Logan	7,747	4,664	2,504	3,772	1,030	19,717
	Sandero		2,310	6,526	12,157	6,664	27,657
	Duster				5,824	7,728	13,552
	Total	7,747	6,974	9,030	21,753	15,422	60,926
Italy	Logan	5,478	6,399	4,621	2,535	1.147	20,180
	Sandero		2,242	17,144	15,285	5,819	40,490
	Duster				5,511	18,894	24,405
	Total	5,478	8,641	21,765	23,331	25,860	85,075
Total 3 countries		15,342	19,305	35,668	56,484	55,929	182,728

Total sales in the three Western European countries reached parity with Romania in 2009. After the Duster arrived in 2011, they were almost twice as much. The refocusing effort was obvious, with the vast majority of Dacias assembled in Pitesti now targeting–due to the crisis and the Sandero's launch–Western Europe.

Table 3.5–Entry range volumes in the Czech Republic, Poland, Turkey and Algeria

		2007	2008	2009	2010	2011	Total 5 years
Czech Republic	Logan	1,912	2,312	1,850	1,959	1,239	9,272
	Sandero		590	896	1,128	842	3,456
	Duster				524	2,333	2,857
	Total	1,912	2,902	2,746	3,611	4,414	15,585
Poland	Logan	2,024	1,755	1,535	2,366	2,163	9,843
	Sandero		559	1,231	1,751	1,546	5,087
	Duster				1,901	3,673	5,574
	Total	2,024	2,314	2,766	6,018	7,382	20,504
Turkey	Logan	8,951	8,323	6,312	10,817	8,397	42,800
	Sandero		1,255	3,477	5,369	4,957	15,058
	Duster				2,982	7,985	10,967
	Total	8,951	9,578	9,789	19,168	21,339	68,825
Algeria	Logan	9,090	11,465	13,677	16,432	15,149	65,813
	Sandero		735	3,650	1,995	1,302	7,682
	Duster				541	2,791	3,332
	Total	9,090	12,200	17,327	18,968	19,242	76,827
Total 4 countries		21,977	26,994	32,628	47,765	52,377	181,741

In terms of Western Europe sales during this period, only Turkey and Algeria saw volumes close to Spanish or Italian levels, although representing much larger market share and therefore justifying that they be defended. Note that as expected, the notchback continued to dominate in these markets, as it did in Romania, Poland and the Czech Republic. This also explains why in the Czech Republic or Poland the Sandero's arrival had little effect on Dacia's weak position when it took responsibility for the Entry range. This casting mistake soon became apparent. Above all, competition from used cars continued to be a handicap here, despite the products being adapted to the local context. The dynamism of the demand being expressed in other ways, along with limited installed production capacities, explains why nothing was done to address the gap between products' potential and actual performance.

DRIVING HOME THE ADVANTAGE AND ACCELERATING THE INTERNATIONALISATION INTO LARGE EMERGING MARKETS: THE DUSTER

Within the Entry family, the Duster assumed the role of a maturity product. As Chapter 4 will show, this could already be observed at the design and production level. It was also true in commercial and policy terms. Designing and selling the Duster meant allowing Dacia and/or the already extremely important "Entry" segment of the Renault range to go upscale while remaining an entry-level vehicle. It was also (and above all) a tool for Renault's intercontinentalisation. Even in its E0/M0 version, the product could be positioned at a price level where Renault was already offering both new and used products. For example, the starting price for the petrol version of the Duster in France was €12,000 (versus €8,000 for the Sandero and €10,000 for the Modus) with the diesel version starting at €15,000 (versus €10,000 for the Sandero and €11,500 for the Modus). Compared to the average price at which Renault models were being offered in France (according to Polk, around €19,347 versus €11,735 for the Dacia), this meant that Dacia cars were much closer to the heart of the product offer. A petrol engine Sandero cost a little more than 40% as much as a Renault, and a diesel version around 50%. The equivalent numbers for the Duster were 60% and 80%, respectively.

That this kind of product was accepted by Renault's trade operations (including the people running its "traditional" range as well as the network) showed how much had changed since 2004-2005, when people used to worry about the Logan's launch leading to cannibalisation and blurring the brand image. Similarly, even without abandoning either the emerging markets as a target or the task given the Entry range of accelerating the Renault group's overall internationalisation, the Duster put an end to the pretence that French or Western European sales were marginal or secondary. Having been designed (at least for its final project phase) during the crisis that–by severely hampering sales in Russia and Romania–had made Western Europe so important to Dacia's aims and Pitesti's prospects, the Duster would henceforth be presented unabashedly as a car that should "go down like a bomb" in France and Europe.

Like the Sandero, the Duster was subject to styling work affecting both its body frame and interior. Once it was no longer necessary for a product to be less good-looking than a Renault for the Company to accept it, people even began to consider normal that it be attractive and started spending a little money on this aspect. Things had changed markedly since the original discourse when the Logan was first launched in France. Sceptics had been reassured by the austerity of this trailblazer. The 2010 launch coincided with the Koleos, Renault's failed effort to address its absence from the highly dynamic SUV segment. Designed and made by Samsung in Korea on a Nissan platform, the car started at €28,000 but struggled to reach 4,000 annual sales in France. In this context, people probably feared that the Duster could harm a product whose commercial life had started so poorly. Having said that, within a very short period of time, it was clear that the two product lines had almost nothing to do with one another.

All in all, the Duster came to defend Renault's Entry range "after the battle was over". For the family (and in particular, for the Dacia range), the product arrived at the right time to transform volume into value, fully legitimising a sales strategy initiated with the Sandero. For Renault in Brazil or Russia, the Duster–which had only been launched 18 months after the Dacia–was commercially crucial in two ways. It was a way to address the specific requirements of markets that, given their global importance (specifically for Renault) would henceforth need to be fully incorporated into people's thinking. It was also a chance to incorporate the fact that in Russia, Brazil and Argentina, these were Renault products that, above and beyond the badge, should be treated as such.

The Duster's positioning in its family and on the market

The idea of positioning a product "above" its two predecessors had been evoked relatively early on. Already in 2003 or 2004 (and particularly in Romania), the press had raised the idea of designing between the M1 and M2 segments a product resembling the Skoda Octavia. In a world where profits and legitimacy were usually acquired by upscaling and attacking higher segments, this may have appeared self-evident. It is not the choice made for the Duster, which sought the same effect with a more original positioning.

Firstly, to save resources and meet tighter deadlines, there was no choice but to maintain the same platform. The search for value would have to respect this constraint, while continuing to adhere to the Entry programme's mindset by adopting the same basic sales arguments ("more for less"). The question became what new body should be built on an Entry version to increase unit values by one and a half times.

The experience that Renault (and more broadly, the global automotive business) had had in recent years meant that this was a relatively straightforward question that would likely be answered one way or the other with reference to the M1 segment. Indeed, after the development of a number of coupé and/or estate versions, vehicle families had tended to evolve towards minivans or–as with the Scenic or the Picasso–long seven seater minivans. These would then be followed by SUV versions (Peugeot 3008, VW Tiguan, Ford Kuga, etc.) coming in both short and long versions (i.e. the Nissan Qashqai and its "+2" version). The Duster tried to mine the same "ore" and offered an alternative to urban SUVs while maintaining habitability closer to the top segment SUV ranges. Above all, it had better non-urban performance.

Asides from bolstering the product's sales arguments in Western Europe, the targets here were the Russian and Brazilian markets, where driving conditions required (much more than they did in Paris, Torino or Munich) vehicles offering the kinds of crossing capacities and ground clearance that characterise off-road vehicles. In Russia particularly, AvtoVAZ turned a model known as the Lada Niva in France into a bestseller. Schweitzer's reasoning could also be applied to this vehicle. Otherwise, the same logic as the one pursued by Renault's Entry teams led Ford's teams in Brazil to offer (based on something known in Europe as the Ford Fusion) a model called the Ford Ecosport, built using a Fiesta platform usually presented as the Duster's big rival. Annual sales in Brazil were between 40,000 and 50,000.

Renovated in 2012, like the Duster this car would also be manufactured and sold in India.

All in all, after five or six years of accumulating commercial experience worldwide, the Entry's sales teams were now in a position to work on a model and its Dacia and Renault variants, using the same fundamental characteristics to position it appropriately in the main markets to which it had been allocated. For the moment, Western Europe, Russia and Brazil would be the leading benchmarks, having progressively replaced Romania, which had been such a crucial reference for the Logan. From 2010-2011 onwards, India would become the fourth pillar for the Entry range, with the Duster becoming, after the Logan failed, the main tool for increasing volumes in this country.

Pricing and the quest for value

Compared to the minivan market where the Entry range faced its next challenge in the shape of the Lodgy, the Duster's positioning somewhere in the category of off-road vehicles, SUVs and crossovers had the advantage of being particularly in useful in Europe, where this segment corresponded in 2010 to more than 1 million new vehicle registrations out of a total of 30.8 million, or 8.3%. Even more important, amongst the biggest segments, off-road vehicles had grown the fastest. Whereas the global market fell by 5% in 2010, new vehicle registrations in this category rose by 15.42%, versus a 4.49% fall for minivans and a 10.09% fall for sedans. In Europe's five biggest markets, it ended up with a market share of between eight and 10 points in 2010.

Table 3.6–Rise of off-road vehicles in European markets in 2010

Country	Passenger cars		Off-road			Minivans		
	Reg.	Change	Reg.	Mkt share	Change	Reg.	Mkt share	Share
Germany	2,916,259	-23.4%	275,690	9.45%	9.35%	423,253	14.5%	-23.11%
Spain	982,015	3.1%	105,560	10.45%	27.46%	130,761	13.3%	6.44%
France	2,251,669	-2.2%	202,074	8.97%	54.94%	343,650	15.3%	-3.28%
Italy	1,959,436	-9.3%	169,318	8.64%	5.03%	208,322	10.6%	-5.07%
UK	2,030,846	1.8%	163,449	8.05%	20.11%	215,900	10.6%	14.28%

In terms of brand product policies, positioning an attractive product on this segment was an opportunity to address a willingness to pay that was hard to find elsewhere. In Europe, the Nissan Qashqai and Peugeot 3008 embodied this form of success. For the Duster (and in line with certain sales routines that were being progressively structured), the problem was as much establishing an intelligent position deviating from these new car product offers as attracting used car buyers interested by such vehicles. From this perspective, the fact that the segment had progressed recently and rapidly would be an advantage since the demand for used cars was very strong and inflated the price, helping the Duster in turn.

By applying pricing rules that consisted of positioning the car at about 60% of the value of comparable new cars and/or of the price for cars in the same category that were three years old and had 60,000 km on the odometer, the Entry teams came up with comfortable price levels and provisional sales volumes that they constantly adjusted upwards. The table below recounts prices for the lower and higher versions as well as the arithmetic average for comparable models, together with book prices for cars that were three years old and had driven 66,000 km[1].

Table 3.7–Pricing of off-road vehicles

Models	Lower price	Upper price	Lp + Up/2	0.6*(Lp Up)/2	Min book price 3 yrs	Max book price 3 yrs	Avg book price
Nissan Qashqai	20,000	30,000	25,000	15,000	12,300	20,400	16,350
VW Tiguan	25,550	37,470	31,560	18,940	14,500	21,700	18,100
Chevrolet Captiva	27,800	34,000	30,900	18,500	13,400	17,900	15,650
Kia Sportage	21,000	33,200	27,100	16,250	10,000	14,600	12,300
Hyundai Santa Fé	37,500	41,000	39,250	23,550	14,600	1, 600	16,600

With prices ranging from €11,900 for a 1.6 L petrol 16V 4x2 version to €18,900 for a Prestige 1.5 Dci 110 cv 4x4 version, the Duster was retailing for 40% less than a Nissan Qashqai and at the same price as a three year old Kia Sportage. Even in opting for the versions with the best driving systems and all-around features (costing more than €15,000), someone purchasing a new Duster would come out on top in comparison with the purchase of a

---

1. The models in question were the Nissan Qashqai, VW Tiguan, Ford Kuga, Kia Sportage or Hyundai Santa Fe but not the Nissan Juke or Skoda Yeti, also from the category to which the Duster theoretically belonged.

three year old used car such as the Hyundai Santa Fé or Nissan Qashqai. In this context, the model enjoyed something tantamount to a monopoly.

The launch may have had lesser resonance in the press than the Logan but the Duster did enjoy a modicum of specialised or other media attention enabling it to achieve notoriety without spending too much on advertising. Similarly, marketing expenses were limited, meaning that—as had been the case with the Sandero—it was logical to allocate capacities to top-selling models. This is illustrated in sales statistics from the first part of the Duster's commercial life, which involved Europe a lone.

Duster sales and the effects on the mix

The Duster was launched in April 2010. This was largely a Dacia operation, hence something affecting the "Euromed" zone. The launch was simultaneous in Romania, France and Western Europe, Turkey and North Africa. It exemplified a "crisis exit" strategy, even though markets were slow to react, if only because of the end of the wreckage bonus system (particularly important in Germany). This return to normality was accompanied in 2010 by extreme upscaling in Germany and also, albeit to a slightly lesser extent, in France, where the wreckage bonus was still in place.

Against this backdrop, partially because the market demanded it and partially because it would lead to a more profitable allocation of the Romanian plant's limited capacities, the Duster's launch soon caused a major deformation in the structure of Dacia's European sales.

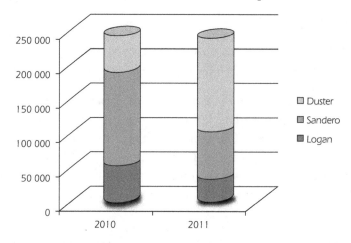

Figure 3.1–The Duster replacing the Logan and Sandero in Dacia's European sales

1. Dacia privatisation agreement, 2 July 1999: Radu Vasile, Romanian Prime Minister and Louis Schweitzer, Renault CEO

© PERUS, Alain

2. Logan launch highlight: journalists' trial in Capadocce

3. Need to restructure the network in Romania: dealer workshop and business, around year 2000

4. New dual brand dealership in Bucarest

5. Success in Romania (Logan MCV)

7 - Preference for simplicity

8 - L90 Project team

10 - Reconversion of a brownfield factory

11 - ... Becoming a modern unit, not particularly automated but satisfying
Renault quality standards

12 - Sandero, a product satisfying Brazilian demand, designed by Renault's Sao Paulo design
centre as the Sand'up concept and manufactured in the country's Curitiba plant

14 - Russia: April 2005 inauguration of Avtoframos factory, with a Logan in the snow.

15 - Expansion in India, announcement by Renault Nissan and Mahindra about location of future production site in Chennai (Madras, India).

Mr. S.K. Das | Mr. Keshub Mahindra | Mr. Patrick Pélata

16 - Signature of construction protocol for new industrial complex at Tangiers in Morocco: Mohamed VI and Carlos Ghosn

17 - Renault Nissan's Tangiers plant (January 2012)

The Duster clearly took over from Logan and Sandero in Dacia's production and sales. 2010 and 2011 witnessed comparable total sales but the Logan and Sandero were down by nearly 20,000 and 65,000 units respectively, versus a 76,000 rise for the Duster. In the Euromed zone, however, things were different. Sales here also stagnated–partially because production capacities were saturated by demand–but the Logan continued to dominate.

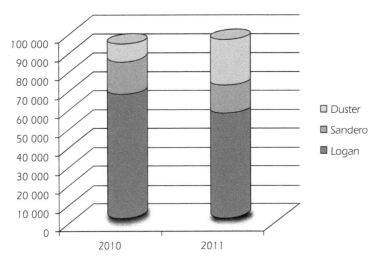

Figure 3.2–The Logan's ongoing domination of Euromed zone sales

In terms of market prospects, these outcomes confirmed trends that Dacia had seen with the Sandero. They affected Western Europe proportionately more than Romania, Eastern Europe, Turkey and North Africa, the so-called "Euromed" zone. Thus, more than 158,000 Dusters were sold in 2011, including 52,000 in France, 24,000 in Germany, 19,000 in Italy, 8,000 in Belgium and 8,000 in Spain. In volume terms, 72% of the Pitesti plant's output was sold in the "Europe" zone. In revenue and profitability terms, the number was even higher.

Analysis of all Entry sales, including Renault sales, leads to very different conclusions, especially if Brazil and Russia are included. These were the two main zones where the range could be extended, and contrary to the way that the structure of Dacia's sales was further deformed by the Sandero and Duster, the Entry programme stayed a development tool that Renault could use to accelerate its presence in the emerging markets, as per its original plans.

Table 3.8–Global sales of Dacia and Renault Logan, Sandero and Duster from 2009 to 2011

			2009		2010		2011	
					année			
Renault	VP	Logan	150 603	67,31 %	190 24	56,49 %	255 306	54,24 %
		Sandero	73 149	32,69 %	145 245	43,08 %	196 428	41,73 %
		Duster			1 453		18 942	4,02 %
	Somme VP		223 752	43,40 %	337 122	50,70 %	470 676	57,84 %
Dacia	VP	Logan	140 419	48,16 %	126 598	36,23 %	95 365	27,79 %
		Sandero	151 151	51,84 %	154 276	44,15 %	86 578	25,23 %
		Duster		68 601		19,63 %	161 203	46,98 %
	Somme VP		291 570	56,60 %	349 475	49,30 %	343 146	42,16 %
Renault/Dacia	VP	Logan	291 022	56,47 %	317 022	46,17 %	350 671	43,09 %
		Sandero	224 300	43,53 %	299 521	43,62 %	283 006	34,77 %
		Duster	0	0,00 %	70 054	10,20 %	180 145	22,14 %
	Somme VP		515 322	100,00 %	686 597	100,00 %	813 822	100,00 %

Thus, Dacia only accounted for 42% of all Entry sales in 2011. The Logan's share was only one-quarter of Dacia's totals, although the product continued to account for 43% of the range's global sales, beating both the Sandero (35%) and the Duster (22%). This must also be considered when analysing the Duster-Dacia volumes today have been supplemented by sales in Russia as well as other sales under the Renault brand name in Brazil and South America. This was the initial intention and the fact that the launch started out being European should not hide the fact that expected volumes for the Renault Duster were–as was the case for the Sandero in 2011–supposed to be at least as substantial in the major emerging markets.

The Duster's ambitions in Russia and South America

Between 2009 and 2011, the Renault Entry family grew by more than 100%, with sales skyrocketing from 223,000 to 470,000 passenger cars. This explains why the Duster's launch has become so important to Renault– in Russia and South America in 2012 and in India in the future–and why the Company has worked so hard to get it right.

This effort has consisted of specifications that both maximise the product's adaptation to local commercial and regulatory circumstances and turn it into a Renault model (see Illustrations below). From this latter perspective, the leadership is aware that the Entry's disproportionate importance to total Group sales means that Renault's brand and image can only be developed in major emerging markets using these products rather than the more traditional range. This signifies that whereas the Dacia range did not have to convey "Renault values", the Duster does. Hence the flattering presentation of the version developed for South America and displayed at the Buenos Aires Trade Fair, with a spotlight cast on things like the car's chrome-plated grills and rear strip.

It remains that modifications were not only aesthetic in nature, with Brazilian and Argentine engineering teams also undertaking major adaptation work to get the Duster to comply with local norms, specifically safety regulations and constraints relating to the different qualities of fuel, the variable state of the road network and specific climate conditions. In communications terms, Renault's emphasis has been that the Duster wants to "symbolise the democratisation of SUVs and making innovation accessible to everybody", reaffirming the Company's ambitions in South America. Renault has hopes of seeing sales in this part of the world rise from 200,000 units in 2009 to 400,000 units by 2013. Note that Renault Entry sales amounted to 116,000 units in 2009 and 225,000 in 2011. Thus, Brazil has accounted for half of all volumes in South America and still does. Renault is more than ready to change this, however, in part by leveraging its greater historical relations in Argentina, where the Company sold 82,000 vehicles in 2010 (market share of 13%, making it the country's third best selling brand) on a market that had grown 26% since 2009.

The timing and mindset with which the Duster was launched in Russia–the market for which it had been initially imagined–were more or less the same. The Duster was presented at the Moscow Trade Fair in August 2010 although the launch took until late 2011. Like the Logan, the Duster was positioned between the ancient Niva–designed way back in the 1970s–and import competitors as a car for social "climbers". This positioning seemed more self-evident and beneficial than it had been for the Logan. It was with this same model–and on a market that had recovered quickly from the crisis–that Avtoframos was hoping to exceed annual sales of 200,000 units. Between 2009 and 2011, Renault sales in Russia more than doubled, rising from 72,000 to 154,000 vehicles, basically thanks to the Logan and the Sandero, whose sales went from 53,000 to 127,000. Clearly, the network here is up and running and prepared not only to sell the Duster but also non-entry level Renault vehicles.

The same strategy might work in India where the Duster could avenge the defeat of the Logan and offer the brand the kinds of volumes that it needs to make key investments in the country's networks and drive the diffusion of the whole of its product range.

HOW FAR WILL THE ENTRY GO?

In commercial terms, 2008 to 2011–which witnessed the launches of the Sandero and Duster–saw the systematisation of an entry method that is being continued today with the Lodgy. This commercial strategy is based on two pillars.

The first, which despite being less clear to the French executive has been the crux of the programme since the very beginning, situates the Entry at the heart of Renault's development strategy in the major emerging markets, particularly Brazil, Russia and (probably) India. The second, resulting from a success that has led since 2005 to chronic under-capacities in comparison with potential demand, consists of allocating production volumes to those markets and models that are the most profitable, specifically in Europe and the Euromed zone.

This second aspect has played a crucial role in the Entry range's profitability for Renault. It has helped to preserve the integrity of a "pull" marketing model associated with low commercial costs. Since the product was designed following a subtle and original analysis of value; because it was positioned more in relation to competition from used cars; and because, within this framework, Logans, Sanderos and Dusters have all enjoyed monopoly positions–as a result, the under-capacity situation has clearly had a multiplier effect on programme profitability.

This combination has sparked widespread support for the programme's paradoxical situation. After working to serve demand from emerging markets that everyone was convinced were destined to expand more quickly than EU markets, Entry range designers quickly realised, even before the crisis, that the Global South would be unable to saturate the productive apparatus by itself. The range offered effective tools for conquering these markets wherever they emerged, but the New Member States were not part of this configuration. Moreover, even though Turkey, Algeria and Morocco offered more favourable conditions, volumes here were also expected to remain limited.

This explains why it was in Russia and Brazil that the range revealed its full potential. It was here that–as per Louis Schweitzer's initial intuition–the handicap of being neither Rolls-Royce nor Mercedes was transformed into a competitive advantage for Renault, on the condition that did not try to flog off its old models here, or else marginally adapted "decontented" current models. By presenting itself commercially and politically as a player that would give serious consideration to the markets' specific requirements–and enable distributors and local engineers to give voice to these specificities–Renault used its Entry range as a platform for its late but rapid development in the BRICs. Destined to offer volumes without which it is impossible to exist commercially or industrially, the Entry would ultimately dominate these markets, to the extent that people now wonder if they might one day be able to accommodate the rest of the range.

The spectacular expansion of the Entry programme has raised questions about the identity of the Renault brand. Developed on the margins of the Company after having more or less freed itself from the normal rules, it has become increasingly difficult to view the Entry range–in light of its diversification, rising volumes and, above all, significant margins–as being separate from Renault's traditional range.

By modifying the geography of Renault's production, markets and profits; by demonstrating that upscaling is not the only way to make money; and by revealing where market value can be found–the Entry's commercial adventure has offered a powerful incentive to advance further down this path. Renault's management is well aware of this and has authorised the programme to pursue its dual dynamic of increasing the number of models being produced as well as the number of markets being targeted. At the same time, the executive has been relatively discrete about this dynamic in comparison, for instance, with the media resonance given to its adventures with electric vehicles or in the Chinese market. This is probably because, for the moment at least, the Entry's full integration is still perceived by many people as highly problematic. For Entry programme managers, it is commercially essential that they be able to deviate from Renault's standard rules. For other programme managers, it would be very difficult to assimilate Entry methods, if only because they are not always applicable to the "core range", and also due to the fact they would be hard to implement wherever structured methods already exist.

All of this has been witnessed on a commercial level. It is an even stronger proposition on an industrial and/or engineering plane.

4

METAMORPHOSES AND CONTINUITIES WITHIN A WIDER EXPANSION DYNAMIC

The successful design of the Logan can be partially attributed to its uncompromising affirmation of certain principles, including "design to cost", single site, reduced automation and "carry over". One of the conditions explaining this breakthrough was the decision to define the project as something out of the ordinary.

By exceeding the most optimistic forecasts, this success paved the way–as shown in the chapter above–to an expansion strategy that was spectacular: geographically, because of its global marketing approach; and in product range terms, by designing a family of differentiated vehicles derived from the Logan platform. The project evolved from a marginal status to become one of the Company's main programmes. The key question during this phase was how to shape this mutation and maintain the principles driving the initial project's success while adapting to new contexts.

Paradoxically, this dynamic of success based on the programme's deployment beyond its original aims did not simplify the missions of the people involved in its design and industrialisation functions but, to the contrary, complexified them singularly.

- Certain design principles that had ensured the efficiency of the initial project found themselves at odds with the new necessities of deployment. Typically, the X90 had optimised the initial hypothesis of a single product on a single site. Now the goal was to deploy a diverse range worldwide. This raised several questions, including which initial options would be kept, how they should evolve and what should be dropped.

- The singularity of the product and target market helped to ensure the project's convergence and facilitated compromises. The variety of targets and the subtle and heterogeneous positioning of Entry products in different markets (translated by the semantic evolution from "low-cost" to "Entry") implied the incorporation of new constraints that might otherwise have been ignored. In turn, this raised questions about the best way of ensuring that the product maintained a clear meaning by seeking appropriate compromises.

- It was uncertain that the X90 would survive, a troubling prospect given its importance. Yet the project would turn this precariousness into a strength by convincing people that it had to contend with unusual constraints. As it steadily "normalised" over the course of its deployment, these mobilisation and persuasion levers started to fade, raising questions as to how to maintain a spirit of sacrifice (i.e. the need to make savings) with a programme that was visibly in such good health.

- The X90 was an exceptional adventure in comparison with the Company's "core" engineering functions, which were experienced in designing products for advanced European markets. This was no longer the case, raising new and difficult questions such as whether it was advisable to permit an ongoing transgression of business policy by a programme that had long list its marginal status; to what extent the Entry programme should, to the contrary, be portrayed as a textbook case; and how to deal within this new context with "cannibalisation" issues, including the allocation of resources between different product lines.

We will review each of these questions by demonstrating how they were handled in turn through the development of the Sandero and the Duster projects

FROM A SINGLE PRODUCT TO THE DESIGN OF A DIVERSIFIED GLOBAL RANGE

Like the Twingo back in the days, the X90 project sought an economic solution to the dilemma of how to achieve simplicity and savings with a single product. The transition to a multi-product solution, like the commercial deployment into different markets, upset this basic approach.

The development of diversified products–whether for the purpose of expanding the range to include different target customers or else to ensure that it was adapted to specific market demands–may have been commercially useful, as demonstrated in the previous chapter, but it also generated research costs and restricted scalability savings on component purchases. Giving the savings logic underlying the Entry programme, this raised concerns about how to control any inflationary effects.

Multiple sources of divergence affecting Entry line components

- A single product doctrine may have enabled the initial launch but it lost relevance over time. Focusing on overall programme profitability meant that the product had to offer access to markets that the initial product (i.e. the Sandero in Brazil) could not satisfy. There was also a need to develop higher-margin cars (like the Duster) and build a catalogue of multiple options to bring the product in line with traditional automobiles.

- In the words of Dominique Bellot, the Entry programme's Technical Product Range Director, "Regulatory changes are anathema to the idea of sharing components across a platform." The choice was whether to apply the most stringent and costly standards to all vehicles on a programme or organise products diverging in Europe and elsewhere.

- "National specificities evoke topics like climate or the quality of the road network but we should also consider customer perceptions, driving habits and subjective standards of comfort. Safety is considered less crucial in Brazil than in Europe. If you spend a week in India, for instance, you realise that horns constitute important permanent safety features. Horns designed for Europe need high-performance replacements. Similarly, if drivers are used to sitting on the clutch and driving at less than 2,000 t/min, they will need better clutches. In India, the quality of inside materials is an important purchasing criterion. Cars sold here emphasize these aspects more than they would elsewhere."

Source: interview with Dominique Bellot.

Systematising a "carry across" approach

The first response was to be rigorous in pooling components amongst different models. "Carry over", which had been implemented on the first Logan project, evolved into "carry across" to standardise a maximum of components and achieve process flexibility on all models derived from the Entry platform. The Sandero shared 70% of its parts with the Logan; the Duster 4x4 and Duster 4x2 were 86% identical. In numerical terms, 46% of their components were the same as on the Logan. More importantly, in value terms, 60 to 70% was the same.

"Carry over" can be defined as a combination of a components pooling strategy and a strategy based on permanent learning across the whole of a family. As the first explanation infers, for Renault this consisted of recovering components from existing vehicles and incorporating them into a new model. This is because it was not enough to simply ensure that components were shared over the long run across a succession of projects. With each new project, some components would be renewed, either because standards required this or because engineers found solutions outperforming components available through "carry over". As such, the percentage of components shared within a family tended to fall over time. "Carry back" countered this by replacing components on an old product with ones developed for the new product. Through this "carry across" process (combining "carry over" and "carry back")–associated with global sourcing–the programme maximised global volumes and technical definition.

An example was when the Sandero's front section was copied on the phase 2 Logan, with instrument panels and dashboards designed for the former also being used on the latter. Similarly, modifications resulting from productivity actions conducted in collaboration with suppliers were systematically incorporated into all models.

It is worth highlighting the engineering competencies associated with this strategy. Comparing the Sandero and the Duster, it is not at all evident that the latter would have replicated certain very crucial parts from the former, such as doors, windscreens or body sides (see dossier illustrations).

Redesigning a product by means of a "design to variety" approach

It remains that "carry across" was not always appropriate as a single solution, especially when markets wanted options that were too different from one another. Questions at this level included whether the "carry over" should be aligned with the most technological options–which would make the programme lose competitiveness for no good reason in markets focused more on frugality–or whether it should go for the simplest solution and give up on markets requiring higher performance levels.

The dashboard example offers a good illustration. The initial design was for a single board "generating an impression of robustness while remaining aesthetically pleasing".[1] This may have been true but it was not appreciated by many of the customers that the Company was trying to attract, notably in Brazil. This was a case of the single component doctrine causing "top down" standardisation and having a significant inflationary effect impeding programme profitability.

Then came the decision to return to the initial doctrine because of the gain in flexibility. A new dashboard was designed. All models shared its hidden structural parts. The visible shell had features that could be modulated for different product range levels.

The Logan's shield was another example of the kind of redesign work required for a wider range. Initially designed as a single part and cast in a workshop located near the assembly line, the approach (fewer parts, no geometry-related quality problems, low assembly costs, etc.) helped to reduce upfront investment in a big casting die or high-power pressing machine. This design choice turned out to be inadequate for a multi-product and multi-brand strategy. Giving a product a Dacia or Renault badge implied further costly investments in injection moulding machines. The decision was made to dissociate the shield and the grille, since the latter offered a cheaper[2] way of accommodating a variety of logos while facilitating product marketing. Similarly, the Logan project had initially chosen to make two versions of this shield, one painted and the other not. To improve the look of the latter, the surface had to be embossed. Yet this damaged the perceived quality of the painted version, a kind of compromise that was unacceptable for the Brazilian market, which is very demanding in terms of external finishing. Ultimately it had to be "de-embossed", generating extra retooling costs for an end result that was ultimately less than satisfactory.

Opportunistic adaptation to inflated standardisation

Regulatory changes were generally problematic for the Entry programme. They had an inflationary effect insofar as they forced it to incorporate equipment that customers did not necessarily perceive as having value

---

1. *R&D Renault* October 2004, p. 30.
2. Grille tooling costs about nine time less than a shield moulding machine.

corresponding to the cost. The impact was greater on this programme because it had made savings into its main competitive advantage. One example was the Euro5 standard, which added €800 to diesel versions' retail price. For a programme like the Entry, this clearly had a significant impact.

Hence a policy of minimalistic applications, with the Company trying to benefit from enforced changes wherever possible by introducing new performance aspects that customers could see. A good example here was the use of multiplexing. Until this point, the Entry programme had relied on wired technology, because this was cheaper and sufficed for vehicles as simple as this. However, regulations forced it to move to multiplexing, something much more complex, by the year 2014. This was a major change with extra costs relating to the electrics system, controls, dashboard, etc. Given the magnitude of the change and above and beyond the systematic search for economic solutions, dashboard redesign work was initiated to create a new module that would, in geometric terms, be entirely interchangeable with its predecessor, lowering the cost of differentiating between European and non-European markets while limiting risks relating to the uncertainty about the actual dates when the new regulations would apply. Alongside of this, new features were also added to the multiplex version.

From single site to multi-site: "design to logistics"

As aforementioned, the Logan project was originally designed for industrialisation on a single site. Its geographic expansion required the deployment of multi-site manufacturing and the integration of local suppliers. Because this was more profitable for transportation cost and customs tariff reasons, vehicles would henceforth be manufactured near the places where they were sold.

Designing a project involving a multinational system–and where some countries lacked any longstanding industrial apparatus–led to vehicle design options that were different from the ones associated with a single site manufacturing scheme. Consideration had to be given to:

• The availability and performance of locally manufactured resources. The single site strategy had enabled a concentration of relatively sophisticated and heavy equipment. Typically, this involved plastic injection moulding maches used for big parts, high thickness stamping machines for parts like axle gears, insert technologies, cataphoresis equipment, etc.

- Transportation costs, which were a function of the volumes requiring transportation. Some components could travel relatively cheaply, but not larger or more cumbersome items. Total upstream transportation costs would tend to account for a higher share of total manufacturing costs, rising (depending on the production site) from 3% to 17% of the price of the components being purchased.

- Taxes and currency effects. Many countries levy high taxes on imported parts to encourage the development of homegrown industries. In addition, currency volatility is a key factor in the cost competitiveness of countries characterised by high economic instability. Between 2006 and 2007, some currencies fluctuated by 30%, which was enormous in an industry with operating margins around 6%.

It is clear to see why incorporating these different variables into location choices and understanding cost structures required the creation of new management tools. Several indicators were developed along these lines. One was the "depth" indicator measuring local integration by the share of locally produced value-added (with some inputs purchased from Tier 1 local suppliers actually being sourced from non-local Tier 2 suppliers). There was also a price competitiveness indicator comparing prices for identical parts made on two different production sites in a benchmark currency.

The project's initial design choices often seemed inappropriate to the new manufacturing logic. Hence the frequent reliance on "design to logistics". One example was the relative cost of transportation compared to the cost of manufacturing stamped parts. The ratio could reach 10:1 wherever a component had not been designed to fit easily into containers. This explained, for instance, the redesign of wheel arches. Otherwise, for large sub-assemblies like body sides, the traditional solution had been to cut the part into three (forward, middle, rear) to make it less cumbersome. The problem is that this would undermine its geometric quality and increase assembly costs. Yet a decision not to cut the part up was also suboptimal, if only because it meant a loss of space for doors. The project's original solution was to transport body sides already fit with doors, thereby achieving a better occupation of space.

More generally, these logistics considerations ran counter to a deep trend in the automotive industry, to wit, modularisation. This strategy, which tended to be associated with highly compact industrial sites, consisted of cutting vehicles up into complete sub-assemblies (such as seats, dashboards or front sections), manufactured by suppliers in plants located near assembly sites and delivered synchronously to the final assembly line. It had several advantages, particularly for highly complex, sophisticated and diverse products. It was also generally associated with purchasing policies giving module suppliers an important design and integration role.

The Entry programme's globalised manufacturing system led to a major revision in this strategy. It was inconceivable that sub-assemblies as cumbersome as the ones involved here be transported between distant sites. Local suppliers had to be found, ones capable of providing certain services that the Pitesti plant's Tier 1 supplier could not necessarily satisfy. In addition, high transportation costs meant that it was necessary to revisit the module's aggregation logic. Certain readily transportable elementary parts that were common to all models (typically seat tracks) could be sourced globally to create significant scale effects. Conversely, parts that were difficult to transport (seat frames, in this example) would never be particularly scalable, even if they were sourced globally. Hence the tendency to take suppliers located near the production sites, and even to bring the manufacturing of certain items (like the dashboard) back in-house. The steering column exemplified "design to logistics", which became key in Renault's globalised industrial system. Paying peanuts to buy the world's best steering columns would have been an expensive way of doing things given how much room a system with this kind of geometry took. What was needed was sourcing from nearby suppliers, a solution that was not necessarily advantageous in pricing terms or in light of certain suppliers' relative immaturity. Hence the reincorporation of assembly operations enabling specific sourcing of parts capable of travelling inexpensively. In turn, this would generate significant price or quality effects.

All of this explains why one of the Logan's leading slogans soon became "make your own rules". The project specifically questioned the lean flows dogma, with its obsessional focus on cost-cutting and/or the problems and risks that this creates. One example was the Duster's wheels, purchased from an Indian supplier with a big price advantage but also the source, at least at first, of some major responsiveness problems due to the fact that it took three months to ship the parts by ocean freight.

The equation "low-cost = simplicity + single product + single sourcing + single site" had to be dropped, with the search for savings sometimes involving a major redesign based on new questions: how parts should be divided to reflect the need for product diversity; manufacturing costs on work done in-house; logistics costs on multi-site systems; tariffs on components imported into the countries where the assembly work was being done; availability and cost of having to have more tools, etc.

TURNING FRUGALITY INTO A LONG-TERM VALUE IN A PROGRAMME ON THE PATH TOWARDS NORMALISATION

Between 2001 and 2010, a conjunction of inflationary factors began undermining the Logan project's strong early performance. External factors included stringent regulatory standards; the global automotive industry's increasingly expensive technological standards; raw material costs, labour market changes in the countries where companies ran operations; and the impact of the 2008-2009 crisis. Internal factors included new complexities caused by the programme's geographic and lineage expansion. The saturation of capacities resulting from increased volumes in 2008 was a profitability driver that found its mirror image in the saturation of the Pitesti site–although a compensatory organisational logic was also at work here. The end result was that a temporary and exceptional sacrifice would generally find its reward at a later date.

Maintaining the programme's frugality appeared under these circumstances as a constant dynamic that could stave off and compensate for any of these inflationary factors. On one hand, this involved a continuous improvement in existing processes (like the Kaizen processes that Japanese industrialists do so well). Conversely, there was the need to control all of the modifications introduced during the life of the programme, even if this increased the possibility, via a ratchet effect, that the project would have to revert to a trajectory considered more "normal" in the automotive business.

Controlling the ratchet effects associated with the introduction of new references

Faced with this constant pressure on existing production, introducing new parts on the occasion of new models' development seemed like an opportunity to restore profit margins. A study by the Ecole Polytechnique's

Centre de Recherche en Gestion[1] has shown how controlling procurement performance, by monitoring cost variances within families of components affects negotiations with suppliers in the sense that agreed reductions in existing production are offset by surcharges on new references. At the same time that they generate technical gains through engineering output, redesigning parts redistributes margins between manufacturers and suppliers. This novelty reconciles product experts (who run their life cycles via limited series or variants), engineers (who view this as a space for inventiveness) and purchasers and suppliers (who reinforce their ability to bargain with their respective hierarchies).

The Entry programme tried to counter these inflationary ratchet effects within the perimeter that it covered: by limiting redesign when this did not seem to offer significant technical advantages; by expanding the scope of "design to cost" to include options and variants, areas that were generally less locked up than the basic programme was; by making sure that different product generations' costs could be systematically traced; and by adopting a follower's strategy (being prudent in terms of quality and cost-efficiency) whenever technologies were introduced. One example was wired technology, which was only replaced by multiplexing solutions when required standards made them inevitable–with work also being done to make the associated costs competitive with traditional technologies (something that has yet to be achieved).

Because of its success in these pursuits (hence in volume and growth potential terms), the Entry programme became attractive to suppliers. Yet it continued to have a strong effect on Renault's global procurement strategies, balancing supplier negotiations across a range of programmes that were simultaneously being undermined by the Entry's "egotistical" stance–an effect reinforced by the fact that the Entry programme began accounting for a rising proportion of total Group activity.

Embedding "design to cost" in the development processes

The goal at this level was to ensure that "design to cost"–an approach that had demonstrated its efficiency throughout the Logan project–would be

---

1. Cohen-Hadria, Y.,Pouvourville, G. de, *L'évolution d'une fonction industrielle: le cas de l'achat*, Postgraduate degree in management thesis, University Aix-Marseille, 1981. Berry, M., *Une Technologie Invisible-L'impact des instruments de gestion sur l'évolution des systèmes humains*, Paris, CRG, June 1983.

sustained and used systematically across the whole of the Entry programme. Towards this end, the programme altered its generic planning approach to try and implement a traditional principle that seemed self-evident yet materialised infrequently–to wit, anticipation. The search for savings required painstaking work, studying exactly which components needed all of their aspects designed. In general, it was difficult specifying upstream phases, if only because insufficient resources were provided to deepen general principles. Yet it could be just as difficult analysing innovative alternatives in the downstream development phases, which were severely constrained by efforts to diminish time-to-market. Hence the frequent abandonment of rupture solutions and reproduction of standard responses.

"Design to cost" within a wider analytical framework

Analytical processes tended to start with senior management expressing a product planning intention. The business units then engaged in a macro-analysis of its feasibility and fed back on product concept options and the overall cost target.

The next stage tried to converge towards a single concept considered capable of meeting the target cost objective. Towards that end, the project would be broken down into subsets, with each allocated a target cost objective declined from the overall cost. Each subset was then worked on by a group including a design engineer, purchaser and product performance manager. This team developed at its own level a technological and procurement scenario culminating in an optimal cost objective. If the outcome of this cost consolidation gave a result sufficiently close to the target (i.e. within 10%), the concept was accepted and everyone moved on to the next stage. If there was too much variance, the concept would have to be reworked.

Once the concept was accepted, the "design to cost" process began with suppliers working along three axes: technology; performance (pitched at a level that was "just right"); and supplier negotiations. Several suppliers got involved in each component. The goal at this level was to cover as wide a range as possible (70% of the components on this project). The process was deployed for about one year and led to supplier contracts based on cost objectives framed in this way.

From that point onwards, people would start looking to further improve a solution that was already robust.

This subtle and very forward-looking approach helped to secure cost forecasts as early as the pre-contract phase.

An opportunistic product range expansion emphasizing speed of execution

The same market attack strategy was used for the MCV estate version and the Duster off-road vehicle. Using basic Entry technologies, vehicles were designed to fit the specific niche of having an unbeatable offer price. This was a "blue ocean" strategy[1] where speed of execution played a paramount role in ensuring that the Company gained maximum benefit before rivals could react.

A similar strategy was pursued with the development of options, an original and important element in the Entry programme. These were also indispensable in helping Entry products to compete with existing competitors in the emerging markets, generally well-equipped cars designed a long time ago. As aforementioned, it was in Western Europe that the least ornate versions were being sold. This meant that piloting the development of options was bound to have a major effect on the programme's overall profitability. The basic version (called the E0) only accounted for 10% of all sales, versus 50% for the first level equipment version and 40% for the second level. Compared to the basic programmes, manufacturers would often spend a great deal of energy on rationalising "ancillary" developments like options and derivatives. These options were generally sold at a high price, meaning that people were less strict on costs: "In general, engineers and suppliers were pretty relaxed about options compared with the savings that they tried to make on the basic version." Things were different with the Entry, however, where these developments came under the "design to cost" approach's rigorously defined boundaries.

A good example of this opportunistic strategy was the GPL derivative. "At the time, Renault had an adapted solution costing around €1,000.

---

1. W. Chan Kim, R. Mauborgne, *Stratégie Océan bleu*, Village mondial, Paris, 2005.

Engineers discovered a doable technology costing around €500. The option sold for €1,200, which together with the €2,000 bonus meant that buyers were saving €800 compared with a petrol model and €2,000 compared with a diesel. This was an immediate success, with the most crucial factor being the speed of execution. We were faster than the others to detect and react to this opportunity."[1]

Piloting greater value: the virtues of a "bottom-up" approach

"In the type of markets we were targeting, it was crucial for us not to fall into a value trap. People tend to always explain why you should offer some option or feature, chiefly because it will bring in new customers. The reality is that the Entry was a category where it was paramount to stay within certain boundaries."[2]

Once this upper limit was set, the question became which features should be kept. Firstly, there were the three "unique selling points" underlying the programme's identity: a novel price/performance ratio; generous habitability; and indisputable reliability and durability (see Chapter 2). Subsequently, two or three distinctive traits would differentiate products in the range and make them competitive vis-à-vis their rivals. All of the other features were to be dealt with "from bottom up", complying with regulations, of course, but no more than that.

The Duster's design exemplified these kinds of choices. Beyond the programme's three generic USPs, the vehicle's three distinctive USPs were its SUV design; its off-road performance that made this "the best of the non-experts"; and fuel efficiency. It was also in relation to these attributes that it incurred most of the costs that made it pricier than the B90 benchmark: big tires, enhancing its off-road status; special gearbox and transmission, plus a chassis that was adapted, reinforced and elevated; and a different body. In total, this added 16% in costs, but the car's excellent profitability (despite being sold at 30% less than the competition) meant that it was worth it.

---

1. Interview with Dominique Bellot.
2. Interview with Gérard Detourbet.

The virtuous circle of price competitiveness/performance: lowering marketing expenses

The automotive industry has been fixated on manufacturing costs ever since the early days of Ford. Yet selling products in a market as saturated and competitive as this one is also very expensive. Marketing expenses are varied in nature, ranging from the cost of vehicle distribution logistics, running a sales force and a point-of-sale or advertising–not to forget customer discounts. The orders of magnitude can be significant (with the industry consensus that marketing generally accounts for 30% of an automobile's total cost). For the Entry programme, whose initial price/performance compromise was very different from the competition and which targeted customers that had not been offered suitable products previously, this meant the possibility of a sales policy that did not have to offer discounts and incurred almost no advertising costs. Not only did this help balance the economic equation but it also enhanced the credibility of the promise.

Controlled expansion linking higher volumes to profitability

The main issue at this level was how expanding the product range and the target markes might perpetuate initial levels of performance and profitability over the long run–and also whether the programme could compensate for the many inflationary factors that it faced both internally and externally.

The figure below shows the overall change in the cost of the reference model, between the first Logan's launch and 2010. It indicates how, for an unchanged product definition, continuous productivity gains achieved during this period were able to offset (-0.4%), inflationary factors caused by rising raw material prices (11.4% over the period), the transformation value (1.5%) and logistics (a minimal 0.6% due to the fact that the reference vehicle was made at Pitesti). It also showed the big impact of regulatory standards (+6.2%) on higher product costs, with enrichment efforts associated with the product targeting strategy only accounting for 2 .4% of the higher cost.

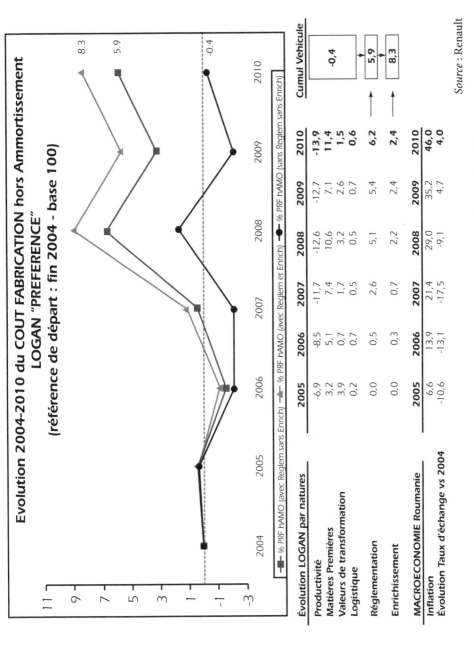

Figure 4.1–Changes in cost of Logan "Preference" petrol version

Beyond the remarkable cost control on this reference model, the question is how the dual expansion of product ranges and markets affected programme profitability. The manufacturer has not communicated any operating margin indicators but we can assume that these factors made a significant contribution during the growth phase. The increasingly systematic use of "carry across", together with the implementation of local sourcing and design strategies, ensured that cost savings were deployed across the whole of the Entry range. Similarly, the "top down" expansion of the product range and the absence of discounts created a gearing effect on margins.

In recent decades, the automotive world has witnessed many volume growth strategies rooted in price wars that were devastating for firms' profitability. In contrast, the Entry family's rise was based on a profitable growth strategy. Above and beyond cash flows, the programme's global success also created useful assets for the Company. New industrial bases, amortised through the Entry programme, became new manufacturing bases that could be used on other models one day. Similarly, new networks were created in countries where the brand had no presence, but which now asked Renault to broaden product catalogues for customers' benefit.

It is worth stressing the originality of the economic growth model demonstrated here by the Entry family versus the traditional automobile model where corporate profitability is said to derive from a "premium" effect. The final section will revisit this important point.

FROM A COMPACT AND UNIQUE MANUFACTURING SITE APPROACH TO A POLYCENTRIC AND GLOBALISED INDUSTRIAL SYSTEM

The Logan seemed to offer a general solution in emerging markets where Renault, like its competitors, was trying to distribute products (such as the Mégane) derived from its European range. The globalisation of the markets that were part of the Entry's world would rapidly lead to an internationalisation in its production system, especially given the ostensible transferability of the manual processes that had been implemented at Pitesti, once they were codified through the Renault Production System (see Chapter 2). The range launched at Pitesti in 2004 with the Logan was deployed the following year in Russia, Colombia and Morocco, and then in

2007 in Iran, Brazil and India, before arriving in South Africa in 2008 in the guise of a pick-up wearing a Nissan badge, followed by the Sandero. In November 2006, Renault was planning global output of 1.25 million X90s by the year 2010. The economic crisis upset these forecasts with only 700,000 Entry range vehicles being made by 2010–progress that was, nevertheless, quite remarkable. This also meant the wider internationalisation of Renault since the Logan (and, to a lesser extent, the Sandero) was the only Group vehicle to be produced on a global scale on four continents, affecting two countries apiece in Europe, Asia, Africa and South America. It was sold everywhere under different names and brands, like the Dacia or Renault Logan, Nissan Aprio, Mahindra Verito or the Renault Tondar 90 in Iran.

Table 4.1–2004-2011 changes in the Entry range's global output

Country	2004	2005	2006	2007	2008	2009	2010	2011
Romania	28,613	146,456	177,253	222,914	242,385	296,110	339,653	327,729
Russia		11,377	50,665	72,761	73,250	51,393	87,329	137,724
Columbia		3,737	15,070	24,643	18,472	18,097	33,366	43,198
Morocco		3,826	13,101	18,904	20,590	23,049	22,185	40,816
Iran			0	15,582	57,535	28,979	45,842	83,071
Brazil			0	47,398	91,868	101,216	150,787	198,791
India			0	18,365	20,015	7,507	10,611	0
South Africa					2,874	10,932	16,080	21,843
World total	28,613	165,396	256,089	420,567	526,989	537,283	705,853	853,172

Since 2010, more than half of all Entry range vehicles were made outside of Romania, translating a quickstep internationalisation that often involved partnerships with other manufacturers. During its first phase, the internationalisation drive often seemed opportunistic, based on ad hoc operations reacting to local markets' deeper development issues. The X90's success brought about a phase of integration as well as a global rationalisation of the Entry's globalised industrial system, one that would henceforth serve as a key ingredient of the Nissan-Renault Alliance.

We start by presenting the different investment scenarios that were mobilised, plus the underlying issues. This will be followed by a review of the different internationalisation stages that the Entry programme experienced during the latter half of the 2000s, before returning to changes affecting the historical industrial base in Romania that went on to achieve new centrality for Renault, with the country turning into a core part of the Entry range, in both product design and process development terms.

Internationalisation of industrial systems: challenges and scenarios

Within the automotive industry, the geographic deployment of an industrial system can be a real challenge given the magnitude of the requisite investments, hence the underlying economic risk. A multitude of parameters are taken into consideration, often producing contradictory effects.

Manufacturing in the same place as where a good is being sold is generally considered ideal in the automotive world. There are multiple reasons for this. As aforementioned, where emerging markets are involved, there is a significant difference in manufacturing labour costs, a factor that had a major direct effect on the Logan project. In addition, it is more costly to transport fully assembled vehicles than spare parts. Local production also eliminates the risk of variations between the currency in which the good is manufactured and the currency in which it is sold. Lastly, state authorities often levy tariffs on imports and/or enforce local contents ratios.

Other arguments include the fact that the local market's size and uncertainty may not justify investing in a highly integrated manufacturing plant. The idea of a geographical hub becomes more important in this case than a country-by-country reasoning. Currency variations associated with national economic policies can also revive the preference for national over long-distance business. For instance, changes in Brazil's monetary policy in 2008 caused a sudden change in Brazilian products' competitiveness across South and Central America, with a rapid effect on automotive imports and exports. Having been an exporter, Brazil became a net purchaser of vehicles, with imports rising from fewer than 100,000 units in 2005 to 660,000 in 2010, and an automotive trade surplus of nearly $6 billion in the middle of the decade turning into a $4 billion deficit five years later. As a result, Renault's Ayrton Senna plant in Curitiba, which was supposed to feed into Nissan's Mexican network to help replace the Tsuru (which had come to the end of its useful life) was actually a Logan badged as a Nissan Aprio. Things turned sour, however, due to the appreciation of the Brazilian real, which rose by 50% against the Mexican peso between 2005 and 2010.[1] The

---

1. The exchange rate went from 4.5 pesos per 1 real on average in 2005 to nearly 8 pesos by yearend 2009.

Ayrton Senna factory was therefore forced to concentrate on the domestic market, since its cost structure was no longer competitive enough for exports. Local industrial capacities were also insufficient to implement the technologies that the Company was trying to push and achieve the necessary level of quality.

Expanding an industrial system internationally can also mobilise several scenarios that vary depending on the level of risk and competitiveness involved.

The "built up" scenario involves simply importing vehicles made in different countries.

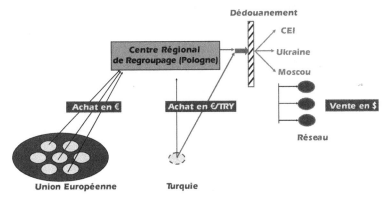

Figure 4.2–Built up scenario

The CKD (completely knock down) and SKD (semi-knocked down) scenarios involve locally assembled vehicles using imported components or sub-assemblies.

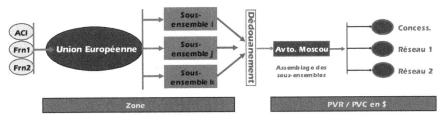

Figure 4.3–SKD production scenario

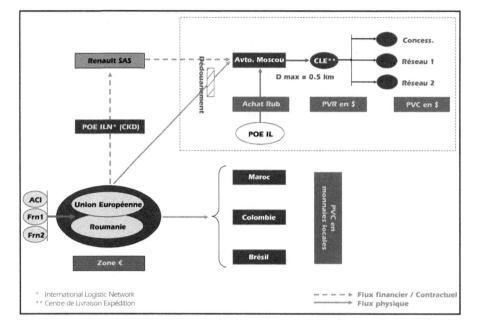

Source : Baudinot, Chahbi, 2006

Figure 4.4–CKD production scenario

These scenarios mean that new markets can be quickly supplied without a company having to risk heavy investment in a local production unit. On the other hand, they are generally uncompetitive in return cost terms, and are sometimes unfeasible where state authorities require major investment in local industry.

In this case, there is a shift to a more advanced local industrial integration scenario matching the high level of commercial uncertainty. This can involve transforming existing local production capacities (brownfield sites, such as the Pitesti or Moscow sites) or creating new greenfield site, like in Tangier (Morocco) or India.

The Entry programme's internationalisation mobilised these different industrialisation scenarios.

An initial phase of opportunistic industrial expansion based on local cooperation

Whereas in Brazil, Renault assumed sole responsibility for launching the Entry range by coming up with products that were adapted or adaptable to its market–and mobilising its Curitiba plant towards this end–in other countries, the Company would turn to local partners to expand its productive apparatus.

At long last, products adapted to the Brazilian and Russian markets

Most of the world's largest automotive groups have been rushing into Brazil and Russia to take advantage of these two emerging giants' current volumes (annual sales exceeding 2 million units) and growth prospects. At the same time, this unavoidable move comes with a certain number of risks, starting with uncertainty about the type of products that people expect in these markets and the volatility of sales (see Chapter 1). Bottom-of-the-range vehicles based on relatively old platforms and technologies (like the Fiat Uno in Brazil) retail here at less than €5,000, meaning that Renault would have to try and position itself on an intermediary market segment while offering more up-to-date products "at the right price". The Entry range finally had products adapted to specific markets, albeit with notable variations. Russia was geared towards Logan, Brazil towards the Sandero (being the market for which this sedan had been originally designed). Moreover, despite being almost exclusively focused on assembling these two products, Brazilian and Russian plants accounted for nearly 40% of the Entry platform's global output in 2011, exceeding the Pitesti plant.

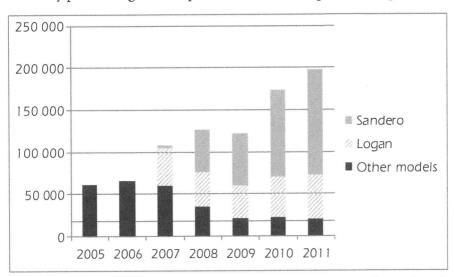

Source : Renault

Figure 4.5–Changes in Renault output in Brazil

Having arrived in Brazil with a wave of other Western manufacturers over the latter half the 1990s, Renault built an integrated production plant in Curitiba called Ayrton Senna, featuring an engine manufacturing unit. In a highly competitive market dominated by Fiat-VW-GM, Renault struggled to come up with a product adapted to a Brazilian market that was very idiosyncratic. These difficulties were aggravated by the Argentinian crisis. The end result was that the production of Clios, Méganes and Scenics topped out at 60,000 units annually.

As noted in the above analysis of the Brazilian market, the Brazilians had predicted that the Logan would fail because its body was so austere. As a result, they were able to negotiate the development of the Sandero—a sedan that they would be the first to industrialise—even before Romania could. The arrival of both the Logan and the Sandero would unblock the situation by offering two affordable modern vehicles. Moreover, the Entry range production would enable the Curitiba plant to significantly increase its output by adding two cars to its assembly line alongside the Clio, the Mégane and other Renault products. With more than 150,000 Logans and Sanderos assembled in 2010, 90% of the Curitiba plant's output was allocated to the Entry range.

Favourable market conditions in Brazil and Argentina (where the production of the Clio had been shifted) caused the factory's output to triple between 2005 and 2010 to become the second biggest producer of Entry range models, behind Pitesti in Romania. The presence of Renault suppliers in the vicinity of the Ayrton Senna plant—alongside other global automotive suppliers—simplified procurement. Success led to the Alliance developing the ambition of becoming a major manufacturer in Brazil. In early October 2011, for example, it announced a 100,000 unit increase in the annual capacity of Renault's Ayrton Senna plant (reaching 380,000 units) as well as a new Nissan plant in Resende (near Rio de Janeiro).

The same year that Renault announced its arrival in Brazil (1998), it founded a company in Russia called Avtoframos, in partnership with the City of Moscow. Acquiring an automobile plant with limited production capacities that had been built by Moskovitch but never used, Renault began exploring this new territory but encountered several problems. The first was significant market volatility, with the economic crisis the Russia suffered following the rouble's depreciation in the wake of the 1998 financial crisis delaying project implementation. When the relaunch happened in 2002—and even more than in Brazil—Renault struggled to come up with products adapted to market specificities. After first considering assembling the Mégane here, it opted for the Clio Symbol notchback, starting with the assembly of a few thousand units assembled on an SKD basis. In 2003, Renault announced a €230 million investment to make the Logan here (with annual capacities of 60,000 units), a vehicle to be sold under the Renault name (see Chapter 1). Lastly, the Company discovered how hard it can be to undertake production activities in this kind of economy. On one hand, Russia was characterised by a mixture of bureaucratic practices and corruption, although local institutional partners could also help to wade through otherwise complex and tense situations. At the same time, the country did not have a particularly substantial fabric of suppliers. The procurement situation was further aggravated by the fact that Moscow was not the geographic centre of Russia's automotive business. Some parts, like seats (which the global automotive industry generally considered as something to be outsourced) were produced in-house in Russia, with many components imported from Romania. And yet, the undertaking was a success, with the Logan production–the only vehicle to have been assembled in the suburbs of Moscow before 2010, when the Sandero came out–averaging 70,000 units over 2006-10, causing production capacities to be quickly raised to 80,000 vehicles/year. As 2009's most widely sold foreign brand in Russia, the Logan accounted for nearly 75% of all Renault brand sales in this market.

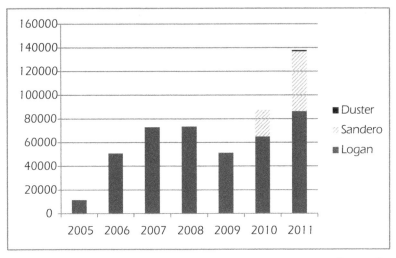

Source : Renault

Figure 4.6–Changes in Entry range output in Russia

Success convinced Renault to accept the challenge of leveraging its Entry range and become a major actor in the Russian automotive industry. In 2009-10, it invested €150 million to double Avtoframos' annual capacity to 160,000 units. In 2008, it signed an agreement with the giant Russian company AvtoVAZ (who, with its Lada brand, accounted for 70% of domestic output) and took a major 25% stake in the hope that AvtoVAZ would use Logan platform to design and produce specific cars (see above).

Penetrating markets in Asia with a local partner: Iran and India

The decision to enter Iran and India was risky given that Renault would not be able to rely on any in-house knowledge of the local economic, industrial and political contexts in these countries. The Company had a rough ride in both, although it faced different problems with its local partners in each.

Table 4.2–Changes in Logan output in Iran and India

Country	2007	2008	2009	2010	2011
Iran	15,582	57,535	28,979	45,842	83,071
India	18,365	20,015	7,507	10,611	Production stopped

Starting with recognition of significant market potential in Iran (one million vehicles sold) and offering the Iranian government an opportunity to reinvigorate national automotive production by developing modern vehicle, Renault's initial plans were extremely ambitious here. It hoped for an annual production of 300,000 Logans (renamed the Tondar 90), with Iran supposed to make a major contribution to its goal of manufacturing more than one million Entry range vehicles by 2010. Renault was hoping to take advantage of this opportunity to counter its French rival, PSA, which had been present in the country for several years already.

To achieve this objective, Renault was forced to negotiate with two local industrialists, Sapaï and Iran Kodhro, with a view towards getting each to partner it in helping to ramp annual production up to 150,000 Logans/Tondars. In an administrative economy such as Iran, assembly operations are complicated. A joint venture called Renault Pars was founded, 51% owned by Renault and 49% by ETCO (a company in which each of Renault's industrial partners held a 26% equity stake). The requirement was that the two Iranian companies be treated equally. Renault would continue to control quality and sell components, but the partners would be responsible for production and marketing. Another significant constraint was the requirement that components production be localised quickly (and largely covered by the Kodhro group's component subsidiaries) until it reached a local contents ratio of 60%. This caused industrial problems because Renault now had to mobilise a local supplier fabric that did not always have the competencies needed to satisfy modern technological requirements. Above all, there was a problem with funding. Yet sales seemed promising at first, with the Todar (retailing at $9,000) recording 100,000 orders during its first week on sale.

This brief moment of hope made the fall from grace all the more disappointing, The fact is that these were not firm orders. Logan yearly output would never exceed 85,000 units, or for below the initial target. Due to administrative interventionism in Iran and the fact that Renault's partners were public sector companies, it was the State that established the Logan's retail price and set this too low. Not only did this cause financial problems for Renault's partners but it also meant that they had no real incentive to produce the vehicle at a loss. Otherwise, the market was further complicated due to certain geopolitical difficulties. In the end, Renault was not able to take advantage of its growth. The Iranian market reached 1.4 million vehicles by 2009, but Renault still lagged behind, including with its French rival PSA. Despite tumultuous relationships with its own partner (Iran Kodhro), this latter company seemed to do better in Iran. With 460,000 unit sales in 2010 (versus fewer than 50,000 for Renault), it had a 30% market share. Having said that, price liberalisation in Iran has opened up new prospects for Renault in this country, and even if it was unlikely to achieve its initial objective, sales growth in 2011 was promising.

Regarding India, Renault entered the market in 2006 with a local partner called Mahindra & Mahindra (M&M), a utility vehicle manufacturer that had already had the experience of cooperating with the American company Ford. Growth prospects in India had become very attractive and it was necessary to have a presence here to take advantage of these opportunities, translating the expansion in the country's middle class population. A joint venture called Mahindra Renault (in which the French company had a 49% equity stake) was founded, with the M&M plant in Nashik (180 km north of Bombay) immediately offering annual production capacities of 50,000 units that would be used, following an investment of €100 million, to assemble Logans. Mahindra & Mahindra also had an operational distribution channel to market this car, badged as a Mahindra-Renault product.[1]

In reality, output only reached 20,000 units in 2007/08, before falling below 10,000 in 2009/10. There was even a suggestion of slashing prices in spring 2010 in a desperate bid to reinvigorate sales. Poorly positioned on (i.e. too expensive for) the Indian market,[2] the Logan was further penalised by a 17% tax on vehicles exceeding 4 metres, a levy that was only determined after local vehicle production had been announced. In procurement terms, local suppliers did not consider Renault's Indian plant a priority since they got more demand from other, higher volume assembly plants. Lastly, relations with partner M&M deteriorated when Nissan entered the picture, with the Alliance deciding that India was a strategic priority. After the two companies publicly committed in November 2006 to the ambitious project of building a new plant in Chennai (ex-Madras), M&M withdrew in 2008, the first sign of a tension that would worsen in the following months and progressively lead to the partnership's dissolution. In early 2011, Renault stopped using its Indian partner's plant, but Mahindra continued to produce the Verito under its own badge.

Renault's future in India would revolve around the Alliance. Given the market's growth prospects and cost advantages (averaging 20% less than the Romania), the Group decided to consolidate its presence here and create its own distribution network and design/engineering centre. It would also look to bolster local component purchases, undertake production projects together with Nissan and explore ultra-low cost solutions (see above).

Opportunities for assembly units: Columbia (SOFASA) and Morocco (SOMACA)

In both Colombia and Morocco, project output was small-scale, amounting annually to ca. 20,000 to 30,000 units assembled, using the production capacities of local plants with whom Renault had historical relationships. Local contents ratios were low in this context, with many components imported from Romania (body parts, seats, etc.). The weak industrial fabric also made it hard funding local suppliers.

---

1. With a Renault logo in the front and a Mahindra-Renault logo in the back.
2. 428,000 roupies, or €7,171 for the petrole version, and starting at 547,000 roupies or €9,165 for the diesel.

Renault had worked together for several years in Colombia with Toyota in a small assembly unit called SOFASA, in which the French carmaker held a 25% stake. Aside from providing access to the local market, this factory also exported a few hundred units to Central America or neighbouring countries like Ecuador–with Brazil remaining mainly focused on Mercosur. The joint venture enabled Renault to conduct a live experiment with the famous Toyota Production System methods, whose organisational mode–involving a permanent reduction in costs–turned out to be particularly adapted to the economic constraints weighing on the Logan's production.

Table 4.3–Changes in Renault Entry range output in Colombia

	2005	2006	2007	2008	2009	2010	2011
Logan	3,737	15,070	24,643	14,558	9,789	15,597	21,424
Sandero				3,914	8,308	17,769	21,774
Total	3,737	15,070	24,643	18,472	18,097	33,366	43,198

When the Logan was brought in, Renault had to search for local suppliers. This led to some cases of technology transfer, one example being a Colombian plastics company called Riduco, which made plastic parts (plates, bins) and components for household electrical products (refrigerators). Riduco was put in charge of making certain parts (shields, dashboards, etc.) that Faurecia had been manufacturing in Pistesti. With the success of the Logan and the Sandero, Renault seized the opportunity to take full control of SOFASA when Toyota decided to exit Colombia in 2008.

In Morocco, Renault leveraged its assembly unit to start building Logans that were initially destined for Northern African markets. Founded in 1959, SOMACA was key to the global configuration that Fiat had put together in the emerging markets (its Projet 178/Palio). It also assembled a few commercial vehicles on behalf of French carmakers PSA and Renault. When Project 178 wound down, the future of SOMACA became very uncertain, especially once the Moroccan government began looking to privatise the company. For several months, its CEO (Larbi Belarbi) had been trying to find a partner amongst the world's big carmakers. The rise of the Logan project was the signal for Renault to engage with him. It ended up taking over SOMACA and using it to produce Entry range cars.

Table 4.4 –Renault output at SOMACA

Morocco	2005	2006	2007	2008	2009	2010	2011
Logan	3,826	13,101	18,904	20,590	18,758	15,484	14,210
Sandero					4,291	6,701	26,606
Total	3,826	13,101	18,904	20,590	23,049	22,185	40,816
Inc. X90 exports				5,093	5,651	19,688	Not available

The quality effects were noticeable and ultimately led to growing part of SOMACA's production being exported towards Europe, where there was a great deal of product demand that the Romanian plant had been unable to satisfy. Morocco's economic partners–mainly Egypt but also Tunisia–were also a big market for SOMACA. A few local component suppliers were able to capture part of its production but the predominant source of parts remained imports. Moreover, the local contents ratio was low. The future of the Casablanca plant, which would also end up assembling Kangoo models, was closely tied to Renault's big industrial project in Tangier (see above).

Affirmation of a globalised Entry industrial strategy within the Alliance framework

The Entry programme was progressively integrated into the Nissan-Renault Alliance via "cross-badging". This started with an exchange of existing productive capacities (ie. in Brazil, despite the Mexican project's failings, or in South Africa), followed by ambitious new hub factories capable of doubling Entry range production volumes by 2014-15.

Spilling over into the Alliance's world in South Africa

South Africa, the Entry range's eighth production country, had a particular configuration due to the fact that Renault used the production capacities of a Nissan factory here. The two partners invested €80 million in the Rosslyn plant to increase annual capacity from 40,000 to 68,000 units, including Entry range products. After 2008, this essentially involved assembling Logan pick-ups. After making and selling more than 10,000 of these vehicles under the Nissan NP200 badge in 2010, the South African plant ended up producing more than its Romanian sister. Adding the 6,000 Sanderos sold under the Renault brand, the Alliance had developed an Entry product offer here that would allow it to consolidate its presence in the South African market. It remains that the country had a relatively dense automotive industry fabric, if only because of the presence of other manufacturers. This meant that Renault could source inputs from large suppliers already operating here, while using the production capacities of its partner, Nissan.

The period 2011-13 was meant to witness the introduction of three new production sites for vehicles derived from Entry platforms located in emerging countries: Tangier in Morocco; Chennai in India; and AvtoVAZ in Russia. The intention was that these units would get Renault over the barrier of 1 million units produced annually, a rare achievement in the automotive industry despite being several manufacturers' overt aim.

The Tangier export platform

It was in proximity to the international scale port of Tanger Med (opened in 2007 and planned for completion in 2012) that Renault decided to build an automotive complex whose annual production capacities would reach 170,000 units during the initial phase, and up to 340,000 subsequently. This investment (estimated between €600 million and €1 billion) reflected the Moroccan government's "Emergence plan" policy seeking to turn the north of the country (geographically closer to Europe) into an industrial production zone hosting companies within free trade zones, much like the *maquiladoras* operating on the border between the United States and Mexico. Some suppliers are already running operations in Tangier, but the Meloussa zone accommodating the new industrial complex has been relatively empty, translating Moroccan suppliers' relatively sparse fabric. Renault has therefore had to negotiate with its own suppliers to get them to come on-site. Asides from certain industrial construction problems, this raised issues pertaining to urbanisation and workforce training/recruitment, with an expectation that 6,000 direct jobs would be created when the operations were running full steam (on top of the 30,000 indirect jobs that optimists predicted).

The initial project, which was given the emblematic name of Hercules to symbolise the rapprochement between Europe and North Africa (15 km across the straits of Gibraltar), also relied on Nissan, which froze its commitment at 70,000 annual units during the 2008 crisis. In 2012, the first vehicles produced on the new Entry platform started to be assembled on the final assembly line. This included a family minivan (the Lodgy), followed by small utility vehicle that would also be declined into a passenger car version. Once again, Renault decided to internalise the production of certain components. 95% of the output was to be exported, notably towards Europe, with local markets being mainly supplied with Logans and Sanderos by the SOMACA's Casablanca plant, destined to increase volumes to 80,000 vehicles a year (including exports towards Europe and other North African markets).

There has also been talk about supplementing these operations in Morocco with a smaller factory (capable of 50,000 units a year) in Algeria, if certain very complicated negotiations with the national authorities prove successful. The Algerian market is the most promising in North Africa, with 14,000 Logans sold here in 2009 (and 3,500 Sanderos), making this the top-selling car in 2010 with a 12% market share (see Chapter 1).

An Alliance factory in India and the ultra-low cost approach

The Chennai (Madras) plant was the Alliance's second joint project in the emerging economies. Although the initial announcement in 2006 concerned Renault and Mahindra & Mahindra, the Indian partner subsequently withdrew from the project and was replaced by the Japanese Nissan, who officially came on board in early 2007. The idea was to create by the year 2015 a greenfield factory in the south of India (where Hyundai and Ford are also present) with an annual production capacity of 400,000 units, representing both Alliance brands.

Due to Renault's provisional withdrawal, the 2008 economic crisis delayed the implementation of this investment of more than €1 billion. Two production lines were planned but only one implemented, with the first Nissan Micra coming off the assembly lines in June 2010. Renault tried after autumn 2009, Renault to reinvigorate the project internally and start making own models, mainly the Duster. Chennai was supposed to become a major production and export hub for a range of Entry vehicles representing both Alliance brands.

With the ambition of achieving a significant position in the Indian market, Nissan and Renault also began exploring the ultra-low cost segment, notably with a view towards competing with the Nano, a car developed by Indian manufacturer Tata. Towards this end, they combined with a local scooter and tricycle manufacturer, Bajaj Auto, to try and develop a $2,500 (€1,900) vehicle to be produced at Chakran starting in 2012. The ostensible objective was to make, mainly in India, 400,000 ultra-low cost vehicles bearing the names of the three brands. The project was abandoned in summer 2011 because of difficulties with the ultra-low cost approach, illustrated by the problems that Tata has had. Despite this failure, the Alliance would continue to exploit India's economic and industrial potential and extend its experimentation with the design and production of low-cost vehicles. The appointment of Gérard Detourbet, involved in X90 projects since 2001 (and Entry Programme Director from 2006 until late 2011, see above interview) as the Alliance's Managing Director for the A segment starting in 2012 showed that this ambition of offering a vehicle positioned below the Entry range in emerging countries such as India has remained very topical.

The partnership with AvtoVAZ

Renault also tried to take advantage of the Russian market's potential. Asides from doubling the Moscow plant's production capacities, it used its alliance with historic Russian manufacturer AvtoVAZ, which is responsible for 70% of domestic production in this country and sells products under the brand name of Lada. In 2008, the two companies signed a strategic agreement that involved the French carmaker taking a 25% stake in AvtoVAZ. In industrial terms, the Russian manufacturer was asked to make vehicles using the Entry platform and market them under three brand names (Nissan, Renault and Lada). There was a technology transfer in the shape of a €165 million licensing purchase and above all a transfer of technological and managerial competencies involving the modernisation of the Togliatti industrial complex.

Having been built with support from Fiat during the 1960s, this site epitomised the kind of integrated complex characterising a planned Soviet economy. Similar to Dacia in Pitesti but on a gigantic scale, this city-factory of 700,000 inhabitants could produce up to 800,000 units a year. Previously encompassed within the Renault organisation's Euromed region, now Russia was an autonomous part of a new region called Eurasia, attesting to the Group's new ambitions for this part of the world.

Within a very short period of time, the partnership was weakened by the serious financial crisis that AvtoVAZ faced in 2009 and the collapse in its sales. Close to bankruptcy, the Russian company only survived because of vigorous intervention by the national authorities, with Renault refusing at first to take over AvtoVAZ despite strong government encouragement and incentives. It injected a little cash into the Company through a rights issue to maintain its 25% stake. After a few months of discussion culminating in a complex financial arrangement, in May 2012 the Alliance came to an agreement with the Russian authorities whereby Nissan and Renault would invest $750 million to take AvtoVAZ over by 2014, via a joint venture in which it would hold a stake of more than 50%.

From early 2010, AvtoVAZ started modernising its assembly line, working on behalf of Lada, Renault and Nissan to reach an annual capacity of 280,000 models derived from the Entry platform. The first cars rolled off the new assembly line in spring 2012, starting with the Lada Largus (derived from the Logan MCV estate) followed by other vehicles with Renault and Nissan badges. The aim was for cars from the three brands to total 40% of the Russian market, with the Entry range making a significant contribution to these volumes. This would be accompanied by a joint effort by the three partners to structure and upgrade the suppliers network's efficiency, a necessary step before increasing the local contents ratio. Renault had struggled to mobilise suppliers for its Moscow factory but the decision in 2010 to double Avtoframos' capacities and the outlook for AvtoVAZ helped it increase Logan and Dacia's local contents ratio from 40% in 2008 to 54% two years later.

Why not China?

China was temporarily considered a possible destination for the Entry range. In December 2002, Louis Schweitzer was saying—even as the Logan project's internationalisation was being concocted—that, "Renault expects to enter the Chinese car market and its partner will probably be the joint venture that Nissan is going to set up with Dongfeng Motor next year." His hope at the time was to sell more than 100,000 vehicles a year in China by 2010. By 2012, however, Renault's presence in China was still limited to a joint venture (Sanjiang Renault Automotive) that was founded in 2004 and never did anything asides from producing a few thousand units of the Master utility vehicle, before suspending all activities due to a lack of outlets. This productive apparatus might have been useful to the Entry range's global expansion. Indeed, Renault had explored the hypothesis of producing the Logan in China. This was abandoned, however, with two main reasons seeming to explain the Entry programme's absence.

Firstly, although the Chinese automotive market has been the world's largest since 2009, ahead of the United States, it was not at all certain that Renault's Entry range offered adapted products. The range did not really satisfy the demands of a customer base that liked luxurious foreign cars. As for the entry segment, it was occupied by a number of Chinese manufacturers offering adapted products at very low prices.

Secondly, Nissan was the Alliance's predominant partner in China. The renewed dynamism of this Japanese manufacturer–whose financial health had been restored without it having to sacrifice its technological competency–meant that it had no incentive to help its French partner enter this promising market (or indeed, any market in Asia). This was especially true once Nissan agreed with Renault on the importance of the Entry range, no longer viewing it as a simple support business but as one meant to make its own contribution by offering different products derived from the Micra's A platform, an alternative to the Entry platform that Renault used for its Entry range.

An implicit Yalta conference agreement seems to have been reached here, with people accepting one or the other partner's predominance in different parts of the world, based on its seniority in that particular region. Joint projects revolving around hub factories tended to be driven by Renault-Dacia in and around Europe (Morocco/Russia) and South America, whereas Nissan would lead in Asia, including India, plus South Africa.

The post-Duster renewal of Renault's Entry range always offered a possibility of changing this situation, much in the same way as other future products might do. It is hard to imagine that given the French manufacturer's ambitions, it will remain absent from the world's two biggest markets: the US; and China. The agreement announced between Renault and Dongfeng in April 2012 may have revived attempts to find room for the Entry range in China, as part of a joint Alliance strategy.

Spatial hierarchisation within the Entry's world

The Entry's vertical and geographic extension meant a new centrality for the Alliance's multipolar space in Romania. Concretising the dreams of Constantin Stroe,[1] the Logan project's success translated into the constitution of an integrated automotive complex here, one developing competencies and commanding logistics flows on a global scale.

Compared to what Renault engineers discovered at Dacia in the late 1990s, the Romanian automotive industry had transformed radically, in

---

1. Managing Director at Dacia after 1990, he was one of the main drivers behind the Romanian manufacturer's privatisation, thus the agreement it signed with Renault. After 2002, he became Vice President of Dacia.

part through its rapid development of product and process engineering competencies. The Mioveni plant has sharply enhanced its volumes, scope and productivity (and quality). In this context, employees have benefited from the Logan's success, in both job and wage terms.

Developing an integrated automotive complex in Romania

Romania would become increasingly key to the Entry's world space. In 2007, Renault decided to accelerate the development of its local engineering capacities by creating RTR (*Renault Technologie Roumanie*), a Romanian version of its Saint-Quentin en Yvelines Technocentre near Paris. The purpose was also to reduce vehicle design costs and transfer upstream development from the Technocentre to Romania, training high-level engineers and technicians willing to start at a salary of around €500-€600.

With a combined workforce of 3,000 employees, RTR tried to consolidate product engineering activities for the Entry range by combining them with process engineering, purchasing, design etc. It worked out of three sites: the Bucharest design centre (1,900 persons); process engineering (500 persons) at Mioveni-Pitesti, in direct contact with the assembly and mechanical plants; and a modern testing centre (300 employees) built in September 2010 at Titu, between Bucharest and Pitesti resembling Renault's Aubevoye facilities in France and featuring 32 km of tracks and around 100 test benches for vehicles and parts. Romania's growing importance to Entry range products' design was remarkable.

In terms of processes and in conjunction with RTR, the Pitesti plant would become a global reference for defining standard manual procedures for the production of vehicles in this range, starting with the early industrialisation of new models (except for the Sandero, which was industrialised in Brazil). These procedures were than disseminated to other industrial sites assembling different versions within the range, whether low-volume units (Morocco or Colombia) or larger series ones.

With Pitesti also serving as a hub for global logistics flows (see above), Renault's presence in Romania involved Dacia as well, through its subsidiaries RTR and RIR (*Renault Industrie Roumanie*), which helped constitute an integrated automotive complex in Romania, thanks to the Entry line's success. The end result was the complex's growing centrality on an international scale.

Progress at the Mioveni-Pitesti plant

Initially sized to produce 180,000 to 200,000 units a year, the Mioveni plant responded to the demand for Entry range vehicles by doubling production capacities to 350,000 units in 2010, or 64 vehicles assembled an hour (one every 55 seconds). This expansion was accompanied by the production of a progressive wider variety of vehicles, with the Romanian plant being the only one to assemble the whole of the Entry range, asides from the Lodgy, which was made in Morocco. At first, it only made the basic Logan L90 model–totalling 168,500 units in 2006–supplemented later that year by the Logan MCV estate version that was only manufactured in Romania, with 100,000 units rolling out the following year. There was also a utility version (the Logan van) targeting professional customers, although volumes were quite limited (fewer than 10,000 units). The following year, Dacia resurrected the brand's historical pick-up. In volume terms, 2006 was characterised by the launch of the MCV estate followed by the Sandero (B90) which would soon move into first place, with the Mioveni plant churning out 150,000 units of this latter by 2009. The following year it was the turn of the Duster to shine, accounting for one in every two vehicles to be assembled in Romania 2011.

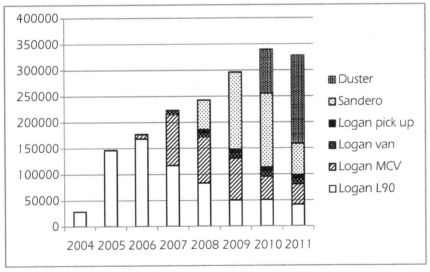

Source : Renault

Figure 4.7–Changes in Entry range output in Romania

The rapid growth in production volumes was accompanied by an increase in staff numbers at Dacia, although less rapidly due to big productivity gains. One simple indicator—the ratio between the number of vehicles produced and Dacia personnel—doubled from 2005 to 2010. Savings derived from learning effects alone cannot explain a change of this magnitude, especially given the under-estimation of productivity gains resulting from the fact that a greater variety of models was being assembled (six in 2010 versus one in 2005). Alongside of this, the models were also being enriched insofar as they were now targeting European markets and therefore had more options. Lastly, the changes also ignored variations in mechanical performance.

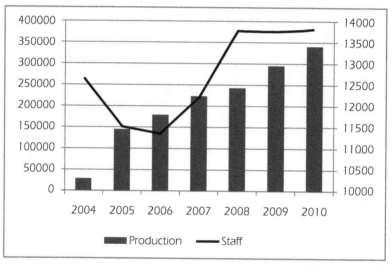

Source : Renault, Dacia

Figure 4.8–Comparison between in changes in Entry range output and Dacia staffing

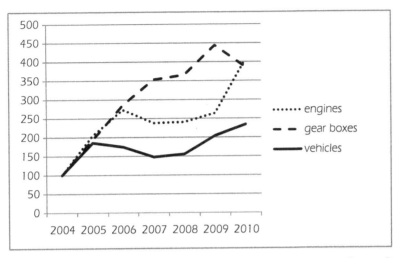

Source : Renault

Figure 4.9–Changes in productivity

The launch of the Duster was a real turning point[1] in the Entry range's trajectory (see above). This was not only because its design implied greater involvement by RTR engineers in Bucharest; or because target customers were different from the Logan or the Sandero; or because different markets' hierarchisation was the opposite of what was usually considered normal (with more luxurious versions being sent to the emerging markets). Beyond this, it caused a significant restructuring of production activities, such as they had been organised for the Logan, with a new focus on the Mioveni industrial complex. The Duster's commercial success accelerated these changes, with the lion's share of the plant being reallocated to this model. By year-end 2010, one in every two units rolling off its final assembly lines was an off-road vehicle.

As a four-wheel drive, the Duster incorporated more advanced technologies than the ones used on the Logan and therefore required new production lines for the mechanical unit and body shop alike. Like all diesel Logans, its K9 engine was imported from Renault's Valladolid plant in Spain, with the gearbox found on its TL four-wheel–drive version being

---

1. The project's internal codename (H79) denoted a new orientation, with different variants derived from the Logan being referred to under the generic term of X90: Logan (L90), MCV estate (K90), pick-up (F90), van (U90) and Sandero (B90). The Indian version would have the code name X89.

produced in Romania. The equipment and shops used to machine and assemble the product were very different from the ones used for the J gearbox fit on X90 vehicles. Whereas most of the equipment used for the latter had been recovered from other sites–meaning that the technologies employed were somewhat obsolete–the new TL gearboxes (and their components) were produced according to standards that were more modern and sophisticated, contrasting with the old machines used to make the J version in the machining unit. The TL assembly workshop was a very well-lit automated environment, full of new machines. It contrasted with the J assembly shop, which seemed relatively old and labour-intensive. Clearly, there had been a qualitative leap forward involving an upgrading to the latest international standards in mechanical plants, extending their life expectancy through the production of the new H4 engine.

Sharing the fruits of success

Significant cuts in Dacia's high staffing levels culminated in a new redundancy programme that led in 2004 to the departure of 5,000 persons (40% of the staff members as of 31 December 2007). Similar levels of departure occurred through 2009, involving between 1,000 and 1,500 employees, or 10% to 15% of total personnel. These were voluntary redundancies, with the Romanian economy's relatively high annual growth rate (ranging from 4% to 8%) offering job opportunities above and beyond natural departures. Staff turnover slowed down in 2010, however, as a result of the Romanian economy entering recession.

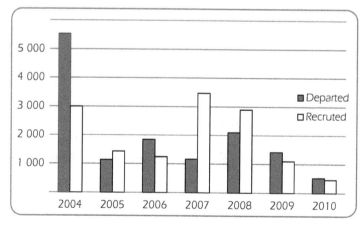

Source : Dacia, DRH

Figure 4.10–Variations in staff turnover at Dacia

Hiring correlated positively with the site's increasing responsibilities and new product launches, notably in 2007 and 2008, with Dacia recruiting around 3,000 employees both years to face its new staffing needs. It was in this context that Dacia would experience its first major strike in early 2008, attesting to staff members' demand that they share in the fruits of the project's industrial and commercial success.

Whereas average national wages rose by a whopping 25% between 2007 and 2008–and even though Dacia's trade unions had already negotiated a 20% rise in 2007 after threatening to strike–tensions rose during the 2008 bargaining rounds. Demanding a 50% wage increase (or 550 lei a month, the equivalent of €148), workers went on strike on 28 March, an industrial action considered legal this time (unlike 2002, cf Chapter 2). The participation rate was high, with the unions claiming that 80% of all workers joined the action (vs. a management figure of 50%). After 19 days of negotiation, there was an agreement on an increase of 360 lei (€97), or 28% in two steps, on top of which came a profit-sharing mechanism based on 2007 earnings amounting to 900 lei (€243). Renault evaluated the total cost of the agreement at €13 million.

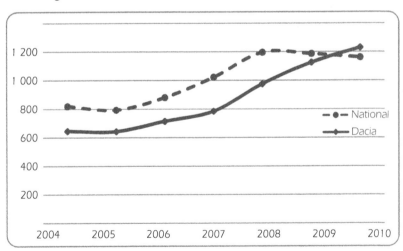

Sources : Dacia DRH (salaire), UE (inflation)

Figure 4.11–Compared changes in real wages (base 2003 Romanian leu)

Until that point, wage hikes at Dacia had matched national trends. As the Romanian economy fell into crisis, real wages stagnated and even began falling, despite the automaker's continued growth resulting from the strong demand for its new products (the Logan MCV estate, the Sandero and the Duster in 2010). This caused major tensions, in part due to insufficient production capacities. Dacia looked like an island of prosperity in a country facing a serious macroeconomic crisis (the recession began in 2010) and unions took advantage of this situation to negotiate a higher share of the fruits of growth. Each year began the negotiating round would be based on bluffing, with unions[1] threatening to go on strike and management–having under-estimated its labour needs–waiting to sign the agreement before revealing production plans. Average wages at Dacia had been 23% below the Romanian average in 2007 but caught up over 2008-2010. Since the Logan's launch in 2004, real wages (measuring purchasing power adjusted for inflation) had doubled at Dacia.

Managing procurement on a global scale

The international deployment of the Entry line revolved around a purchasing policy that was adapted to the local context due to the need for localisation to keep costs under control. In turn, this engendered a whole series of component and vehicle flows that had to be managed in a way that minimised logistics costs–more or less the same order of magnitude as labour costs–starting from the centre of this world, Romania.

A pragmatic approach

Logan's suppliers in Roumania in Pitesti did not systematically follow Renault as it moved abroad, creating a need for the Company to find new suppliers in its new operational centres for those components that were difficult to transport (i.e. seats, dashboards). This involved a variety of solutions: sourcing from a global supplier that was already present in the country; search for a local supplier (technology transfer solution); renegotiation of "make or buy" arrangements by re-internalising certain kinds of production (seats in Russia); or managing intellectual property rights on components.

Renault's mechanical driving systems (engines and gearboxes) would be imported, except in Brazil where the Curitiba plant included an engine unit, with gearboxes coming from Chile. Thus, localisation manoeuvers

---

1. Dacia had many unions at first but this ended up with SAD enjoying an almost hegemonic position.

tended to involve body work. For most main components, Dacia's suppliers in Romania did not track its international deployment. This did happen, however, for certain generic components where local producers were able to offer an alternative at attractively competitive prices, notably when the component (i.e. batteries) was being made for a retrofitting phase operation. Regarding dashboards, Faurecia EAPS tracked the Logan project in three countries while collaborating with local industrialists who were responsible for producing this component. Conversely, Johnston Control stayed in Mioveni, meaning that other suppliers (i.e. Faurecia or Lear) took over to supply Logan assembly lines elsewhere. Lacking any partners in Russia, Renault decided to assemble the seats itself here. Where a local manufacturer was involved, the supplier would be invited to engage in a technology transfer, although this solution could be delicate to manage when this meant being replaced by a direct competitor, like what happened with car seats when Faurecia and Lear stood in for JCI.

The questions raised at this level related to intellectual property rights on component development studies. To avoid paying design costs several times over (always a possibility given the internationalisation drive's unpredictable nature) and to improve cost control, Renault opened up the black box of design costs that were usually amortised via component prices. By directly funding development costs, it was able to break such costs down more precisely and renegotiate certain supplier standards (such as discount rates, often twice as high as the ones Renault used). It was also able to recover, under certain conditions, intellectual property on studies facilitating the international deployment of the Logan's production on those occasions where the main supplier (the one who had done the studies) did not follow Renault abroad.

A general local procurement organisational system was impossible in this context. In the words of Philippe Cayette, Entry range Purchasing Manager from 2004 to 2008, "We didn't have any model [and] ended up with schemes that were pretty complicated". Each country was dealt with on a case-by-case basis reflecting its particular constraints (i.e. the local contents ratio required by government) or opportunities (absence or presence of an automotive industry fabric, production volumes). By remaining focused on costcutting targets and with support from the project management team–including the direct involvement of Gérard Detourbet to sort out any difficult situations when necessary–local buyers were able to devise adapted configurations. In Iran, for instance, despite the requisite 60%

local contents ratio, the impossibility of finding a competitive solution for fuel tanks led to a redesign of this component's metalwork. The outcomes in purchasing policy terms did not always correlate with Renault's commercial and industrial success in a country. For instance, the Logan's success in Russia was not accompanied by a sufficient localisation of components production. These were largely imported from Romania, adding to the cost. Conversely, Renault's commercial failure in India with Mahindra was mitigated by the discovery of a very competitive industrial sector (20 to 30% cheaper than Romania), hence the decision to opt for a local contents ratio of 67% versus 54% in Russia. Globally, the rate varied between 20% and 30% on low volume sites (Morocco, Romania), while raising to more than 80% in Brazil, thanks to the engine factory here.

Towards new supplier relationships

The recent period (2010-2012), marked by construction of new hub factories, has been particularly useful in analysing how the effects on Renault's procurement policies, especially given the parallel negotiation of a contract renewing the Entry platform. Renault may have given suppliers strong incentives to come with it when the Logan experiment started in Romania, but the attractive volumes (over 1 million units) put it in a strong negotiating position. Whereas Renault had to pay suppliers' design costs for the first Logan, it was now able to ask them to pay this themselves by recouping their investments through subsequent production activities, as is generally done elsewhere. Attracted by Logan platform volumes of around 1 million units a year, Renault's suppliers have had an incentive to track its international operations or negotiate intellectual property rights in case of a technology transfer with another supplier if the companies that designed a particular piece of equipment does not follow Renault into a particular country.

Given this production scale, Renault has been squeezing suppliers–the goal for the next generation was to be 30% down on the Logan–since rivals in different countries would be marketing products competing with Entry vehicles sold under the Dacia or Renault brand name. The principle of systematic outsourcing was to be reconsidered within this overall negotiation, with the focus now on reaching the best decision on a case-by-case basis. The trend towards re-internalising certain functions that used to be outsourced has reflected two factors. On one hand, systematic outsourcing led to a loss of in-house competencies and reduced Renault's ability to negotiate with suppliers, a major weakness in an organisational model revolving around cost-cutting (explaining why the Entry team systematically explored alternative technical solutions to the ones suggested by a supplier to demonstrate the feasibility of less expensive options). Otherwise, in a model focused on earning a few pennies on all components, comparative analysis of in-house ("make") or outsourced ("buy") production costs would be subjected to deeper criteria than the simple economic efficiency of outsourcing, which has often been over-estimated. The new factory in Tangier would be an opportunity for Renault to re-internalise certain functions, including seats assembly, given that suppliers here have not proposed any economically useful solutions.

Managing logistics

With the Logan family's deployment and proliferation of variants that would be particularly popular in industrialised European markets, production capacities at the Mioveni-Pitesti industrial site were increased to 350,000 units/year. At the same time, the Romanian automotive market–in which Dacia still had 60% share in 2003–collapsed, to such an extent that the factory basically became an export base for both finished vehicles being shipped to different markets worldwide but also for components sent to the Entry line's seven other assembly units. The Logan's unexpected global success forced the Renault group to deal with both these challenges by coordinating the activities of its Dacia Pitesti factory with those of a specific subsidiary (*Renault Industrie Roumanie*) managing the Mioveni ILN global logistics hub on a global scale, making this a fully-fledged member of Renault's International Logistic Network (ILN). Renault Mioveni has become the Group's biggest logistics centre today, surpassing the historic Paris *Grand Couronne* centre in 2007. With more than 250 employees (versus 330 in 2006-07), it exported the equivalent of 300,000 vehicles in 2010.

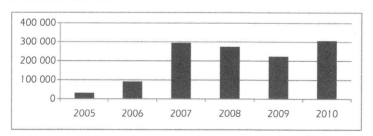

Source : Renault

Figure 4.12–Changes in INL logistics hub activity (equivalent units shipped)

This became ground zero for all Logan assembly sites' procurement, handling all parts manufactured by Dacia's Pitesti body shop and mechanical plant before they were shipped to the assembly sites. The main items were engines and transmissions that, outside of Brazil, were not produced on-site. It is also worth mentioning certain body parts such as pressed sheet metal, whenever small assembly volumes meant that an expensive investment in a pressing workshop was not justified.

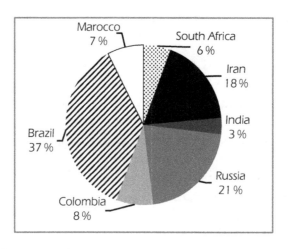

Source : Renault

Figure 4.13–Breakdown of 2010 Mioveni ILN logistics hub budget

The ILN would also handle parts from eight suppliers located in the Mioveni suppliers park. For some components, this involved global companies. For others, the components came from local companies working out of Romania (74) or elsewhere (231). Although certain voluminous components–or ones produced within a cycle (dashboard, seats) –had to be produced locally, it made sense, for economies of scale reasons, to make parts characterised by few components (and low costs) on a single site, before redistributing them worldwide to the Logan's different production lines.

Suppliers and assembly plants flows

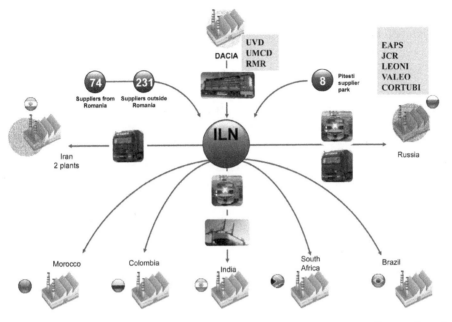

Source : Renault

Figure 4.14–Customer and supplier flows at the Mioveni ILN logistics hub

In sum, this has been a key hub in the Logan's global production scheme, a transit centre for all of the input flows of components requiring subsequent re-shipment globally. Once again, the organisation evolved constantly in a bid to cut costs, whether associated with handling costs or inventory levels, which fell in spring 2010 to two days of activity. Beyond these efforts at ILN, the importance of logistics costs led, at a more design upstream level, to the incorporation of a "design to logistic" approach cutting component development costs (see above).

ENTRY TEAM DYNAMICS

The question then became how this spectacular expansion phase would play out in terms of the Entry team's organisational dynamics–and how a compact team mobilised around a radical but simple revolutionary project was transformed to the extent that it would be able to pilot a diversified global deployment.

Quite understandably, the first development involved team-development. From an initial group of around 10 members in 2002, the programme team grew to 20 persons in 2010, mainly reflecting an expansion in technical and product functions mirroring growth in its range and target markets. Team members' average age and experience remained unchanged at something like 47 years old in 2010, versus 45 in 2002. This attested to the fact that the team was comprised of highly experienced individuals coming from different automotive businesses (and who also knew how to lead new product projects). Another explanation for the Entry programme's coherent dynamics was the relative stability of its leading actors. For instance, its number one, Gérard Detourbet, took over in 2001. Dominique Bellot joined in mid-2005, replacing Odile Pantiatici, who served as Engineering Project Manager throughout most of the Logan project's first phase. This stability struggled in the face of the programme's success, however. Missions' average duration fell from five years for the first team to about four years for the 2010 team. This reflected their changing nature (with initial launches deploying for longer than derivative products and capacity-raising efforts) as well as greater attractiveness within the in-house labour market of acquiring experience in the Logan programme. At first, it was little more than an adventure—and a relatively unattractive one, at that. By the end, it had become a career trampoline.

The second major change was the group's substantial internationalisation. Where 30% of the first team had had some international experience, this rose to 50% by 2010. Beyond the Entry programme's core team, the Entry family's development coincided with an engineering internationalisation dynamic that was unprecedented at Renault. Although there was nothing new about internationalising production sites in the automotive business, this had been a revolution in development engineering.

The Logan started as a Technocentre car. Its first internationalisation stage had been the July 2008 move to the Pitesti engineering centre (RTR, *Renault Technocentre Roumanie*) as the product evolved over the course of its marketing phase. All of the changes affecting the Logan were done at Pitesti (quality solutions, further cost-cutting, product evolution and incorporation of regulatory constraints). In early 2010, a Romanian Technical Range Deputy Director was appointed and the Design Centre hosted a delegation working on the second industrialisation of versions made in Russia.

The next project was 50% Technocentre and 50% Pitesti. The 79 (Duster) broke down as 30% Technocentre, 70% Pitesti. An important ingredient of this design system was still lacking, however, to wit, a testing centre, although this was in the process of being built and would be operational for the next project. At the same time, as the centre of gravity for developmental work being shifted to Romania, the programme's bigger target countries hosted engineering units responsible for adaptations and variants that were specific to each region in Brazil and India, under the leadership of the four Technical Range Deputy Directors (America, Russia, South Africa/Iran, India).

So far, the advantage of this change have been manifest, including a 2:1 ratio in engineering hours; better understanding of local market hierarchies (but also industrial and social contexts); and decision-making processes more compact than at the Technocentre, hence faster–or in the words of Dominique Bellot, "Things are quicker there, it's like the Utility Vehicle Engineering Development unit." Clearly, the change also came with several risks. However natural it seemed that central engineering's leadership be legitimised, the major peripheral centres like Brazil found it hard to swallow their subordination to another decentralised engineering unit, which may not necessarily have had the same orientations or priorities.

The third transformation axis involved the team's modes of intervention. The Logan's epic journey started under the sign of the project team's "commando" interventionism. As the scope of the Entry programme expanded (and as it lost its marginal status), the institutionalisation and generalisation of its thinking and behaviour necessitated other modes of intervention. It was no longer enough to be the exception–the rules themselves had to be taken on. The expansion and complexification of the space of intervention implied being able to theorise practice to make it transmissible and deployable. This was possible now because the programme had a consistent and validated base of experience that could be used to question existing processes and standards. "Initial technical choices generally involved exceptions to business rules. Now, with more than one million Entry vehicles on the road–including the Logan, out since 2005– we have cars that had driven 310,000 km, we have thousands of Turkish taxi drivers who have proven the durability of these exceptional technical options."[1]

The end result was an affirmation of new technical references, including through the formalisation of design approaches like "design to cost". This was a significant change in the scheduling and modes of intervention of

---

1. Interview with Dominique Bellot.

different businesses within the development function, involving an anticipation of design details, the involvement of suppliers and a willingness to question the status quo.

It remains that this bureaucratic way of structuring things suffered from a number of well-known limitations: it was heavy; its application was constrained by particular cases, which could only be dealt with through planned approaches; it mobilised hierarchies and sometimes had very little effect on basic operational decisions; it rarely called on people's sense of initiative or inventiveness, etc. Hence the importance of management trying to share its vision, providing meaning to encourage people to "tackle problems". This was a symbolic kind of management[1] that did not define any methods precisely but constructed semantics to communicate key messages, proposing "meta-rules"[2] based on meaningful examples to help people interpret things and act "in the spirit of the Entry programme" when facing a particular situation.

The six meta-rules of the "Logan spirit"

Keep it simple. Simplicity was one of the programme's main design strengths, driving savings, quality, durability and speed of execution.

Stingy on Spending. Self-explanatory.

Adapt technical standards. Systematically asking about the justification for business rules within the context of the Entry programme. A key aspect of Entry engineering.

Be Pragmatic and Opportunist. The history of the Entry programme was always associated a doctrine's affirmation and with contradictory examples. The ability to remain focused on a general goal, while rebounding anytime in case of unwelcome surprises (or taking advantage of opportunities) was one explanation for the Entry programme's success. There were many examples involving product definition and a variable focus on different countries depending on customers' often unpredictable reactions.

---

1. Midler C.: "L'acteur projet, portrait d'un rôle d'influence", *Revue Gestion 2000*, No. 2/93, April 1993, Louvain-La Neuve, Belgium
2. F. Jolivet and C. Navarre: "Grands projets, auto-organisation, méta-règles: vers de nouvelles formes de management des grands projets". 1992 Paris, mimeograph

Decide and Implement in Short Cycle. The competitiveness logic underlying the Entry programme typified strategies highlighting first mover speed. Having created a new market (or a Blue Ocean approach, to recycle a concept formulated by Kim and Mauborne), the goal was to exploit this original solution as far as possible before others reacted, something they would inevitably do. The rapid development of derivatives such as estates, pick-ups or GPL versions, typified this approach.

Transcend Geographic and Cultural Frontiers. Thinking in global (and not exclusively European) terms was probably one of the Entry programme's main specificities in a milieu of engineers, designers and marketing specialists bathing in a Western automotive culture.

Within these transformations, it was also possible to find certain traditional organisational development attributes caused by an activity's growth. We will demonstrate, however, that they mainly translated a managerial dynamic rooted in a quite peculiar form of growth, to wit, the management of lineages, whose logic will be characterised more precisely in Chapter 5.

Interview with Gérard Detourbet, Entry Programme Director

Gérard Detourbet, how did you become Entry Programme Director?
It's been a long journey. I've been with Renault for 30 years and worked in almost all of its automotive industry and engineering businesses. After studying mathematics at university and a first job in operational research and planning back in the 1970s, I was appointed Project Manager for R25 bodies manufactured at our Sandouville plan, before being put in charge of a decentralised methods plant. I then ran central assembly methods in 1985 before moving in 1991 from the body work to the mechanical unit, where I served as Project Director on several engine projects until 1997, when I took over the Mechanics Department and joined Renault's Management Committee. Then in 2001, I was put in charge of developing vehicles and a production system at Dacia.

This journey is important because it gives me the wherewithal to succeed with this project. I've got a lot of experience and legitimacy in terms of automated and manual production processes, involving both mechanics and body work. I know the people who can supply us with our engineering skills, means of production and components because I've already had many opportunities to negotiate and work with them. Basically, this means that I can no longer be "trapped" by the opinions of "experts", something that was very useful when we had to break traditional rules to meet the goals of this very original project. It also helped me to avoid any mistakes when building our teams, and to understand how much pressure to put on our engineers and technicians.

Alongside the competencies that I've acquired over my career, I have some personal attributes that are also very useful. People say that I'm tenacious and even thick-skinned, that I never give in. Actually, in professional life I've often argued with senior management, sometimes getting pretty close to leaving the Company. In fact, it was after a kind of fight that I started to shift gears and ended up on the Logan project.

Given your background, what did you learn from the way in which the Entry programme has been run?

The first thing is that I've had a great time. Which is actually why I've agreed to lead the Alliance's new low-cost vehicle project.[1] A Programme Manager runs the whole business. You're in charge of operational margins and really have to get involved. It's much more than what project managers or product and process designers do, all things that I did earlier.

I also learnt a lot about international development. It is by attacking markets that you understand them. At first, the platform had a potentially incomparable advantage, which was the Logan's arbitrage between size and price. Later, we discovered when entering different national markets that this wasn't enough. In Brazil, for instance, people want visible performance and change their cars frequently. Russian customers have a different set of demands. Hence the need to develop adapted local engineering while maintaining a maximum of joint standards. We were able to achieve this modulation by combining a progressive development of local engineering with "carry across methods".

---

1. Renault-Nissan

Starting with a single product (the Logan), you led the deployment of a diversified and globalised family. How did you do this?

The programme kept a clear identity. The mission was to explore territories that were new for the Renault Group, with a view towards establishing robust and durable commercial and industrial bases, ones we could use to drive the Group's further expansion. When people think about international development, they tend to start with factories. But when you enter a country, you also have to think about how to build an efficient network, otherwise you won't sell anything. In India, for instance, we had a manufacturing partner but no network, which explains our problems there. Moreover, networks are big investments. A dealership costs between €1 million and €5 million, meaning that if you are trying to cover a big territory and need 300 dealerships, you can spend as much as €1 billion. Hence the need to help investors make ends meet by achieving sufficient sales. Unlike Rolls Royce, Renault cannot sustain a dealership with just a few unit sales annually.

This is what we had in mind throughout the programme's expansion drive. We weren't trying to build a complete Entry range and develop it little-by-little. Our focus when attacking a market was to ascertain the best product that could use the Logan platform. This explains why Brazil was an important target. Renault's prospects here were fading despite the Scenic, plus at first the market didn't want the Logan sedan. This is why we designed the Sandero based on the Logan, which we also introduced. Now for instance, we have an 8% market share in Brazil, more than double in five years.

Similarly, the Duster was conceptualised starting in Russia. We clearly saw the global trend towards SUVs but the Renault group didn't have a product to satisfy demand in the emerging economies. Although these were very successful vehicles in Western Europe, for us at Renault they were little more than icing on the cake. Of course, the icing was very attractive, certainly as far as our two vehicles were concerned.

One of the central responsibilities of a programme management team is to control product definition. Saying that you are adapting to local markets does not mean completely delegating all "product" choices to national subsidiaries. Short-term and overly "retrospective" reasoning does not help us look to the future. The Entry programme invented new markets that didn't have any references to rely on at the time the decisions were made. A good example was the Logan in Brazil. At first, the market didn't have any sedans and local managers told us that they didn't want the Logan. So we brought out the Sandero and Logan together and noticed that Brazilians were also buying Logans. We resuscitated a market for sedans that didn't exist but which does now.

At birth the Logan was marginal project but as it broke through, how did your relations evolve with the rest of the Group? And how did you maintain the "Logan spirit"?

Within the programme team, I always paid a lot of attention to people I'd hired in my team. I often employed colleagues who I knew, who had strong technological competencies, were capable of deep analyse and understood the details of the decisions that had to be made. This played a big role in preserving the Entry programme's specific methodologies.

I always resisted homogenising with Renault's other programmes and businesses. For instance, I remember a time when we were supposed to define the substance of our brand identity. The questions were what a Renault should offer, what functionalities, what styling, what ingredients, what level of performance, etc. All programme directors attended these meetings. I was often the only person to say "no", I'm not doing it, it's too expensive. The programme could only thrive if it maintained, regardless of the implications, the appropriate ratio between costs and sellable performance.

Clearly, this caused arguments at the time. It still does today. For instance, some people say that a Logan sold in Russia as a Renault "is not a Renault". This is the kind of thing that headquarters also says when it forgets national variations. A Russian Renault is not a Brazilian Renault which, in turn, is not a European Renault. To build an image in the country, I think they have to start by selling cars that customers know and are able to evaluate. The Entry programme helped at this level.

But you also have to know how to say no to short-term demands, differentiating between potentially lucrative demand and mere noise. You have to know how to ignore superficial media buzz. For an Entry vehicle, being behind the curve is not as dangerous as offering a feature that cannot be sold.

A basic principle in defining a car is how to maximise value at a particular sales point. Since the car cannot be sold at more than X, the only USPs[1] we should consider are ones that create the highest sales value, offering customers the highest level of service while remaining compatible with X.

---

1. Unique Selling Points.

Towards that end, there are two successive methods that we can use. The first is "deboning" which defines the zero version of the Entry corresponding to the level such that if we'd have if we took off or diminished a single feature, we could no longer sell the car. The second is "reconstruction", which consists of introducing USPs for each country along with specificities from the home country or else ones reflecting standards or geographical factors. This is how we managed the value created by each car.

In sum, a great deal of groundwork was done regarding what customers want or more precisely in terms of what you could sell them. We would then work on what kinds of recurring characteristics should be found across the range. Typically, for us, this started with size and reliability, all of which costs money. In terms of reliability, customers don't perceive this immediately but it means that we can offer them a three-year guarantee without it costing us too much.

As the programme succeeded, did the Company start to view it as a textbook case?

Not sufficiently. I spent a lot of time and energy trying to formalise our processes, specifically our "design to cost" methods. For a while, I was in charge of a project that consisted of structuring specific Entry methodologies (see above) and defining what we should do to target a specific car price. I tried to popularise this and come up with a mathematical translation of what I'd done for my own purposes. I gave a lot of lectures and ran workshops. Unfortunately, this didn't really convince people, or not enough.

Why?

Resistance is quite normal. Actually, we were lucky to have been the only programme that could say "no" from the beginning. People reacted by thinking that if we could do this, so should they. I had the right to liberate myself from certain Renault constraints. This meant that others had the right to not learn from our example if they so desired.

On the other hand, what did work was the way we let the programme's founders spread across the Group. It is the destiny of any group with the particularity of being a provider and transmitter of know-how that others will try to hire away members. Some people could import our methods, but this wasn't always possible when they found themselves in a conformist environment. After a while, people get tired.

And the future of the Entry programme?

With the Lodgy and the small utility vehicle that is coming out soon, we are already witnessing a second generation for the Entry programme. If we consider the interior and more generally the perceived quality and content, there has been a visible break with the past, something that we also find with the new Logan. We are introducing functionalities that have been on other cars for several years, including automatic navigation and speed limitations. There are also automatic windshield wipers and lights. All of this has been done on a low cost basis. The end result is that we cut these functionalities' costs by a factor of three or four, and sometimes more.

We have also applied the same reasoning for the Lodgy as for the Duster, by asking what new development was likely to generate the most additional volume. At the same time, this product was a real challenge, if only because models of this kind are starting to be dominated and replaced worldwide by SUVs. This is more of a European project (and even a French one) that has been regressing more than it has been progressing, that is, unless our price point stops (and even reverses) this trend and enables the product to find new outlets. We have limited this risk, however, by ensuring that 80% of the car's design is shared with the utility vehicle that will be coming out soon. The combined numbers for both products are a lot more impressive.

And beyond the Entry?

This is a programme that I am currently developing based on the idea of making a small car with a very different price point, which radicalises the whole approach. Even more than with the Entry, we have to make a choice here. We need to take advantage of the great things that we achieved with the Logan, which consisted of considering what should go into a car and what doesn't need to be there. This really was the number one question for us and being able to answer it is precious know-how.

In conclusion, we would like to ask again why all of this has not been treated as a textbook case by the rest of Renault or the competition, and whether this might still change?

Regarding Renault, I remain optimistic and believe that this will happen. For the others, to be honest, the later this happens the better it is for us!

I think the explanation is that many people believe (or have believed) the sterilising argument that low price equals low margins. Renault's Entry programme has shown that this is not true. Yet it seems to me that many people are still wondering whether it is worth developing an Entry range.

One day they won't be asking this anymore. They will think that cars should always go upscale and add new features. Because in my view, this is a huge mistake. The story of the Logan shows that the opposite is true.

Interview with Bernard Jullien and Christophe Midler.

SECTION III

LESSONS AND QUESTIONS ABOUT AN EPIC ADVENTURE

This third section revisits the main lessons taken from–and questions associated with–the Logan's epic adventure. This happens on two levels.

Firstly, the Logan symbolised *"low end disruption"* for Renault, using Christensen's sense of this term,[1] meaning a kind of innovation that unsettles a market's structured organisation and the of competition associated with this by offering consumers products and services featuring the same basic attributes but sold at a radically lower price–an approach that end up unveiling previously unsuspected demand. The archetype is low-cost airliners, whose emergence have caused a reshuffling in the air transport market over the past 30 years, with certain former leaders even disappearing from the scene. These kinds of "disruptive innovations" are generally driven by new entrants, with established firms focusing on product and technology improvements and maintaining their stabilised representation of the market–an approach that, in terms of organisations and routines, restricts their ability to design something radically different.

---

1. Clayton M. Christensen, *The Innovator's Dilemma: when new technologies cause great firms to fail*, Boston, Massachusetts, USA, Harvard Bfactoriess School Press, 1997.
    Clayton M. Christensen, *The Innovator's Solution: creating and sustaining successful growth*, Boston, Massachusetts, USA, Harvard Bfactoriess Press, 2003

The crux at this level is to determine if and how Renault was able to overcome the difficulties that an established company will face when it contests the prevailing industrial model and produces "disruptive innovation". This case study is useful because it analyses the conditions in which such a strategy emerged at Renault and also because it elucidates the lineage dynamic that allowed its implementation and producing the ensuing benefits, which were not certain at first.

In turn, this leads to a broader question, namely what comes next. This includes whether Renault–by broadly disseminating its Entry experience– is likely to become a disruptive company contesting the automotive industry's currently dominant design, embodied by German manufacturers. Note that Christensen and two of his colleagues actually dreamt of their strategy being adopted by General Motors in China.[1] Otherwise, it might be more realistic to assume that Renault will likely break the Entry (and electric vehicle) product line down into variants as diverse as traditional ranges are, following approaches that will ensure the specificity of these dynamics while perpetuating savings through reciprocal learning. A final question is how competitors will react to this new market opening process, and what the consequences will be for the dynamics of Renault's Entry programme.

This brings us to a second level of analysis highlighting the more global dynamic of the modern automotive industry in the face of societal changes and the ensuing need for transportation. It is clear that Ford–which, in the early 20th century, became the first company to view automotive mobility no longer as a peripheral luxury reserved for affluent customers alone but as a product focused on the priority needs of a mass customer base that was expanding rapidly in line with changes in American capitalist society at the time, epitomised by the glorious adventure of the Ford Model T.[2] Disruptive innovation, as introduced by Henry Ford, had a big impact on the automotive industry: by making it enter an era of mass production; and, on a societal level, by driving the transition towards what some call the "consumer society" and others Fordism.[3] It is unclear today whether we are

---

1. Clayton Christensen, Thomas Craig and Stuart Hart, "The Great Disruption", *Foreign Affairs*, March-April 2001, p.92
2. Jean-Pierre Bardou, Jean-Jacques Chanaron, Patrick Fridenson and James M. Laux, *La révolution automobile*, Albin Michel, Paris, 1977.
3. Michel Aglietta, Crises et régulation du capitalisme. L'expérience des Etats-Unis, Calmann-Lévy, Paris, 1976.

facing another mutation of this magnitude–or how to tie together the different trends at work in our "new age of mobility", to reuse the subtitle of a book by Georges Amar.[1]

It is by exploring these visions of global industrial competitiveness–as well as the place that automotive mobility occupies within society–that Chapter 6 will conclude this book. This will involve demonstrating the extent to which the approach used with the Logan broke with a dominant design that focused on top-of-the-range vehicles and mobilised sophisticated (or "sustaining", to use Christensen's terminology) innovations. The purpose was to extend and deepen ongoing technological trajectories by targeting affluent buyers both attracted by the new services on offer and willing to pay for expensive technology. Subsequently, the innovations would progressively diffuse downscale (into the midrange and then into bottom-of-the-range small cars) following a banalisation of these technologies and as a result of the cost-cutting that occurred thanks to the shift towards mass production. One perfect illustration of this shift from the top to the bottom-of-the-range, sometimes referred to as a new variant of "*trickle down*" economics, was the decision to equip these cars with all kinds of electronics (ABS, ESP, GPS).[2] Within this design approach, automakers found it advantageous to position themselves with top-of-the-range cars (in the so-called "premium" segment) because it helped them to master these processes and was conducive to the upscaling or "premiumisation" that was considered the best way of succeeding in this industry. By using disruptive innovation to upset the status quo, the Logan helped people to perceive and defend an alternative automotive economics that might be described as "*trickle up*", one whose virtues would justify structuring a political and institutional context capable of increasing the number of paths available for exploring the sustainability of the automobile in general, and of the European automotive industry in particular.

---

1. Georges Amar, Homo mobilis, le nouvel âge de la mobilité. Eloge de la reliance, FYP editions, Limoges, 2010.
2. The expression "trickle down economics" has been associated in the United States with a neo-liberal vision of supply-side economics ('Reaganomics'). The theory promised that reducing taxes and other social charges (hence social expenditure) weighing on the wealthiest households would "free up" wealth and generate direct spending, creating positive effects for the poor. Reproducing an idea suggested by Alain Lipietz in *La Société en sablier* (La Découverte, Paris, 1995) to broaden this concept to include all of society, the present text adheres to this vision of the positive externality of wealth being moved from the wealthiest (top-of-the-range) to the poorest (bottom-of-the-range).

5

MANAGING DISRUPTIVE LINEAGES WITHIN THE AUTOMOTIVE INDUSTRY

The notion of "dominant design" was developed by Abernathy and Utterback in a study that had also focused on the automotive industry.[1] Academics have portrayed this as the archetypically progressive stabilisation of a maturity phase, in line with the upheavals witnessed during the late 19th and early 20th centuries. This does not mean that there is no longer any room for innovation–but the idea now is that whatever happens is to some extent pre-programmed by current learning. As is often the case, the real world has shown–quite spectacularly since the 1990s–the limits of this theory, with the concepts of "de-maturing" and "intensive innovation" arising in economic and management literature[2] to explain clear contradictions with the theory that sectors stabilise progressively. One of the main challenges facing the automotive industry today is how to manage innovative activity in a mature and very capital-intensive industry.

The question then becomes whether the Logan should be considered innovative. Some observers disputed this when the car first came out, considering it out-of-date in comparison with the rivals on display at trade fairs in 2004. Full of electronics and various features, they embodied a traditional vision of innovation as a process increasing products'

---

1. William Abernathy and James. M. Utterback, "A dynamic model of process and product innovation", *Omega*, 1975, pp. 639-56. Chapel V., *La croissance par l'innovation intensive, de la dynamique d'apprentissage à la révélation d'un modèle industriel, le cas Tefal*, Phd Dissertation in Engineering and Management, Ecole des Mines (Paris), 1997. Benghozi, Charue, Midler, *Innovation Based Competition and Design Systems Dynamics*. the Harmattan, 2000. Hatchuel A. and Le Masson P., "Innovation répétée et croissance de la firme: microéconomie et gestion des fonctions de conception", *Cahier du CGS* No. 18, 2001, Paris.
   William J. Abernathy: The Productivity Dilemma. Roadblock to Innovation in the Automobile Industry, The John Hopkins Press, 1978.
2. William J. Abernathy, Alan M. Kantrow and Kim B. Clark, *Industrial Renaissance: producing a competitive future for America*. New York: Basic Books, 1983.

sophistication by adding continuously and cumulatively to existing products' performance.

Clearly this was not an entirely inaccurate vision. It could even be quite dominant in the automotive world, where almost all engineering and design teams tended to use it as a guiding principle. In this view, a "sustaining" (cf Christensen, op. cit.) kind of sophistication of innovation occurs against the backdrop of a stabilised benchmark. Christensen has demonstrated to what extent mature companies excel in this respect. Internally, the sophistication of innovation places great value on accumulating expertise in strong and long established businesses, injecting a sense of progress into design centres and marketing departments, encapsulated in the use of different metrics to evaluate and compare solutions. Externally, on the other hand, the focus is on satisfying those customers who are the most interesting commercially, i.e. who already own existing products and would naturally want to replace them with others featuring superior performance and functionalities.

Christensen contrasts the sophistication of innovation with "disruptive" innovation, which breaks with the logic of always doing "more of the same thing better" and accepts the need to question certain long-established standards of "progress" to emphasize different ones. This generally involves significantly reducing sales prices and promoting simpler products by determining that certain kinds of performance are superfluous and abandoning them. The idea is that these kinds of innovations target customers and markets that mature companies have generally ignored, probably because they consider them too small and not lucrative enough. But it also demonstrates that these are generally the markets holding the greatest promise for the future, involving as they do young people and countries embarked on a rapid development path. In addition, exploring their values paves the way for the kinds of breakthroughs enabling subsequent attacks on more traditional sophisticated products.[1]

In this sense, the first lesson from the Logan project was to demonstrate the importance of (and conditions for) implementing disruption strategies.

Our analysis has shown how it was possible in a company like Renault to develop and conduct a €5,000 car project of this kind. The originality lay in the fact that this is an established company undertaking low end

---

1. For analysis of different axes of innovation in the automotive business, cf. *Réenchanter l'industrie par l'innovation; stratégie et management de l'innovation dans l'industrie automobile*, Christophe Midler, Remy Maniak and Romain Beaume, Dunod, Paris, 2012.

disruptive innovation. As pointed out by Christensen, generally it is new entrants that follow this approach, one example being air travel. Established companies are likelier to realise what they might lose through disruptive innovation rather than what they can win. The question then becomes what a mature company like Renault gains by developing a product that is so different from the automotive values of the Company's professional engineers or business people.

The second lesson from the second section is the importance of lineage management.

Using a notion formulated by Chapel[1] (1997) and Hatchuel and Weil[2], lineage management strategy is no longer driven by innovation grounded in successful but isolated projects. Instead, the crux is the ability to build a sustainable trajectory of successive innovations introduced by repeatedly changing the identity of the products, markets or technologies involved. In addition, innovation studies have often highlighted clever one-off projects that transcend the status quo when they first come out. Yet in today's competitive environment, an isolated innovative gesture–however heroic it is–cannot ensure a firm's long-term competitiveness. This is because it can be copied quickly and even overtaken by the competition. Instead, what counts is the ability to repeat this innovative rupture (an oxymoron, since by definition breaking with the past means not reproducing what came before) in a way that ensures long-term success. Clearly, this repetition must occur under conditions of economic efficiency, based on a learning economy that maximises the re-use of whatever technological, industrial and commercial knowledge was developed during previous actions. It is the kind of capacity that can be found today, for instance, in Tefal's spectacular success with household appliances[3] or Apple's success with mobility accessories.

The Entry line's deployment might be described as a classic example of lineage management. If the Logan project ended up a "winner", this was because it extended and amplified initial success with a surprising range of projects that ensured the Entry programme's ultimate success. This was a

---

1. Chapel V., *La croissance par l'innovation intensive, de la dynamique d'apprentissage à la révélation d'un modèle industriel, le cas Tefal*, PhD in Engineering and Management dissertation, Ecole des Mines de Paris, 1997.
2. Le Masson P., Weil B., Hatchuel A., *Strategic management of Design and Innovation* Cambridge university Press.
3. Chapel, op. cit.

multi-pillar long-term learning process associating ongoing changes in markets and products with the rationalisation of industrial processes and the continuity of learning as a strategic focus. It also involved the ability to maintain meaning and preserve the principles underlying various updating actions reflecting market contexts, products specificities and regulatory opportunities.

At this point, it would be useful to revisit the organisational levers that seemed so decisive in this ability to organise an effective management of the Entry lineage.

EMERGENCE AND MANAGEMENT OF A DISRUPTIVE LINEAGE

Key role of the Managing Director

Giving credit where it is due, the obvious first lesson when analysing the Logan's epic journey is, as Chapter 2 demonstrated, the extent of senior management's investment in disruption strategies, to both kickstart the adventure and sustain it in the face of the deep-seated scepticism that it was bound to provoke. Similarly, senior management was also crucial in agreeing compromises (like having the Logan carry the Renault brand name in Russia) and in reversing decisions (like the one to bring the programme back to France), all of which–unsurprisingly–created a trajectory full of good and bad fortune.

There is an obvious parallel with another quantum leap that Renault is currently attempting with electric vehicles, an effort that its President launched and has continued to drive. Analysis at this level goes well beyond this one company, however, with authors such as R.A. Burgelman[1] describing these forms of strategic management as initiatives that senior management actually select and steer on a ex post facto basis.

---

1. R.A. Burgelman, Strategy is Destiny: How Strategy-Making Shapes a Company's Future, The Free Press, 2002.

Programme management teams and "real live" intrapreneurship

It remains that senior management's ability to take action necessarily goes beyond ad hoc (albeit powerful and indispensable) impulses and expressions of support. In complex organisations like automaker companies, permanent structures are needed to relay and "thicken" strategic directions and turn them into adapted and concrete modalities of action. This is particularly important when the practices in question clearly break with established processes and traditions.

Chapter 2 showed the importance of structuring powerful project management teams to engineer an initial break. The book's second section showed how programme functions became a key lever in piloting the Entry line's long-term expansion. The history of the project clarified with ingredients were indispensable to this capacity for action. They included a broad perimeter of responsibilities–ranging from design to sales–deployed over the long run (unlike project functions that cease when the commercial work begins); as well as significant autonomy expanding the scope of the project. Similarly, some ingredients were indispensable for the exercise of this responsibility. One was having an identity that was geographic (the X90 platform), hierarchical and therefore social in nature. Another was the existence of a global contract (the only–albeit significant–constraint at this level being the relationship between sales price and profitability) organising, within the Company, a free choice of compromises between different parameters affecting the overall equation. Respondents all highlighted the crucial nature of these ingredients, as well as the importance of contextualising Renault's success in overcoming this daunting challenge at the time it did this. In the words of Jean-Marie Hurtiger, a key protagonist, "This was an era when we are still talking about a golden age of project management. Since then, we have gone backwards. The Logan would not have succeeded with the organisation set up in 2005."

What this shows was the difference between an intrapreneurship function and heavyweight project management, with the former not only incorporating product but also the management of a differentiated range comprised of successive generations deployed across a variety of markets. The success of the Renault's epic journey as described in this book was specifically based on the ability to maintain its identity within a dynamic that increasingly strayed from the hypotheses underlying the initial programme. Maintaining or above all constructing/reconstructing this identity (the "Logan rules of excellence") in a trajectory as changeable as this one was implied a constitution, sharing and transmission–despite changes in personnel–of what leading project figures called the "Logan's spirit" and everyone else its culture.

This culture was particularly difficult to maintain over the long run due to the fact that it transgressed the existing norms that had created the identity of the Company and its different businesses. "Breaking the rules" cropped up frequently in our interviews as one "Logan rule of excellence".[1] Lean management, total quality, modularity, partnerships with major suppliers, the search for maximum safety–all of these approaches would be scrutinised if they did not help to meet programme priorities.

All of which raises questions as to the best way of characterising the lineage management that was implemented so successfully during the Logan's epic adventure.

The Logan platform, a concept generating disruptive lineage

Lineage management has been defined as a coordinated twofold expansion of knowledge (about markets or technologies) and products, in a bid to maximise continuous learning. The starting point is the dual nature of this expansion and the "generating concept"[2] underlying the lineage, one that defines its meaning without necessarily constraining it or setting limits. The "DNA" of the initial Entry project resided in the vehicle's technical identity, an original compromise bringing simplicity, robustness and habitability together with bargain basement prices. The same can be said about the approaches associated with the original design ("the Logan spirit"). The Logan's platform, a child of the Entry line's approach, also enabled (and even stimulated) a variegated kind of learning without any loss in coherence.

The rules guiding this programme extension were as follows:

- Permanent and systematic exploration of new market opportunities. The programme did not stop with the first success. Even as it would exploit markets successfully, it still tried to build new ones, as reflected in the Programme Director's comment that he never had any time to lose. The

---

1. Cf. Peters T. and Waterman R., *Le Prix de l'Excellence*, Dunod, 2004.
2. Le Masson P., Weil B., Hatchuel A., *Strategic management of Design and Innovation* Cambridge University Press.

goal here was to constantly explore potential new countries, even when they were not an initial target market for the programme's.

- Identification of specific values to be highlighted in the new market–with the variant's specific Unique Selling Points coming on top of the platform's generic competitive advantages.
- Guiding new product design in a way that creates value only in these target areas. Continuing to cut costs on other features that should be the "bare minimum". Clearly, there was a direct relationship at this level between the sums invested in the vehicle and the arguments that sales staff (or the advertising campaign) could use. All of the car's costs were sold, something unlike "normal" cars, as Chapter 6 will discuss.
- Systematic pooling of technical learning, procurement, etc. for all programme products and factories, to maintain standardisation effects and simplicity.
- Speed of execution when developing these variants to benefit from the effects of trends or temporary regulatory actions played out on a global chessboard.
- Fast and flexible industrial investments to test new markets' robustness. This kind of ongoing foraging was bound to encounter a number of surprises. The Logan's epic journey demonstrated to what extent expansion is characterised by initiatives falling short of their goals, and by strategic reversals taking advantage of unforeseen opportunities.
- Opportunistic, ex post facto use of the programme's successes to take advantage of the kinds of often unforeseen circumstances characterising the global markets. For instance, a vehicle designed for Russia sold like hotcakes in Europe and generated substantial margins there. Hence the programme's emphasis on manufacturing facilities' production ratios.

It is worth highlighting the originality of this lineage logic, based both on the specificity is of its initial "generative" concept and on the organisation ensuring subsequent deployment.

The Logan's starting concept had great potential–given its exploration of new markets and originality compared to the existing range–for technical learning. Its option value was clearly superior to what was achievable through the renewal of a traditional model, whose advantages and limitations would be easier to identify.

Yet it would also be wrong to view the whole of the Logan's epic journey as something pre-programmed in the project's DNA. What was required was an ex post facto management of the project's initial deployment, one implying unforeseen expansion drives and significant revisions, maintaining all the while a coherent "spirit". Over the course of its long history, Renault has often been at the origin of innovative automotive mobility concepts. The product lines that came out of these efforts were not always as portentous as the Entry turned out to be.

In turn, this casts a spotlight on the conditions enabling a management of this sort. On one hand, there were the opportunities associated with initial concepts whose utility resided more in their expansion potential than in any input they had in the short term. Generally (and as happened with the Logan and electric car projects), intuitive and wilful senior managers were behind the process. A number of current CRG research projects are trying to define methodologies enabling an a priori evaluation of the potentialities associated with innovation concepts. At the same time, it is also crucial to ascertain what kinds of organisations can construct and maintain such learning trajectories over the long run, ensuring that these potentialities translate into concrete outcomes. The organisation and management of the Entry project might well be viewed as a model down the road.

Innovation's new geographic trajectories

One of the conditions enabling the successful implementation of this sort of lineage management was clearly the originality of its geographic deployment. The traditional trajectory of an innovation moves from its country of origin to a somewhat exotic peripheral country. Product specialists and engineers working out of headquarters design products for customers they know, with journalists writing about them for newspapers they read. This is done for obvious practical reasons but often also reflects the ethnocentrism characterising established companies. As a former automotive industry marketing director said in the 1980s, "The president would never have accepted a model whose style did not work for his wife or children." Within the aforementioned "dominant design" concept, a company's sociological and cultural identity is crucial. Examples include the "big Americans" of the 1950s, the "German quality" of later decades, etc.

For quite some time, automotive companies' already long-standing globalisation did nothing to significantly alter the idea of a trajectory spreading out from a group's historic central headquarters to the edges of its sales territories. Today, however, this vision is out-of-date. The entire geography of innovation must be rethought.[1]

The history of the Logan project reveals a trajectory that is much more globalised and torturous. Having been intended for Romania where it would not have bothered anyone, the Logan changed its look and embarked for Brazil, before returning to Western Europe and France, following which it emigrated to Russia wearing a badge that had been previously prohibited. At each stage, the project would materialise further, choosing a battleground that was favourable to it, learning things and gaining strength, accumulating the wherewithal to overcome situations that would have been unsurmountable during its initial emergence phase. Breaking with the past, however incongruous this might have appeared at first, became inevitable.

Innovating "on the edges of the empire"; using the world as a gigantic learning space to nurture revolutionary innovations without being exposed to headquarters' dominant "creaticide" forces; and taking full advantage of favourable circumstances found in local contexts–these were the key lessons learnt from a Logan project that also corroborated the intuitions of several recent researchers[2], starting with Prahalad[3], Christensen[4] and G.A. Moore[5], who often focused on the automotive industry.[6] The geographic deployment of the Entry programme fit particularly well with Moore's bowling alley metaphor, in that the programme was trying to steadily build up key local markets that would give it legitimacy and help it learn, if only from its errors (Romania, Brazil, India). Yet at each step, it continued to envision the possibility of deploying more globally. This could involve reacting to

---

1. Yannick Lung, "Repenser la dimension géographique des trajectoires d'innovation", forthcoming in Christophe Bouneau and Yannick Lung (coord.), *Les trajectoires de l'innovation: espaces et dynamiques de la complexité (XIXe-XXIe s.)*, Peter Lang, Bern, Berlin, Brussels, Frankfurt, New York, Oxford, Vienna, 2012.

2. The term "reverse innovation" is often used to describe such trajectoires, translating the normally ethnocentric attitudes of large industrial groups originating from the older industrialised countries.

3. Prahalad C.K., 2002 "Strategies for the Bottom of the Economic Pyramid: India as a Source of Innovation", *Reflections,* Vol. 3, No. 4, pp. 6-14.

4. Christensen C.M., Bower J.K., "Disruptive Technologies: Catching the Wave", *Harvard Business Review,* 1995.

5. Moore, Geoffrey, *Crossing the Chasm: Marketing and Selling High-Tech Products to Mainstream Customers,* New York N.Y., Harper Bfactoriess, 1991.

6. Jean-Bernard Layan, "L'innovation péricentrale dans l'industrie automobile: une gestion territoriale du risque de résistance au changement ", *Flux,* No. 63-64, 2006, pp. 49-53

"tornadoes" with a quick redeployment towards initially unexpected targets; changing scale; or adapting relational modalities to new market circumstances.

There is also an easy parallel to make here with Renault's other quantum leap forward, namely the electric car, which the Company might test drive in Israel. The logic that applies here is one that might be difficult to find in contemporary marketing classes. Yet it involves the same new strategy of following a sinuous but opportunistic and cautious innovation trajectory, seeking favourable breeding grounds at the edge of an industrial empire that remains the preserve of a dominant design concept.[1]

This is an important lesson in innovative geography at a time when the Western world is worried about possible de-industrialisation and the role that large globalised groups might play in this process. What is clear is that although the Renault Group had been running commercial and industrial operations on a global scale long before the 1980s, it would have been unable to conceive and above all implement these kinds of globalised innovation trajectories. Innovating via globalisation surely constitutes one of the main lessons that the automotive industry has learnt during the 21st century. Undeniably, this has opened up new possibilities, one example being the electric vehicles, the eternal loser of the unfair fight against the internal combustion engine design that, quite symptomatically, continues to dominate the more mature markets. Failing to seize global opportunities for more ecological cars means giving other companies–like Chinese manufacturers?–the time and opportunity to gain a lead that will be hard to claw back later on. Yet there is also another lesson at this level, one undermining the reassuring theory that regardless of headwinds, innovation always goes from the older industrialised countries towards rest of the world instead of the other way around.

---

1. C. Midler, R. Beaume: "Project-based Learning Patterns for Dominant Design Renewal: The Case of Electric Vehicle", *International Journal of Project Management*, No. 28, 2010, pp 142–150, F. Charue-Duboc, C. Midler, "Lorsque les enjeux environnementaux donnent lieu à des innovations stratégiques: comment piloter ces trajectoires exploratoires? Le cas de la stratégie véhicule électrique de Renault, *Revue Française de Gestion*, July 2011.

Brand management as the condition for affirming a specific identity

Another key factor helping the Entry line to expand was its association with the (re)construction of a new brand, Dacia. It was not too difficult transgressing home country business rules in exotic foreign countries, or if the volumes involved were confidential. Clearly, the Entry line's return to Europe's traditional mass markets would have become much harder if not impossible to achieve had the Renault brand name been used. Inter-brand differentiation also played a key calming role at this level, endowing the programme entity with salutary autonomy.

FROM "BUSINESS TO CUSTOMER" TO "BUSINESS TO SOCIETY"

In the end, one of the lessons learnt from the growth of the Entry line was the fact that the very concept of market demand–as it tends to be envisioned in B-to-C consumer goods companies–can be broadened. The Logan's irresistible rise entailed more than a clever anticipation of end users' needs. The sociological school of innovation, led by Madeleine Akrich, Michel Callon and Bruno Latour,[1] has revealed the limitations of asymmetric analytical schemes differentiating between providers "that innovate" and a public "that resists or adopts" an innovation. This model can be enhanced by the more symmetrical construct of alliances to highlight the wide variety of social actors contributing to the success of the Entry programme. The Romanian government, for instance, helped by supporting the reconversion of the Pitesti site and resisting open competition policies coming out of Brussels. It also sparked initial domestic sales of the Logan by levying taxes on import rivals' sales price. Also worth mentioning were the Iranian authorities, who for internal policy reasons, blocked the deployment of a programme that clearly satisfied demands expressed by a whole segment of the population. Then there was the change in Brazilian monetary policy, shaking up a whole scenario that had been based on manufacturing for export out of Mexico and creating an opportunity to produce for domestic sales. Lastly, there were the powerful multi-brand distribution networks found in Russia or Brazil, whose support had to be earned by creating products that end users would want because they carried the Renault badge.

---

1. M. Akrich, M. Callon, B. Latour, "A quoi tient le succès des innovations ?", *Gérer et comprendre*, Vol. 97, June 1988, September 1988, pp. 4-17, 14-29.

Management literature has long spoken scathingly about "engineers' products" and advised readers to "heed the customer". Analysis of the Logan programme's expansion argues in favour of a more sophisticated understanding. If this epic adventure could occur, it was because protagonists had, from the very outset, integrated into their strategy and practices the idea that a new product—once it is being rolled out on the same scale as an automobile—no longer targets customer users alone but a complex and multiform "customer system" incorporating heterogeneous components that can be large/small, material/social or private/public in nature. The actors in our story were able to mobilise, in Romania for instance, parties ranging from the Minister for Industry to trade unionists or the owners of the crumbling garages that dot an Eastern Europe characterised by potholes and extreme climate conditions. Indeed, the programme's "made in France" aspect explains why the French narrative ended up disputing its overall success.

The Entry programme was managed as a kind of prototype for the "Business to Society" leadership that has also been witnessed in other Renault product lines. One clear example of this has been electric cars, where a close link exists between private individuals' mobility needs and local urbanisation measures, without forgetting environmental protection or energy policies.

HOW WILL COMPETITORS REACT?

Competitors' possible responses need to be analysed beyond the Entry line's manifest success. "Disruption" strategies imply that battlegrounds are areas that dominant rivals have overlooked. By the same token, successful strategies attract competition to the markets they create. The automotive industry has many stories of companies that caught up more or less successfully and quickly with rivals. For instance, the R5—an innovative concept created in 1972—only lost its leadership in the B segment when enthusiasm rose for the GTI (Golf GTI in 1976 and 205 GTI in 1983). For average size minivans, the response was particularly rapid, with three years elapsing between the first Scenic (sold in 1996) and the Xsara Picasso, launched in 1999.

Competitors' reaction to the Logan remains today—eight years after it was first launched in Romania—quite underwhelming, with PSA once again having postponed the project until spring 2012, after agreeing an alliance with General Motors.

There are two explanations. On a strategic level, this was a time when manufacturers like VW or PSA were early mobilising diametrically opposed strategies developing, for instance, premium product lines (the Audi for VW or the DS for PSA). Between implementing a strategy and the basically unavoidable development of less polluting modes of transportation, there was almost no room to spare for fighting over the Entry.

At the design level, the genetic specificity of Renault's Entry range (and the sophistication of processes that led to this) becomes clear. Reacting rapidly to market success meant cloning a new body onto an existing platform. Rivals had no chance to attack the Logan in this way, unless they were willing to lose a lot of money. Yet gaining market share in a not very lucrative niche suffering from a mediocre image seemed scarcely justifiable. If traditional cars' declination into variants does not draw much of a response, the received wisdom is that this is just as unlikely to happen with new entrants copying successful approaches in countries characterised by low labour costs. A good example here was the Tata Nano. Contrary to popular belief, it is hard designing an economic car to be both high quality and profitable. The chapters focusing on this "impossible challenge" demonstrated the complexity of such an exercise. Much design intelligence is needed to know how to spend money when such expenditures are supposed to be "the bare minimum" and maximise a company's ability to leverage customers' perception of value. Subtle engineering and hard work is needed to reconcile something that appears at first as quite contradictory: adapting to local markets while standardising components; internationalising production while maintaining quality standards; and global sourcing while increasing local content ratios. All of this is supposed to sustain a collective competency that creates a differentiating asset which can be hard to appropriate quickly. Thus, contrary to certain often heard narratives, developing disruptive products does not mean subjecting oneself to emerging global competitors. Instead, it means orienting differently a design competency that has already become quite advanced.

The final chapter revisits this point by demonstrating that the Logan's success hobbled dominant thinking in European industrial strategy by presenting product sophistication and advanced technology as the only effective arms for competing with emerging rivals.

MANAGING THE DIFFERENTIATION-INTEGRATION DILEMMA IN A MULTI-PRODUCT LINE FIRM

For a global company like Renault, the big question is its ability to achieve a lasting integration of product line identities that are both differentiated and durable. It is doubtful that Renault can abandon the "sustaining" strategy it pursues with its traditional ranges. Indeed, this confrontation understandably caused big arguments in the Company. If the Renault Group had become overly focused on the Entry line's success and lost its status as a generalist group to become an entry-level manufacturer, the failure of its global strategy would have been self-evident–especially because the Company, like its rivals, had been pursuing other disruptive strategies alongside of this, including the development of a electric vehicle programme, a new and major original product line requiring significant management. The question here was how to manage the differentiation/ integration dilemma, to reproduce academic terminology formulated by Lawrence and Lorsch.[1] Today, this concept of innovation has been upgraded following research into areas like design management[2] and ambidextrous companies,[3] all of which is extremely important in today's context where intensive innovation comprises only one aspect of Western companies' competitiveness prospects. In practice, this is an issue that other companies have already dealt with quite successfully, starting with Apple, capable of generating and managing lines as different as Macs, iPod, iPhones and iPads while organising their mutual dependencies and minimising their inexorable cannibalisation.

Several issues have yet to be resolved relating to what kind of learning is possible between the different product lines and whether the Entry's integration requires a redefinition of Renault's strategic identity.

---

1. Lawrence P., Lorsch J., "Differentiation and Integration in Complex Organizations", *Administrative Science Quarterly*, No. 12, 1967, pp. 1-30.
2. Le Masson P., Weil B. Hatchuel A., *Les processus d'innovation – Conception innovante et croissance des entreprises*, Hermès, Paris, 2006.
3. O'Reilly III C,, Tushman M. 2004. The Ambidextrous Organization. *Harvard Business Review*(62): pp. 74-82. Ben Mahmoud-Jouini S., Charue-Duboc, F. and Fourcade F., "Favoriser l'innovation radicale dans une entreprise multidivisionnelle: Extension du modèle ambidextre à partir de l'analyse d'un cas", *Finance Contrôle Stratégie*, Vol. 10, No. 3, pp 5-41.

Inter-product line learning

Despite being defined by its clear break with existing traditions, the Entry line's development required resources that already existed within the Company. The overall savings achieved by managing the Company on a product line basis resided in a maximum sharing of assets created within each line. Above and beyond consistent financial returns, this raises the question of how the rest of Renault benefited from the Logan's success. There appear to be a multitude of responses.

This inter-product line learning transits through three channels. Firstly, there was the pooling of the assets that the Entry line had created. The deep-seated meaning of the programme was, to rephrase Gerard Detourbet, the exploration of new markets and construction of foundations enabling industrial and commercial investments conducive to the subsequent development of group brands worldwide, specifically in those zones where Renault had no presence. Then came the transfer of procedures with which the programme had experimented successfully, using them in turn to develop other procedures. Lastly, there was the dispersion of individuals who left the Entry programme to apply their experience on other missions.

Although it is too early to measure the reality of this kind of inter-product line learning, we can try. Gerard Detourbet did say in his interview how hard this can be, given that the programme's very existence depended on its marginal status, meaning that it always relied on its specificity to combat solutions and approaches shared by other programmes. It would be illogical to expect the Logan to be considered a model by programmes that it had refused to resemble.

Design approaches

The know-how built on the back of successive Entry range projects' success was a great source of learning that helped the whole of the range, in both technical and procurement terms (the Logan's "carry over" onto other programmes). One big opportunity to transfer these competencies was created with the plan to simultaneously renew the Logan and Clio (Clio 4) platforms by 2013-14. Whereas the former is still governed by the principle of doing the "bare minimum", the latter must offer superior features creating value for buyers. Negotiating with suppliers simultaneously–notably about unseen components–is a chance to set prices at exactly the right level. The appointment of the Entry range's former Director for

Procurement, Philippe Cayette, to the position of Deputy Programme Director (Clio 4) created a situation where knowledge gained on the Logan project could be transferred elsewhere.

Relationships with suppliers

Supplier relationship management was clearly the learning aspect that was most likely to spread from the Entry experiment to the rest of the Group, given its significance within the project. The Logan's international deployment to low-cost countries enabled in-depth knowledge of local industrial fabrics. Irrespective of the effectiveness of firms' evaluation procedures, there was little information to garner from purchasing managers' missions of seeking suppliers in these countries. The development of daily interpersonal relations within a production activity framework densified the Company's social networks and helped create better quality knowledge. This global supplier shortlist helped Renault to cut procurement costs, notably in India. Thanks to the Logan project's goal of controlling and reducing costs–dominated by external supplies (80% of the vehicle's value)–the purchasing function was able to better assess what it really costs to source inputs from outside the Company. Procurement professionals often cooperated with suppliers to seek original cost-cutting solutions, revealing their ability to produce at much lower costs than the industry generally expected. For some components like dashboards, prices were cut by half or more (compared to an equivalent component on the Mégane) without significant loss in customers' perceived quality. On this occasion, project development induced Renault to bring certain components' production back in-house, because internal production costs might be lower than outside suppliers'. This also resuscitated lost competencies. One notable example was seats production, brought inhouse in Russia and Morocco, whereas received wisdom in the automotive industry was that this should be externalised to a global leader (Lear, JCI, Faurecia or Delphi). The reversal of the outsourcing trend was one of the most original lessons drawn from the Logan project's deployment.

Sharing industrial assets

The Entry programme enabled solid new industrial foundations in countries where Renault had no strong presence (Romania, Russia, Morocco, etc.). Its capacities for producing traditional products may have been close to saturation but in time–and given the standards of quality and performance it has established–Renault should be able to develop production bases for other models.

On a commercial level

The Entry programme made a significant commercial contribution in various ways. Firstly, a new asset was created–Dacia, whose image was thoroughly renewed. For Renault's networks, this was not only an opportunity to learn to work on a multi-brand basis with the same manufacturer but also to experiment with other sales methods. The fact of not having to "push" a product (via discounts or exchanges) to sell it was something no other brand had let dealers do before. Similarly, for Renault the Dacia brand's development was a very strong incentive to better its own brand identification by re-examining "best practice". Given the opportunity with this range to minimise "marketing expenses" considered normal elsewhere, people finally had a chance to study such costs and ask how necessary they really were in other areas.

Entry sales volumes helped create national networks that enjoy a good reputation today and could be interested in distributing other products supplementing and diversifying their current product offers. In Russia or Brazil, markets where distribution is highly concentrated and done on a multi-brand basis, the Logan and its product lines became powerful tools for convincing "mega-dealers" that adding Renault to their portfolios–even if this meant dropping other brands–could be a good strategic decision. The crux at this level was the product and its suitability to local demand. The fact of not having to distribute overly broad ranges comprised of products or variants that the manufacturer imposed–and which the distributor considered difficult to sell–was just as important. Stocks of Entry models were easy to carry because they were relatively homogeneous and therefore turned over quickly. Distributors felt that Renault understood both them and their customers. Even if they were less well rewarded than by other carmakers, they became allies of Renault's commercial development. The assets built up with the help of the Entry line then became available to the remainder of the Renault range.

Cooperative arrangements with partners

Since Renault's failure to acquire Volvo, the Company had systematic reflected on how it might manage cooperative agreements with other manufacturers or partners. A deeper analysis of this failure induced Renault to become more effective at managing its relationship with Nissan, a company in which it held a 34% equity stake but no overall control. The explicit idea now was to develop an alliance.[1] The same approach would apply to the management of AvtoVAZ or the cooperation with Daimler. Similarly, the Group made sure to respect the specificities of the companies that had become its de facto subsidiaries, including Samsung and Dacia. The idea was to derive value from the competencies of companies acquired to reinforce the whole of the Group.

Asides from the exemplary case of Dacia, the Logan's international deployment was a chance to agree partnerships within diversified configurations to establish different production structures. This involved two state sector companies in Iran; a municipality (Moscow) and an automaker (AvtoVAZ) in Russia; and two local firms in India (M&M and Bajaj). All of these new experiences caused singular problems, but their failings enhanced Renault's overall learning.

THE CINDERELLA OF THE RENAULT GROUP?

Beyond its big contribution to Renault Group results and the learning associated with the Entry programme's many different technical aspects, there was still a question how Renault should incorporate this success story into its general narrative.

Analysis of Renault press releases and international advertisements shows how embarrassed the Company was with this spectacular success. It preferring talking about the electric vehicle programme, a great innovation but one that has yet to materialise.

---

1. Blanche Segrestin, "Towards new governance structure for merging organizations? Lessons derived from the Renault-Nissan Alliance", *International Journal of Automotive Technology and Management*, Vol. 6, No. 2, 2006, pp. 199-213.

Table 5.1–Importance of Zero Emission initiative in Renault Nissan Alliance communications

Number of Renault-Nissan Alliance press releases	2006	2007	2008	2009	2010
Electric vehicles			11	23	30
Other topics	4	3	9	5	5

Source: Renault Nissan Alliance press releases.

Several factors explain this circumspection. The first probably relates to the programme's general savings focus. Having frugal communications was redolent of the approach prevailing in other programme areas. Remember that the Entry programme's marketing expenses were half as high as the brand average. The cars were selling, meaning that the only pressure was factories' ability to satisfy demand. The question then became why spend so much on advertising communications when all of the other corporate functions were being constantly asked to make sacrifices.

The second aspect was Dacia's role in the Renault Group. The Logan project and its product line symbolised renewal and dynamism for the Dacia brand. The Entry programme's assimilation with Renault, on the other hand, was always perceived as a major risk for the Group's eponymous brand. We have already seen the problems that Renault faced with the Logan in Russia. A decision reflecting temporary economic pressure from powerful Russian distribution networks clearly ran counter to the positioning strategy that the Group was pursuing with its other young brand portfolios.

The communications strategy had been constant since the late 1990s, despite all of the problems faced over this time. The Renault brand has been trying to reconquer a strong image of continuity but experienced problems at the top-of-the-range. The global crisis over this period also reinforced the "sandglass effect", hitting the middle-of-the-range.

Faced with rivals' communications praising the traditional values of a premium product offer, Renault decided to emphasize its difference without being too explicit ("drive the change"). In part, this reflected the difficulties with slogans specifying the kinds of value proposals that customers everywhere tend to like.

From this perspective, advertisements for the Duster–which mocked some peoples' efforts to achieve social status by paying over the odds–was an exceptional communications strategy for both the brand and the whole of the European automotive industry. The communications challenge was not to present Entry vehicle purchases as a constraint (the customer would like to buy another product but cannot afford to) but as a positive choice based on the fundamental values of an individual's capacities and freedom from the symbols of social differentiation that are so often associated with automobiles. Instead, the emphasis here was on people's ability to budget their automobile purchase rationally. This explains the communication's emphasis on the marginal population of customers that had already bought Dacias despite income levels allowing them to buy other new models had they wished. This customer base of "clever buyers" was presented as "lead users" with whom others might wish to identify. The approach was highly critical of traditional car marketing (promoting a vehicle with the basic argument that you cannot buy another). It became a "trend" in its own right, emphasising the quality of a product offer and praising purchasers for their nous.

It is clear that the Group's complicated relationship with its predominant but minority shareholder–the French State–impeded publicity for the Entry model. Given France's ongoing employment focus, people were never going to be happy about increased investment abroad; French engineering's centre of gravity being shifted to Romania; or the greater number of cars being re-imported into Western Europe (especially France).

All of which caused an interesting reversal for the Entry line. Many observers started with the view that the project was a risky financial bet. In the end, however, backing from Renault's President was based more on a globalised economic and social vision than on profit maximisation. Ultimately, the product line was very profitable and useful. But it was an ugly sister and as in the Cinderella story, nobody liked talking about it.

CONCLUSION: RECIPROCAL LINKS BETWEEN STRATEGY AND INNOVATION

Ultimately, the Logan was an emblematic case revealing the complex relationships that existed between the Company's innovation and strategy processes.

At the beginning, everything resembled the way things are generally spelt out in strategy books. The innovative process was born out of an explicit strategic formulation dating from the 1990s, which Schweitzer had broken down into four chapters:

- A global production volume target of 4 million units by 2010. Since the 1980s, Renault's annual world sales had fluctuated between 1.5 and 2 million vehicles. At the time, a significant jump forward seemed indispensable to ensure the firm's long-term survival.
- Market targets. Given the saturation of the more mature markets and Renault's competitive position in them, the lion's share of future growth would have to be in the emerging world, led by Eastern Europe and Asia.
- A product strategy of attacking markets not from top-down but "at the centre", thanks to modern products adapted to the mobility needs and rising purchasing power of emerging economies' burgeoning social classes. Hence the necessity of innovative projects reflecting the fact that Renault–like its competitors–did not have any cars adapted to such markets, if only because its general strategy at the time was to derive products from cars designed for European markets.
- The scale of Renault's operations had to be doubled through alliances. This was because there was no hope of increasing the firm's production capacities or developing new commercial networks through its own efforts alone.

Things quickly became much more complex, however. There were recurring surprises forcing a number of reversals and renunciations, caused both by global strategic shocks and innovation's unpredictable dynamic.

For the Company as a whole, the concrete strategic actions that had materialised during the late 1990s in the form of plan 2010 reflected, as is generally the case, unexpected opportunities. These included the failed alliance with Volvo, the acquisition of Dacia and Samsung and the alliance with Nissan–all operations that occurred in 1997 and 1998. Although Renault had premeditated the general framework and scope of these actions, the moves it actually took on the global automotive chessboard were full of surprises that were big enough to have a significant effect on the innovative project's trajectory, in terms of both opportunities and constraints. A prime example was the most spectacular of all Renault's strategies, namely its alliance with Nissan. In terms of opportunities, it is clear how the Entry programme's move into Central America and South Africa benefited from synergies with Nissan's need for greater capacities. In constraint terms, there was the "Yalta" arrangement between Renault and

Nissan, which had previously impeded programme deployment in China. This was clearly a major obstacle to development, one that is hard to understand from the perspective of the Entry programme alone.

The unexpected scale of the Logan's success totally upset initial deployment plans, which had been based on the clear complementarity between the range and its markets. Renault was supposed to attack Western European markets with strong and sophisticated products; Dacia would then hit emerging markets with more basic products. There were many surprises at this level. In product policy terms, the range would soon be enriched with products like the Sandero or Duster, which was particularly strong. In market terms, Dacia had huge success in France and Europe satisfying customers' demand for basic mobility products (whereas Entry vehicles were generally sold in the emerging markets as part of a more uprange product mix). Dacia also succeeded with its very responsive reaction to regulatory opportunities (with versions like the GPL in Germany). Alongside of this, the Renault range had been struggling after failing in a bid to reorient the top-of-the-range around very original products like the Avantime or VelSatis. The midrange was becoming banal and competitors were starting to take a lead in niches that Renault had invented a few years previous (with, for instance, the C4 Picasso unseating the Scenic). Globally, the 2009 crisis[1] was a very difficult period for the Group, and although Entry product sales continued to skyrocket, it was hard to maintain overall performance statistics (see figure below). Yet despite the positive effects on the Group treasury, the Dacia products' success cast a shadow over Renault's other products. Something perceived within the programme dynamic as a strength and success would be analysed by experts as a sign of the Renault Group's weakness.

1. Bernard Jullien and Yannick Lung, *L'Automobile à la croisée des chemins,* La Documentation Française, Paris, 2011.

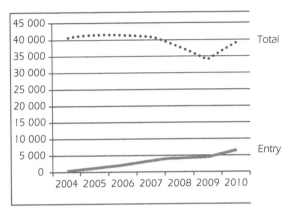

Source : notre recherche

Figure 5.1a–Estimated changes in Group and Entry programme revenues, in € mio

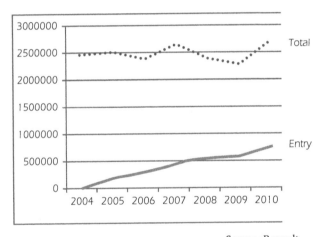

Source : Renault

Figure 5.1b–Changes in vehicle volumes, sold by Renault Group and by the Entry programme, in number of vehicles

This chapter began with questions about the more or less innovative nature of the Logan. The conclusion is that this was an emblematic example of Schumpeter's "creative destruction". It succeeded in relaunching a growth dynamic but also destroyed existing hierarchies and equilibria. This resulted in Renault having to reformulate–because of the Entry and around the Entry–its strategies, positionings and identities.

6

QUESTIONING THE DOMINANT DESIGN
IN THE AUTOMOTIVE INDUSTRY

Chapter 5 analysed the success of the Entry programme (epitomising a disruptive product line) and the breakthrough of the Sandero and Duster in both mature and leading emerging markets such as Brazil and Russia. The fact is that eight years after the Logan was launched commercially, it has not had to face any real competition. Even within the Renault Group or the Alliance, there is a certain sense of marginality if not discretion about this undeniable success story. In other words (and in line with our original focus), it is not at all certain that it will become a "model" for the industry, despite possessing—more than most sustaining innovations that Renault, Nissan or their rivals have tried to generate from one model to the next—the characteristics of significant and profitable innovation.

This is somewhat surprising in light of the automotive industry's capacity (or incapacity) to renew itself. For Christensen and other economists writing about technological change in the wake of Abernathy and Utterback's seminal research in this field, industrial firms as a whole can only benefit to a limited extent from innovations and market opportunities, or the profits they generate. According to this thesis, industrial development often mirrors cycles associated with major innovations characterised by a succession of expansion and contraction phases, with the latter reflecting an exhaustion of innovations' potential and calling for the advent of new ones.[1]

"Evolutionist" writers—led by Giovanni Dosi[2]—have suggested a "technological paradigms" construct to account for major innovations in

1. Jullien B., "Relativiser le statut de la rupture dans la théorie évolutionniste", *in* Baslé M., Delorme R., Lemoigne·J.L., Paulré B., *Approches évolutionnistes de la firme et de l'industrie*, L'Harmattan, Paris, 1999, pp. 207-228.
2. Dosi G., "Technological Paradigms and Technological Trajectories, A suggested interpretation of the determinants and directions of technical change", *Research Policy*, Volume: 11, Issue: 3, Publisher: Edward Elgar, 1982, pp. 147-162.

an industry. In this representation, companies (each in their own way) have cause to perceive and exploit the potentialities associated with innovation. To benefit from this shared potential, they follow–by innovating and accumulating learning–specific "technological trajectories" that differentiate them from one another along technical and commercial lines. Having said that, to be effective, innovative activities must be relatively focused. This leads to a progressive rarefication of opportunities and decreasing returns from the innovation. The paradigm ultimately runs out of steam.

In today's automotive industry, these limitations can be seen in the way that rising costs necessarily result from the "always more of the same" approach that Christensen deems characteristic of sustaining innovations. Engaging in this kind of innovation becomes possible only if it is reserved for customers characterised by the greatest willingness to pay. One consequence is an increasingly problematic abandonment of "basic" customers who are either no longer able to access innovations or are only offered them once lead users have been served first. The different ways that dominant paradigms or models of innovation are being exhausted imply an industry crisis calling for a new kind of Schumpeterian creative destruction. Dosi has spoken of new explorations[1] and the emergence of "pre-paradigmatic phases" where industries seek "new paradigms". It is at this level that companies prosper. Generally, these are new entrants who, according to Christensen, introduce disruptive innovations that "de-saturate" the market by redefining what kind of product offer is relevant and the sum total of characteristics structuring its pricing.

By interpreting things thusly, the automotive industry would appear to have been in crisis at the time the Logan line was being deployed. For many reasons, the automotive paradigm (and its ability to offer sustainable paths for national companies and industries' development) was already being exhausted even before the Logan was launched. It then entered an obvious crisis four years after the Entry programme hit the market.[2] Although the Logan and its product line appeared excellent anti-crisis tools, the automotive industry "exited" the 2008-2009 crisis without significantly revising its conceptions or practices. This explains the success of the Logan

---

1. March J.G., « Exploration and exploitation in organisational learning », *Organisation Science*, Vol. 2, No. 1, 1991, pp.71-96.
2. Bernard Jullien, Yannick Lung, *L'Automobile à la croisée des chemins*, Paris, La Documentation française, 2011.

as a counter-model, with competitors remaining deaf to the strategic suggestions that often come on the heels of this kind of success. In the end, there is no guarantee that people benefited from it as much as they could have.

This chapter focuses on these surprising outcomes by discussing this new battle between David (the Logan) and Goliath (the dominant paradigm), and the shape it has recently assumed. Everyone seems convinced now that salvation can only be achieved through upscaling. Yet as demonstrated by the success of the Logan and many other indicators, neither the automobile's crisis in the mature markets nor the challenges laid down by the emerging markets (or even the demands of sustainability) seem to argue in favour of the dominant paradigm—or its contemporary avatar, "premiumisation"— being considered the only way forward. Quite the contrary, the Logan's example suggests the usefulness of opening up new possible spaces and enhancing the exploration of new paths.

To feed this interpretation, we start with the obvious exhaustion of the paradigm in question, followed by a discussion of how people started to focus on the top-of-the-range, considering it both the best way out of the crisis and an inspiration for public policy. Lastly, we show how the Logan and its lineage can offer credible alternatives to today's "monolithic thinking".

EXHAUSTION OF THE TRADITIONAL AUTOMOTIVE PARADIGM

The crisis that the automotive industry faced in the large developing countries in 2008-2009 broadly reflected significant over-capacities that had long been identified and whose unsustainable nature was revealed by the magnitude of the fall in sales. In certain cases (USA, United Kingdom, Spain), there was a phenomenal collapse due to the fact that demand levels had long been inflated because of easy credit (particularly, mortgage lending), which made it possible to sustain demand without distributing purchasing power.[1] In other cases, it was limited by support policies like "wreckage bonuses" that implied a major downscaling effect for customers as well as a big fall in sales once these measures ran out of steam.

---

1. B. Jetin et M. Freyssenet, "Conséquence de la crise financière ou crise d'une forme de capitalisme: la faillite des Big Three", *Revue de la Régulation*, No. 9, 2011.

In the United States, the adjustment involved a massive destruction of capacities through the closure of many of the Big 3's industrial sites, with Chrysler and General Motors almost going bankrupt in 2009. In Europe, such closures were extremely rare even if many companies saw a reduction in capacities. It remains that significant over-capacity continued after the crisis, causing a price war that was very damaging to the profitability of automakers (especially generalists) once demand started to weaken in 2Q 2011.

This analysis—widely accepted by manufacturers, analysts and public authorities alike (particularly in Europe)—was tantamount to considering that the level of demand witnessed after the crisis peaked represented a return to normal levels. With 13.5 million units sold in Europe in 2011, estimates of over-capacities ranged between three and thirteen million vehicles, depending on whether the observer considered that the assembly sites in question should "normally" run two or three shifts. The idea was also that the European, North American and Japanese markets were all saturated—meaning that it was a lost cause to seek profitability in these parts of the work without any seriously cutting capacities and costs or delocalising all entry-level vehicles to countries featuring lower wage costs.

People were forgetting far too quickly that between 2000 and 2005, many studies had predicted that the American market would reach 18 million units by 2015, with the European market hitting the 20 million mark. They also forgot that Europe's fleet was getting older and that more and more households were satisfying their automotive needs with used cars.

As the automobile historian Jean-Louis Loubet noted in 1995,[1] this sense of a saturated automotive market was already very widespread in France (and particularly at Renault and Peugeot) in the 1930s. At the time, the demonstration had been made that problems were caused by the unavailability of affordable new cars, with market saturation in the automotive sector broadly depending on the split between new and used car purchases, reflecting public policy and manufacturers' product policies. All available indicators show that without anybody really noticing the difference, this split has changed markedly over the past 20 years.

In France, four emblematic indicators covering the period 1990-2010 illustrate this:

---

1. Jean-Louis Loubet, 1995, *Citroën, Peugeot, Renault et les autres. Soixante ans de stratégies.* Paris, Le Monde-Éditions, 1995, 637 p.

- Car ownership rose by seven points (from 76 to 83%), as did the number of households with two cars. The total fleet of passenger cars under the age of 15 varied between 29.5 mio and 35.5 mio;
- The fleet's average age rose from 5.9 to 8 years;
- The average period of ownership rose from 3.7 to 5 years;
- The proportion of households that bought used cars rose from 50 to 60%.

This was an era when household purchases fell from 1.83 to 1.2 million passenger cars (or 0.8 for fleet purchases). Manufacturers and networks' customers began accounting for an increasingly narrow and aging minority of all car owning households. Indeed, this was an accelerating trend due to the devastating effect–in France at least–of higher new car prices, accentuated by competition from other, non-automotive household spending items, such as property, eating out and telecommunications (Figure 6.1).

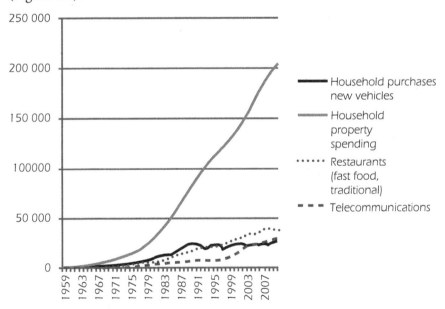

Figure 6.1–Breakdown of household spending between property, eating out and telecommunications in France

This resulted in a big shift in the structure of automotive spending, creating a situation where operational expenditures totally outweighed vehicle acquisition costs (see chart below).

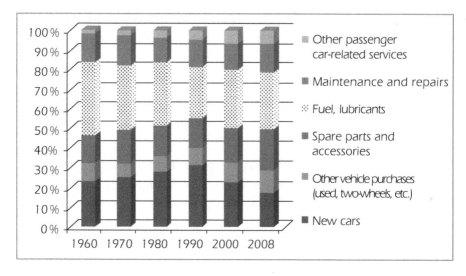

Other passenger car-related services

Maintenance and repairs

Fuel, lubricants

Spare parts and accessories

Other vehicle purchases (used, two-wheels, etc.)

New cars

Source : INSEE.

Figure 6.2–Changing structure of driving expenditures in France (1960-2009) (in %)

Manufacturers responded to these changes through sustaining innovations that tried to accelerate perceived product obsolescence and gain market share. As a result, customers seemed to be more and more demanding. After all, they were fewer in number now; meaning that each would be courted more strenuously. Managers deduced that they should develop increasingly extensive product ranges and renew them more frequently, using innovation and sophistication to attract customers to each new generation.

Since the willingness to pay for this kind of technological or functional sophistication was continually decreasing, objective improvements in the features on offer did not imply an extra willingness to pay, other than by consumers from the most affluent households. This meant that the few consumers who were susceptible to the new narrative became a Holy Grail, with the quest assuming the form of a proliferation of product launches attempting (usually in vain) to attract the remaining customers' attention. These launches were like SOS signals sent out by an industry that was losing its way. Having noticed that consumers were allocating an ever smaller percentage of their budgets to automotive purchases, manufacturers tried to take what they could from those who were still likely to be interested in their goods.

The exhaustion of this paradigm seems therefore to have resulted from a form of market saturation that tended to view the automobile as a normal (and even inferior) good. Manufacturers responded collectively to this saturation effect by competing more fiercely. This amplified the phenomenon, however, instead of making it more manageable. Economists might analyse this as a classic case of "no bridge", one where everyone participates in a game without noticing that this collective phenomenon is in fact helpful to everyone.

One effective way of describing the competitive dynamic, when envisioned thusly, is the construct of "excess quality",[1] linked to the relatively widespread view that customers have become increasingly demanding. If excess quality means offering potential customers new or improved product characteristics[2]–features that are likely to gain a modicum of support but for which people are willing to pay little if anything–this would mean that improvements in product quality require efforts hence costs that are increasingly difficult to offset via price hikes and/or extra volumes. It would also imply that because of competition, vehicles become increasingly varied and are renewed more often, making it harder to make a profit from them. In this case, lowering total costs becomes what games theorists call a dominant strategy, i.e. the best one even if (as shown by the famous "prisoner's dilemma") everyone loses if everyone behaves in this way. In the automotive business, no one appears capable of escaping the need to diversify their product ranges and renew them more often. Towards this end, each participant knocks on to the value chain any and all of the costs and risks generated thusly. Nobody is able to differentiate their product offer significantly and/or sustainably. Everyone must manage a number of bad surprises and very few good ones. Nobody dares to take the risk of undermining this dynamic, but everybody hopes to become the best at carrying it out by becoming leaner, more flexible, purchasing better, delocalising better and consolidating better.

---

1. The reference to excess quality in the automotive business was inspired by John Wormald who interpreted this, however, in somewhat different terms. See Maxton G. and Wormald J., *Time for a Model Change: Re-engineering the Global Automotive Industry*, Cambridge University Press, Cambridge, 2004.
2. Product characteristics and/or their definition as vectors of characteristics are key concepts in the differentiation-based economic analysis proposed in Lancaster K.., "Socially Optimal Product Differentiation", *The American Economic Review*, Vol. 65, No. 4, Sep. 1975, pp. 567 of 567-585.

Once people start upping their bids for technologies and services, the only way forward becomes products that are more expensive and substantial, yet whose retail prices can only go up by a minimum amount. There is a very strong premium on premium goods, given the decreasing differential in volumes between different brands, and between top-, mid- and bottom-of-the-range models. Similarly, the willingness to pay associated with each of these categories continues to vary. From the second half of the 1990s through the mid-2000s, almost all manufacturers worldwide displayed a desire to maintain and/or develop a presence in the top-of-the-range. Lexus, Infiniti or Genesis for Toyota, Nissan or Hyundai; Ford's acquisition of Jaguar, Land Rover, Volvo or Aston Martin (grouped together with Lincoln and Mercury in the Premier Automotive Group between 1999 and 2008); GM's acquisition of Saab; VW's development of Audi or acquisition of Bentley, Lamborghini and Bugatti, not to mention its close relations with Porsche (or the launch of the Phaeton, its electric car); Fiat's efforts to relaunch the Lancia as a premium brand; Renault's attempt to reconquer the market for vehicles priced at more than €27,000 (specified in the 2006 Ghosn plan); or PSA's launch of the C6 and its building of a "top-of-the-range vehicle" competitiveness centre in Rennes, followed by the extension of its DS range. Everyone was singing from the same sheet, talking about the need to have a premium product. A few groups did this and were portrayed as big winners. Most did poorly.

Above and beyond the manufacturers, motorists were offered vehicles by a system that was only interested in a small proportion of the population and would let the others express themselves on the largely self-organised used car market This was where renewal needs became the adjustment variable in most households' automotive budgets. For a growing percentage of households, the automotive consumption system (being able to drive) was managed as a costly social obligation,[1] with people trying to reduce the cost by only paying what was unavoidable (to wit, utilisation costs, starting with fuel) and focusing only then on discretionary variables such as vehicle purchases.

In short, where it might be possible to imagine that—given more or less satisfactory ownership levels—the supply of automobiles would henceforth

---

1. Froud J., Haslam C., Johal S., Jullien B. et Williams K., "Les dépenses de motorisation comme facteur d'accentuation des inégalités et comme frein au développement des entreprises automobiles: une comparaison franco-anglaise", in G. Dupuy et F. Bost, *L'Automobile et son monde*. Editions de l'Aube, 2000, Paris, pp. 75-96.

be geared towards enabling households to spend proportionately less in this area while gaining something in quality terms, what happened instead was a curious phenomenon in which automotive budgetary coefficients tended to stay the same even as most households' cars got older, shifting their spending from acquisition to utilisation costs. Vehicles improved because the "social" benefit derived from this behaviour diffused much more slowly and much less widely than would have been the case had the offer of new vehicles been more in sync with what most households could and wanted to spend in this area. Attempts to reduce emissions or improve road safety were tantamount, from this perspective, to measures requiring households to own vehicles satisfying both points of view. As noted in many arguments about carbon taxes or low emission zones, such measures are deemed problematic today. This is because they mainly hit the more fragile populations, or the owners of the oldest vehicles, whose lifespans are often extended—making it harder for them to satisfy increasingly rigorous carbon or particulate emission standards. In turn, this stigmatises the poor's automotive behaviour.

THE FOUNDATIONS OF "PREMIUMISATION", VIEWED AS A "ONE BEST WAY"

This competitive interaction occurred in a context characterised in many developed countries by growing disparities in income and assets. The situation was de facto beneficial to specialist manufacturers but also to the Volkswagen Group who (together with Audi) disputed the specialists' domination in premium segments and benefited like they did from the specificities of the German market. In countries where mortgage lending was common practice, this auspicious context was amplified by the property bubble that occurred over this period of time. Once people's ability to borrow no longer reflected their disposable income but the increasing value of households' property assets, demand rose for automobiles, especially for premium vehicles due to an optimism sustained by bankers. The idea here was that households (even ones that did not earn much at work) could become rich by purchasing houses and reselling them to buy new ones. Spanish dealers selling German brands asserted that many households had, during this crazy era, added their Audi Q7s or BMW X5s to the sums they borrowed to acquire property assets, certain that these could not help but gain in value over the years to come.

German manufacturers benefited from this external context, much in the same way as Japanese manufacturers working in the United States during the 1980s took advantage of the second oil crisis. Both benefited in a way their competitors could not, due to people's disbelief, based on recent history, that the products in question might become less marginal in commercial terms. Without their having to do much, the Germans' market share and profits grew very quickly in Europe. Daimler and BMW, for instance, each added 3 to 6 points in EU market share between 1990 and 2005. Since the American market experienced (for similar reasons) an analogous evolution helping the same German manufacturers (plus more recent premium brands like the Toyota Lexus or the Nissan Infiniti)–and because the "nouveaux riches " in Chine or Russia very much wanted the same products–the trend was interpreted as being structural in nature. Financial analysts, who mainly focused on corporate profits, rapidly equated a company's presence in the top-of-the-range with the be-all and end-all of an industry. Managers working for leading manufacturers were happy to adhere to a vision whose new priorities bolstered the love many already felt for automobiles.

Hence the advent within the automotive industry over the past 20 years or so of what modern economic sociologists call a new "conception of control" (in Fligstein's sense of the term).[1] The conception dominating the automobile (above all in Europe) views the top-of-the-range as the factor that pre-determines and initiates the characteristics that all product ranges will adopt within a few years. Hence the need to be present in this segment– the willingness to spend money on (expensive) automobiles puts companies in direct contact with lead users by endowing their vehicles with new systems or traits that often diffuse later to all vehicles.

In the end, the whole of the industry began to focus on this one outcome:

- For generalists, profits on expensive cars would help to subsidise lower margins on smaller vehicles and, potentially, market share;

---

1. "Conception of control" is the term that Neil Fligstein used to analyse the industry and define rules structuring its productive sphere, viewed here in much the same way as Bourdieu saw social fields in general, meaning a kind of domination where the parties being dominated accept (often enthusiastically) a logic serving the dominant parties' interests. See N. Fligstein, *The Architecture of Markets: An Economic Sociology of Twenty First Century Capitalist Societies*, Princeton and Oxford: Princeton University Press, 2001, 274 pp.

- Reputations earned on "premium" vehicles affected the rest of the range and enabled, everything else remaining equal, higher prices than the competition could practice in mass segments;
- Suppliers were well remunerated for working with these manufacturers, benefiting temporarily from innovations they were asked to make or that they initiated;
- Customers hoped that premium vehicles' resale value would deteriorate more slowly. Reasoning in "total cost of ownership" terms,[1] they viewed ostensibly irrational choices as quite rational.

THE LIMITATIONS OF THE DOMINANT CONCEPTION

In global automotive geography terms, this conception implied that design tasks be run out of the developed countries that, more than others, featured a customer base apt to acquire enough high unit value products. The idea was that emerging economies' vocation was to host and potentially adapt technologies, products and platforms initially designed for and in the Global North. Thus, growth in the emerging economies' automotive markets and output would not threaten sectorial stability or the oligopoly by means of which this was structured.

This logic was rooted in a trickle-down automotive economy whose basic argument was that "doing more can doing less". The marketing version of this view saw innovative commodities as being irremediably expensive at first, hence reserved for consumers with the most purchasing power, the "safest taste" or the greatest aptitude for prescribing (i.e. lead users). It is only then that the demand for an innovation generalises, motivating investment and learning, benefiting from economies of scale and becoming accessible to the greatest number. The economic version of the trickle-down approach refers to the necessity, within a market economy, of allowing wealthy people to become even wealthier so the economy can prosper as a whole. Supply-side economists view this as defending entrepreneurial capitalism from egalitarian demands for an income redistribution that runs the risk of depriving corporate creators of necessary incentives. From the demand side, this is the idea that an economy also needs to discover the latent needs of its more affluent members as well as

---

1. TCO: Total Costs of Ownership (notably including utilisation costs, new car retail prices and resale values).

ways of satisfying them profitably, so they can be subsequently disseminated to the masses.[1]

Here we are giving trickle-down economics construct a specific industrial and automotive interpretation[2] inspired from Lipietz's *La Société en Sablier*,[3] which defends the idea that the 1990s were characterised by amplified business cycles explained by the replacement of blimp-like Fordian income distribution systems with more hourglass-shaped forms. The result was a rise in the number of households receiving both less and more than twice the median income. This comes with the idea that in this situation and given the "ideological circumstances" leading to it, the new consensus was that the only sure way of driving business was to get the wealthiest to consume more by making them even wealthier or by attracting, for instance via tax measures, these sated consumers' attention to whatever else that they might spend their money on. Thus, in a paragraph meaningfully entitled "getting the rich to consume", Lipietz wrote:

"The greater the concentration of wealth, the harder it becomes to convince people to consume. Yet in monolithic neo-liberal thinking, getting rich people to spend is the only thing that can reinvigorate production. Governments end up with the belief that it would be good for the rich to become even more richer so they can consume more, purchase a third car, hire servants and gardeners and go out for dinner. (...) In reality, the only focus is on the top half of the hourglass. They are ready to subsidise the hiring of servants and automobile purchases. They are willing to get rid of capital gains taxes on financial savings as long as these sums end up 'unsaved'" (1998, p. 45).

For a long time, the trickle-down model did not seem compatible with mass industry and Fordism. Experimenting with many innovations or new technologies at the top-of-the-range went together with the idea that the real test lay in the transition to mass products.

For many activities, the trajectory towards an "hourglass society" invalidated this diffusion and development model. Where the synchronic

---

1. In recent years, the press has often characterised "Obamanomics" as an attempt to create "trickle-up economics", in contrast to the trickle-down economics that have dominated since the times of Reagan.
2. As indicated in the introduction to this third section, the connotation is broader than the one customarily used to define trickle-down economics, focused solely on lowering taxes and social charges on society's wealthiest.
3. Alain Lipietz, *La Société en sablier*, La Découverte, Paris, 1995 rééd. En Poche en 1998.

or diachronic distances between the rich and poor are relatively small, trickle-down can be a socially feasible compromise. This is because the middle (and even poorer) classes join a society's enrichment model, meaning that they have a justifiable hope of being able to rise up the ranks within a reasonable period of time. This results in large "Chandlerian" companies managing portfolios of brands that each feature their own product ranges, so that the same organisation can see the coexistence of "premium" brands staging and initiating innovations alongside mass brands organising the diffusion thereof. Here, trickle-down becomes a rule that– via different logics of inter-firm competition and by managing brand portfolios and products from different brands–does a relatively good job of organising work. This was how things worked during the golden age of General Motors, with its "Sloanian" model. As Louis Schweitzer noted in his interview, GM's signature brand at the time was its basic brand, Chevrolet. For the Ford Motor Company, it was Ford.

On the other hand, when income distribution becomes more "competitive" in nature[1] and leads to the development of a form of dualisation–because income from work is being distributed more unequally and income from assets gains importance –the distance between the rich and poor increases synchronically, with the poor losing hope that they can access the wealth model. Here, trickle-down does not work very well, increasing the probability of dualised supply and demand for the same goods.

In the automotive business, it is possible to see the embodiment of this dynamic in the specific competitive system mentioned above. Unlike other sectors, the automotive industry can only address part of the population participating in the market for new cars. This was always the case, due to the existence of an alternative–used cars, allowing households to continue driving despite new cars' excessive prices. This has created a situation where the attributes of this general dynamic tend to produce specific repercussions, namely the absence of a dualised product offer. Many automakers found themselves restricted to increasingly narrow areas of commercial

---

1. In the "productive models" approach developed at the GERPISA research network by Robert Boyer and Michel Freyssenet (*Les modèles productifs*, La Découverte, Paris, 2000), manufacturers' ability to design suitable "product policies" depended on the fit with prevailing "modes of income distribution". Such modes would be called "competitive" when they were scarcely(if at all) regulated and translated into relatively major inequalities (therefore justifying, for example, the moniker of trickle-down economics).

opportunity limiting the space where they might diffuse their innovations to solvent customers. In the end, this meant that profits were sought from the outset at the top-of-the-range instead of during mass innovations' diffusion phases.[1]

The justification was the industry consensus that having a presence in such segments was the only thing making it possible to develop the image and pay the technological entry ticket needed to attract customers who—even for smaller and cheaper vehicles—would quickly express their desire for limited numbers of vehicles with similar characteristics. Convinced that this was the only way to go, the specialists built smaller cars. The big generalists, on the other hand, wanted their own brands and premium models because they wanted the trickle-down effect to play out.

The VW Group and its remarkable success with Audi embodied this strategy, which seemed to renew the traditional Sloanian strategy and adapt it to today's non-Fordian context. By disputing BMW and Mercedes's monopoly at the very top-of-the-range and benefiting from the associated profits and image, the Group ensured that Audi trickled down to VW and VW-Audi to Skoda. VW became the dominant group in Europe and beyond, enjoying (and nourishing) a conception of industry control that suited it to such an extent that challengers were economically and technologically forced to defend themselves. This domination can be partially explained by the Group's special access to a German market that offered, along relatively Fordian lines, strong foundations and a solid company governance compromise that it could use to build success. The three European generalists (Fiat, PSA and Renault) who lacked these advantages seemed forced to fight for scraps from VW's table. Specialist companies like BMW and Daimler shared a very large premium market with VW and defended together with it the made in Germany meta-brand, in much the same way as French luxury producers defend their national brand. Fiat, Renault and PSA could do little to avoid progressively being cast out from the upper, upper midrange (M2) and increasingly lower midrange (M1) segments.

Based on European sales of the main models produced by the five French and German carmakers over 2004-2009, we have devised a commercial domination indicator by comparing sales volume in Europe for the six

---

1. Jullien B., Pardi T., 2011, "In the name of consumer: the social construction of innovation in the European automobile industry and its political consequences", *European Review of Industrial Economics and Policy*, No. 3.

German brands[1] with the three French brands[2] for all models sold in Europe in the same segments. Where the indicator exceeds one, Germany dominated the statement, and vice versa. Thus, on the lower midrange segment, for instance, PSA and Renault were approximately selling as many vehicles in Europe in 2004 as VW, Audi, BMW and Daimler combined. By 2009, however, the Germans were selling two and a half times as many units as the French.

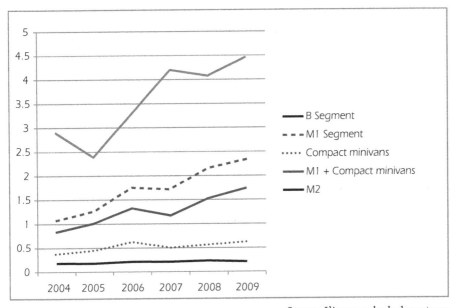

Source : L'Argus, calculs des auteurs

Figure 6.3–Shifting ratio of European sales
by German brands/French brands

Fiat was the first to experiment in a trajectory that, for a while at least, the two French groups thought they could escape. Today, they are increasingly restricted to the B1 and B2 segments and find it harder to defend the M1 segment where they still have advantages that they try to maintain via compact minivans and the different ranges they could develop along these lines. It remains that these relatively clear-cut indicators attest to French carmakers' eviction from different product ranges by their German counterparts. Trying to imitate VW and the German industry in its own backyard–and by so doing, defending a conception of industry control that

---

1. Audi, BMW, Mercedes, Mini, Smart and VW.
2. Citroen, Peugeot and Renault (excluding Dacia).

suits the Germans more than anyone else–has not necessarily been the best way to go for the French groups or for the automotive industry as a whole.

In fact, without this having been explicit in senior management's strategic narrative or developed through corporate strategy and/or state industrial policy, several alternatives have arisen, as witnessed by Renault's Logan or Entry range. These can be interpreted as conceptual innovations rooted in a form of tradition for Renault (i.e. minivan variants). They go beyond this, however, potentially conveying a counter-model for the development of an automotive product offer and/or for contesting the German conception of automotive industry control. Indeed, when the people responsible for building the Entry range were asked, they explicitly contrasted their quest for a "bare minimum" with vainglorious chatter about product quality. This lay the groundwork for a logic that was more or less diametrically opposed to the one that prevails customarily, with the maxim becoming that the party that "does the least does the most". The new development logic was based on a form of trickle-up economics whose contours and attractiveness merit further explanation.

THE LOGAN'S EPIC ADVENTURE: PREMISES FOR DEVELOPING A NEW MODEL?

The aforementioned alternative principle is based on the idea that people can alter their beliefs to develop cars that are equipped, at the very least, with what the competition offers, before focusing on regulatory and commercial requirements. The result has been changing specifications being communicated to engineering and/or purchasing departments, characterised by levels of demands generating very different price-performance compromises for "basic" versions. In turn, this has potentially created room for selling something more than the minimal features whose extra costs customers are willing to pay. It lets people control the creation of value via these features, instead of having to hypothesize that such value exists simply because everyone offers the same accessories. In turn, this made it possible to avoid the aforementioned excess quality syndrome. Companies no longer had to offer absolutely everything, because they were uncertain whether customers had the necessary willingness to pay. This reopened a space of opportunities that had been closed in the dominant paradigm. In addition to the benefits for the company initiating this approach, a number of economic, social and ecological virtues have justified its receiving political support.

During the "post-crisis" or "pseudo-post-crisis" period of 2010-2011, the prevailing conception of control did not dissipate but, quite the contrary, increased in power, even though it should have withered away because of the search for an automotive development logic rooted in economic, ecological and social sustainability. The threefold structure at play here revolved around growth in the emerging countries; new driving systems; and rationalisation/consolidation/concentration. The goal was to find ways of pursuing a trajectory first launched by Henry Ford, without making any fundamental changes either in the population of actors exerting influence, or in technology, or in terms of the automobile's positioning within different consumption and mobility systems. Contesting certain assumptions made in 2008-2009 when many managers deemed it impossible to exit the crisis in the same condition as the ones prevailing when it first erupted[1]–and when some were predicting a "second automobile revolution"[2]–global carmakers (led by VW) reaffirmed the domination of trickle-down automotive economics. Credible alternatives, such as the ones explored in this book, did not seem to have been taken particularly seriously.

This difficulty signifies that in an oligopolistic business like the automobile, there is no spontaneous possibility for "automotive systems" to open up and enable the exploration of sustainable new development paths, even when there is good cause for launching this kind of movement. Once sustainability problems have been identified and it became obvious that not dealing with them is damaging (something that applies particularly to the non-German parts of the European automotive business); and once it is clear that there is a high probability that strong states like China will enter the breach–it becomes politically essential (particularly in Europe) to open up fields of possibilities that competitive logic tends to close all the more powerfully due to the fact that they are sustained rather than destabilised by public policy.

Because analysis at this level varies depending on whether lessons are being drawn from the Logan's experience in the old automotive countries

---

1.   Pélata P., "L'avenir de l'auto se construit dans la crise", *Sociétal*, No. 70, 2010, pp. 39-47.
2.   Michel Freyssenet (dir.), *The Second Automobile Revolution. Trajectories of the World Carmakers in the 21ˢᵗ Century*, Palgrave-Macmillan, Basingstoke et New York, 2009; Bernard Jullien, "La seconde révolution automobile et ses contours", *Sociétal*, No. 70, 2010, pp. 54-61.

(especially Europe) or in the emerging world, we will study the conditions in which such changes can occur in both contexts.

Is the political promotion of disruption possible and desirable in Europe?

In the automotive business (particularly in France), a common complaint is that consumers do not love their car sufficiently; that they do not see it as a status symbol to the same extent as they used to; and that this undermines the competitiveness of the industry because people develop an overly rational and insufficiently emotional relationship with their cars. Whether such changes can be viewed as reasons for losing hope says a lot about the problems created by the trickle-down worldview. The perception here is that at least some of society is demanding cars that are less expensive and less polluting; more rational and discrete; thus less damaging and value-destroying. Hence the need to combat the status quo and put an end to fiscal, normative and enforcement attacks on the automobile, creating the conditions for universe that is more favourable to premium proposals. Automotive journalists, "automobile clubs" and financial analysts all converge around this point.

On the other hand (and far from the views of radical ecologists or road safety ayatollahs), certain financial and ecological constraints–along with the aforementioned competing expenditures–induce behaviours that lead to downscaling and to more and more people buying used cars. Unable to find an automotive product that they can fully endorse, households tinker around on the edges of the system that is currently recognised and promoted, opting for solutions that are relatively ineffective at addressing the constraints affecting their automotive spending or ecological problems. The few times (like the Logan and its lineage) where the offer was structured differently, demand would materialise and the profitability of the products in question would be assured. Key social and ecological questions would be dealt with more effectively.

As noted by J.-M. Normand, "For German manufacturers, there is no problem that cannot be resolved through technology. This faith seems unanimous. Unlike their French counterparts, the German Green Party is not reputed to be particularly in favour of anti-car measures or city centre driving restrictions."[1] What this means is that with very little disruption and in a way that is entirely coherent with the price positioning of a mix that is systematically superior to their challengers, German carmakers and suppliers are inclined to accept additional normative constraints on products whose characteristics and modes of utilisation they have no intention of fundamentally changing. They deal with this by adding technical features, solving safety problems with ABS, ESP, multiple airbags… all of which generally bulks up the cars question. If (as is the case today) drunk driving were criminalised, the response would consist of offering alcohol tests capable of stopping drivers from turning on the ignition if they are over the limit. Similarly, emissions have been reduced through the use of catalytic converters, improved engine efficiency or hybridation, rather than by reducing vehicles' size, weight, maximum speed or acceleration.

Similar to what happened with the Logan, one alternative (or at least a correction) would consist of showing that another path is socially and ecologically sustainable. This would involve attending to a greater proportion of these challenges by using environmental approaches and/or altering vehicles' authorised characteristics, thereby alleviating the demands and constraints weighing on the vehicles themselves. It would also accelerate improvements that are less tied to the perfecting of the vehicles than to their conditions of utilisation. In short, rather than forcing road users to coexist with purchasers of German cars by getting them to buy increasingly expensive cars (that people are only willing to buy used), there could be restrictions on speed, horsepower and wheelbases. By shifting new car standards closer to what most households are willing to pay, a space of different opportunities could open up.

Collectively, the main justification for this more balanced vision consists of asserting that the focus should not be on registering new cars that pollute or are accident-prone but on the sum total of cars on the road. If, for the

---

1. In an article entitled *Les allemands aiment leurs berlines* ("Germans like their sedans") published in Le Monde magazine on 3 March 2012 and enthusiastically reproduced by websites like "Automobiles Club", Jean-Michel Normand wrote: "Between France and Germany, figures reveal two very different relationships to the automobile today. On average, when the French buy a new car, they are willing to spend up to 45% percent of their annual income on the purchase. In Germany, the number is 55%, Here however, smaller cars (equivalent to the Renault Clio or Volkswagen Golf or below) only account for one-third of the market, against nearly half in France. Conversely, luxury models represent 8% of all sales in Germany vs. half as much in France."

aforementioned reasons, the existing fleet of automobiles expands and grows older, this means that "faith in technology" deserves to be mitigated by affordability concerns. In this view, it is clearly preferable that a household purchase a Sandero or a new Logan–even if it does not achieve a Euro 6 standard and has fewer Euro NCAP stars than the latest German sedan costing €42,000–instead of continuing to drive a 10 or 15-year-old car that is maintained to a very mediocre standard and will be replaced by another used car that is around five years old. More generally, if people want to "clean up the fleet" because they are doubly interested in better road safety and lower emissions, it is crucial that the vehicles currently on the road maintain, as long as people are driving them, the features that they were supposed to have at the outset. However, it is only politically and socially possible to implement this idea and transform it into constraints and controls if more vulnerable populations do not feel that it stigmatises them. Hence the need for affordable alternatives.

The rejuvenation and homogeneity that would result from cleaning up the current fleet constitute key factors that are at least as important as vehicles' technological improvement. Rejuvenating and (subsequently) maintaining a relatively young fleet can be a public policy objective at least as legitimate as the traditionally preferred approach of perfecting new vehicles. Certain choices will have to be made, but because people rarely go down this road, there is little probability of anything else being decided. Along these lines, what happens at Brussels when the EU defines different standards is relatively typical of the trickle-down economic conception of control. Convinced that manufacturers are only interested in maximising profits and minimising constraints, environmentalist and "road safety" lobbies tend to opt for a form of maximalism by using ABS, airbags and catalytic converters, or by implementing pedestrian guidelines. By so doing, they find "natural" allies amongst different suppliers and German manufacturers, resulting in normative European policy following a very trickle-down path that largely emphasizes sustaining innovations to the detriment of fields of opportunity open to partisans of more disruptive approaches.

In the case of the Logan, it was clearly the need to satisfy normative demands that, as we have seen, was the main if not only factor explaining higher manufacturing return costs. In more innovative projects like the one run in France's central Poitou Charentes region–whose president, Ségolène Royal, launched a 2008 tender for designing and manufacturing electric vehicles costing €5,000–the decision not to offer "electric cars" but "motor-powered quadricycles" instead was crucial to actors like Eco Mobilité, due to the fact that just authorising these kinds of "cars" meant a surcharge of €5,000. Similarly, it has been accurately said that if so-called "ultra low cost" vehicles like the Nano wanted to attack European markets, they would have to survive the gauntlet of these standards and retail at something closer to €5,000 rather than the €1,500 price tag found in India.

Clearly, this does not mean that it is absolutely necessary to abandon any and all normative demands and allow European consumers to drive all different kinds of vehicles, even ones lacking emission controls, safe braking systems or trustworthy road handling. This would lead to a loss of any control over externalities or the ability to structure industrial or research policies. Yet clearly, to open up a space of possibilities in the automotive world and contest the trickle-down trajectory, regulation must favour more than sustaining innovations alone. Disruptive innovations based on different price-performance compromises must also be encouraged and not dissuaded.

As one automobile executive said in an interview with La Tribune newspaper,[1] "The battle against CO^2 emissions will raise car prices more than ever before. In response, manufacturers must either go upscale or think up cheaper products. In any event, we find ourselves in a situation where people have less money and generally spend less on their car." The executive in question was V. Besson, Product Strategy and Markets Director at PSA, who was being asked about the strategic intentions underlying the C-Cactus (Concept Car) project that Citroen was developing. "Completely rethinking design and rationalising the number of parts and choices of materials as far as possible, what we are trying for is a compact car. Characterised by minimal production and utilisation costs, it needs to be very light, have little horsepower, minimise pollution yet run at a respectable speed."

The project was uncovered in 2011, despite the fact that people had been constantly talking about it since it was first introduced in 2007, when a 2013 launch was being envisioned. Clearly, the power of the upscaling narrative; PSA's successes with the DS3, 3008 and 5008; and the Group's difficulties in late 2011–all these trickle-down automobile economics kept the project on the back burner. After all, projects of this sort show that the

---

1. Verdevoye A.-G., Citroën veut ressusciter la 2CV , *La Tribune*, 8 March 2011.

trickle-up vision initiated with the Logan can benefit from a wide range of variants and enrich a business with the know-how and commercial traditions of many manufacturers, French and Italian in particular. To give shape to these intuitions and help trickle-up challenge trickle-down solutions in Europe, they need real support. This has to be political.

Disruption as a development strategy in the emerging markets

Tracing the Logan and its lineage's industrial and commercial history in the emerging markets, we have seen what an extraordinary tool of intercontinental development this became for Renault. It happened because the product was the most financially accessible for customers; technologically the most "appropriable" in terms of industrialists and local repair shops' know-how; but also because it took local demands seriously and did not impose a single way of looking at the automobile by letting manufacturers working out of a central design unit determine its characteristics.

Above and beyond the focus on meeting the specific needs of the Central and Eastern Europe markets for which the product had been originally imagined, the story of the Sandero in Brazil or of the Duster in Russia indicate that it was the construct of having a "bare minimum" that made it possible to integrate local industrial or commercial contexts in all of their variability (with the entire post-Logan engineering function having been redesigned specifically to enable such flexibility). In terms of principles, this meant that the "doing more can doing less" approach that companies often apply when dealing with customers is not only commercially unsuitable because it is too expensive but also has an "imperialist" dimension. Implicitly, Brazilian and Russian consumers are being told "we know better than you do what is good for you". Conversely, the "doing less means doing more" approach characterising the "bare minimum" credo is a way of allowing local teams to determine where the value (the "more") resides for a customer, without being affected by the formal or informal standards that European, American, Japanese or Korean engineering teams have interiorised.

The goal at this level is not only to engage in decontenting[1] practices to squeeze prices and/or satisfy local contents ratios, but also to empower actors who might then sense that the company behaving thusly is really interested in their market, and maybe even in their wage levels, instead of its own dictates. Once again, the "premiumism" that has been so powerful in large global manufacturers' strategies in China seems an easy solution benefiting from profitability if not sustainability. This is because premium vehicles sales by definition target the margins of the population for whom complying with European or American aesthetic or symbolic canons is a normal thing. This is the population that travels, exports and spontaneously equates driving car Americans or Germans' dream cars as a sign of success.

If disapproval of such attitudes were to intensify; if focusing growth on domestic demand were to become an imperative; if a certain redistribution of the benefits of these actions were to occur; and if a modicum of coherency with energy, regeneration or industrial and technological policies were to become a key focus for an increasingly accountable political class–in that case, manufacturers will only be able to embed themselves in the emerging economies affected by such trends by responding proactively to these legitimate demands. Brazil is about to force manufacturers already working in the country (or who want to move there) into this configuration. This would mean not only selling a few locally assembled Scenics but building up the Curitiba site to make Sanderos or Dusters there, getting local engineers involved and submitting their specifications far upstream to local dealers. All of this should considerably change the medium-term sustainability of Renault's development in Brazil.

Along relatively similar lines, Renault is looking to enter China's electric vehicles market, not to add a new brand and a few models to a competitive landscape that is already very hard to read but to help Dongfeng develop an electric car, something that the Chinese government already considers a priority. Similar to its thinking about what might attract Brazilian consumers, Renault's Entry teams have designed a product whose potential has been revealed in other markets, including Western Europe. It may well be that things done in China with Dongfeng will become just as important for developing electric vehicles in Europe.

The trickle-down automotive economy seems to fit the Lisbon strategy and the general belief in a reassuringly global division of labour where

---

1. This is tantamount to removing from existing products anything that is not indispensable, thereby cutting costs so as to be able to offer the car at a lower retail price.

cognitive work, the knowledge society, innovation and "high-tech" remain the attributes of older industrialised countries from the Global North, with production, manufacturing and factories going elsewhere without anyone missing the pollution or troublesome workers. The Logan's history over the past decade or so has demonstrated the ups and downs of a "strategy" that the global automotive industry (particularly in Europe) has interiorised. But by showing that innovation cannot be assimilated with sophistication, it has revealed that innovation, in the broad sense of the term, is a development strategy that can also be sustained in the emerging world. Once the capacity to innovate is conceived of as something global that can be distributed better, it becomes clear that the Global North has as much to learn from the Global South as vice versa. The ability to act as a stakeholder in the innovation phenomena taking place in these new development territories is just as crucial as maintaining strong capabilities in carmakers' historic heartlands.

For those companies that benefited least from sustaining innovations, the attraction of this development trajectory in (and by) the emerging economies should be very strong. Their ability to develop less expensive products on B and C platforms– as demonstrated by the Logan–is a crucial advantage. Before the Logan, the highly enviable destiny that the Iberian markets had reserved for the French brands during households' first equipment phase (in the 1970s-1980s) had already shown that offering products compatible with middle classes' limited but increasing budgets can be determinant. Tata's alliance with Fiat –which was highly successful in Brazil–also seems to fit this analysis. On the other hand, VW had a terrible time with Suzuki while trying to develop the wherewithal for expansion in India. Projecting VW's engineering teams into this context was bound to fail due to their lack of adaptation to local circumstances.

The fact that the Chinese market placed such an extraordinary emphasis on "premiums", or that the Russian market featured similar characteristics for a while, helped to accredit the thesis that trickle-down automotive economics also apply in the emerging world. However, the growing profitability gap between German and other European carmakers quickly created a difference in their investment capacities, and then in the volumes associated with each platform. This has made it difficult to assess the suitability of a trickle-up approach in the emerging world's automotive economy. Yet the history of the automobile in general (and the Logan in particular) indicate that the latter approach is likely to attract local counterparts.

The attraction of this alternative is particularly obvious in Europe due to the fact that the EU's enlargement led in the 2000s to a number of countries from the continent's central and eastern regions becoming new member states and therefore being subjected to European common law, which requires a free circulation of used vehicles throughout the region. The new member states that tried to get around this constraint (or who actually succeeded in doing so) were systematically fined, with the rule remaining uncontested to this day. The end result is that households have clearly increased their ownership levels but without injecting any real dynamism into the new car markets. Germany sold off its surplus used vehicles, enabling national manufacturers to protect their resale values and therefore facilitating these vehicles' sale to German households without having to deal with a demand for new vehicles adapted to Central and Eastern Europe circumstances. The trickle-down automotive economy is fully functioning here and has changed what could and should have been an emerging local market (as the Logan's designers had forecast back in the early 2000s), transforming this into a delocalisation zone. Fiat, PSA and Renault have been trying to reinvigorate their lower ranges, which the trickle-down automotive economy transformed (despite rising volumes) into a part of the mix that has become highly disappointing in profitability terms. Where the virtues of a less top-of-the-range positioning (and strong cost-cutting) would have played in their favour, the trickle-down automotive economy structured a giant workshop instead, with employees at most able to buy imported used cars. Local markets have been incapable of developing any consistence, with the countries in question quickly facing competition from new pretenders from the former Soviet republics or the other side of the Mediterranean. They never had any real chance of developing a fullblown automotive industry. Renault's RTR engineering centre in Romania remains the exception.

History cannot be rewritten but we can at least try to perceive the rational, effective and inevitable nature of the dominant path in which Europe is embedded. The least we can say is that this has been problematic from many different perspectives, especially in terms of the European industry's collective ability to play a key role in the future of the global automotive industry. Without trying to draw simplistic lessons from the Logan's adventure in terms of how this might affect the automotive industry in general–something that would be tantamount to depicting Renault's trajectory as a "one best way"–the argument could be extended beyond what the designers themselves would have said, in order that we might perceive alternatives and identify means (and even tools) to promote them.

* * *

Starting with the history of a car whose destiny seemed highly improbable, we have been able to demonstrate that this singular adventure has revealed significant developmental potentialities making it possible to improve humans' coexistence with automobiles and with one another. It remains that these path have yet to be fully explored. The paradoxical hence unexpected success that this book has explored–a car that sells at bargain basement prices but remains more profitable than any other–undermines the dominant (we would be tempted to say monolithic) thinking that prevails regarding the competitiveness of automotive firms and, more generally, developed countries' industries. Having sophisticated products and advanced technology is not the only way that developed countries can compete with ambitious emerging economies. We have shown that although monolithic thinking might help certain countries because of their industrial traditions and markets, it is in no way inevitable or even a "one best way". The protagonists of the Logan project were all sufficiently intelligent to understand that transgressing dominant conceptions can be useful. This final chapter has shown that the same lesson applies to everyone, including politicians, regulators and users, who are often imprisoned by conceptions portrayed as the sole alternative.

The automobile is much more than a means of transportation. Through its different dimensions and the various challenges it faces, it is a laboratory for new industrial and societal theories. The role of social science researchers is to provoke debate rooted in an observation of facts. This has been the aim of the authors of this book based on our analysis of the adventures of the Logan, which in our opinion constitutes a highly emblematic case study. Our final ambition is that the debates and perspectives that we have launched here will resonate successfully in the same way as this friendly automobile has done.

Appendixes

APPENDIX 1–HIGHLIGHTS OF THE LOGAN'S EPIC ADVENTURE (THROUGH YEAREND 2011)

Autumn 1995: Louis Schweitzer introduces 2015 growth plan to Renault executives

Autumn 1997: Louis Schweitzer visits Lada plant in Russia as part of Jacques Chirac's presidential delegation

1998: Avtoframos company founded in Russia, in partnership with the City of Moscow

March 1999: Creation of X90 (Logan) programme and appointment of Jean-Marie Hurtiger as X90 Project Director

29 September 1999: Renault acquires 51% stake in Dacia

2000: Launch of SuperNova, made in Pitesti

1 March 2001: X90 Logan exploratory project phase starts

5 February 2002: X90 pre-contract

July 2002: Style decided; X90 contract signed

October 2002: X90 ROP

2003: Launch of Solenza, made in Pitesti

2003: Decision to invest €230 million to have Avtoframos make the Logan

28 May 2004: X90 marketing agreement

2 June 2004: Logan global launch at Renault Technocentre

9 September-December 2004: Logan launched in Romania and Eastern Europe

May-July 2005: Logan launched in Algeria and Morocco

June 2005: Logan launched in France, Spain and Germany

September 2005: Logan launched in Colombia

8 September 2005: Logan dCii launched

2005: Renault joint venture with City of Moscow initiates Avtoframos plant operations. JV is 24% owned by City of Moscow and 76% by Renault

2005-2010: Ayrton Senna plant at Curitiba in Brazil is dedicated to the Entry programme. Production volumes triple. Factory becomes programme's second largest site after Pitesti.

July 2005: Logan launched in Russia

October 2006: Dacia Logan MCV estate launched

November 2006: Nissan and Mahindra decide to build Chennai plant in India

2007: Work starts on future Tanger Med plant in Morocco (inaugurated in 2012).

February 2007: Dacia Logan van launched

May 2007: Logan launched in Brazil

2008: Agreement signed with AvtoVAZ to develop vehicles using Logan platform

February 2008: Dacia Logan pick-up launched

June 2008: Commercial launch of Dacia Sandero

July 2008: Dacia Nouvelle Logan launched

October 2008: Dacia Nouvelle Logan MCV estate launched

March 2009: Duster (Dacia's first concept car) introduced in Geneva

July 2009: Dacia Sandero Stepway launched

August 2009: Duster introduced at Moscow trade fair

April 2010: Duster launched in Euromed (Romania, Western Europe, North Africa)

October 2011: Decision to raise Ayrton Senna plant capacity to 380,000 units. New Nissan plant built in Resende

Yearend 2011: Duster marketed in Russia and Brazil

APPENDIX 2–LIST OF INTERVIEWEES

Name	First name	Company	Function
BELLOT	Dominique	Renault	Product Range Technical Director
BONITEAU	Maxime	Renault	Deputy Director for Entry Programme in Russia
BEN LARBI	Larbi	Somaca	President
BOYER	Hervé	Faurecia	South Europe Vice-President for Interior Systems
BREISS	Philippe	Valeo	Renault Customer Director Lighting System
CAMBIER	Bernard	Renault	Director for Sales, France
CAMBOLIVE	Fabrice	Renault	Director for Sales, Romania
CARRE	Vincent	Renault	Entry Programme Marketing Manager
CAYETTE	Philippe	Renault	Programme I Deputy Manager
CAYETTE	Philippe	Renault	Entry Programme Purchasing Project Manager
CIAVALDINI	Bertrand	Renault	India Project
CRAPF	Karsten	Renault	Entry Programme Marketing Director
DETOURBET	Gérard	Dacia	Entry Programme Director
DETEIX	Jean-Noël	Renault	Entry Programme Body Works Project Director
DETRUN	Jean	Renault	Director of Logistics
DOROBANTU	Adriana	Dacia	Dacia Human Resource Department

DUFOUR	Gilles	Renault	Vice President, Purchasing
ESTEVE	Christian	Renault	President of Euromed
EUDELINE	Jacques	Dacia	Director, Mechanical Plant
FINARDI	Patricia	Renault	X90 South America Logistics
GATIGNOL	Antoine	Renault	Entry Programme Purchasing Project Manager
GIURGESCU	Alexandru	Renault	ILN Logistics Hub
HURTIGER	Jean-Marie	Renault	X90 Project Director
KERGUIGNAS	Michel	Renault	Labour Board
LE VOT	Denis	Renault	Director for Sales, Russia
MENARD	Luc-Alexandre	Renault	Director for International Operations
MORILLO	Jacques	Dacia	Director, Bodyworks Plant
MOVILEANU	Nicolae	Delta Invest	Founder, General Manager
NEFFA	Patricio	Renault	Director, Russia Project
OLIVE	Jérôme	Dacia	Director Dacia-Renault Romania
OLTEANU	Martin	Dacia	Dacia Human Resource Management
OPRESCU	Alexandru	JCI	Operations Manager
OREVICEANU	Anca	Renault RTR	Communications Manager, RTR
PAVELESCU	Nicolae	Dacia	President, Dacia Automobile Trade Union

PIOTIN	Jean-Frédéric	Renault	Director for Sales, Romania
POUILLAUDE	Christian	Renault	Sales Manager, Brazil
PTACEK	Jan	Renault	Director for Marketing, Russia
SICOE	Gabriel	Dacia	Public Affairs Director, ex-Human Resoures Director
STEFAN	Nicolae	Faurecia EAPS	Quality Manager
STEFANOIU	Viorica	Faurecia EAPS	Sales Manager
STROE	Constantin	Dacia	Vice-Chair, Dacia Board of Directors
SCHWEITZER	Louis	Renault	Chief Executive Officer

LIST OF FIGURES

LIST OF TABLES

REFERENCES

ABERNATHY W.J., *The Productivity Dilemma. Roadblock to Innovation in the Automobile Industry*, The John Hopkins Press, 1978.

ABERNATHY W.J., *Kantrow A.M., Clark K.B.*, Industrial Renaissance: producing a competitive future for America, New York, Basic Books, 1983.

ABERNATHY W.J., *Utterback J.M.*, "A dynamic model of process and product innovation", *Omega*, 1975, pp. 639-56.

AGLIETTA M., *Crises et régulation du capitalisme. L'expérience des Etats-Unis*, Paris, Calmann-Lévy, 1976.

AKRICH M., *Callon M., Latour*, B., "A quoi tient le succès des innovations ?", *Gérer et comprendre*, Vol. 97, June and September 1988, pp. 4-17, 14-29.

AMAR G., *Homo mobilis, le nouvel âge de la mobilité. Eloge de la reliance*, Limoges, FYP éditions, 2010.

BARDOU J.B., *Chanaron J.J., Fridenson P., Laux J.M., La Révolution automobile*, Albin Michel, Paris, 1977.

BAUDINO L., *Chahbi M., Les problématiques et les enjeux du développement à l'international : Le projet Logan*, Mémoire de Master Projet Innovation Conception (*Masters in Project Innovation Design Dissertation*), Supervisor C. Midler, Ecole Polytechnique, 2006.

BENGHOZI P.J., *Charue F., Midler C., Innovation Based Competition and Design Systems Dynamics*, Paris, L'Harmattan, 2000.

BEN MAHMOUD-JOUINI S., *Charue-Duboc F., Fourcade F.*, "Favoriser l'innovation radicale dans une entreprise multidivisionnelle : Extension du modèle ambidextre à partir de l'analyse d'un cas", *Finance Contrôle Stratégie*, Vol. 10, No. 3, 2007, pp. 5-41.

BERRY M., *Une Technologie Invisible – L'impact des instruments de gestion sur l'évolution des systèmes humains*, Paris, CRG, juin 1983.

BOYER R., *Freyssenet M., Les Modèles productifs*, Paris, La Découverte, 2000.

BURGELMAN R.A., *Strategy is Destiny: How Strategy-Making Shapes a Company's Future*, The Free Press, 2002.

CHANDLER A. D. Jr., *Strategy & Structure: Chapters in the History of the Industrial Enterprise*, Cambridge, MIT Press, 1962.

CHAPEL V., *La Croissance par l'innovation intensive, de la dynamique d'apprentissage à la révélation d'un modèle industriel, le cas Tefal*, Thèse de doctorat de l'Ecole des Mines de Paris, spécialité Ingénierie et Gestion (*PhD thesis, Ecole des Mines de Paris, specialisation Engineering and Management*), 1997.

CHARUE-DUBOC F., *Midler C.*, "Lorsque les enjeux environnementaux donnent lieu à des innovations stratégiques : comment piloter ces trajectories exploratoires ? Le cas de la stratégie véhicule électrique de Renault", *Revue Française de Gestion*, juillet 2011.

CHRISTENSEN C. M., *The Innovator's Dilemma: when new technologies cause great firms to fail*, Boston, Massachusetts, Harvard Business School Press, 1997.

CHRISTENSEN C. M., *The Innovator's Solution: creating and sustaining successful growth*, Boston, Massachusetts, Harvard Business School Press, 2003.

CHRISTENSEN C. M., *Craig, T.*, Hart S., "The Great Disruption", *Foreign Affairs*, March-April 2001, p. 92.

CLARK K.B., *Fujimoto T., Product Development Performance: Strategy, Organization and Management in the World Auto Industry*, Boston, Harvard Business School Press, 1991.

CHRISTENSEN C.M., *Bower J.K.*, "Disruptive Technologies: Catching the Wave", *Harvard Business Review*, 1995.

DOSI G., "*Technological paradigms and* technological trajectories, A suggested interpretation of the determinants and directions of technical change", *Research Policy*, Vol. 11, No. 3, Edward Elgar, 1982, pp. 147-162.

DUBREIL Y., *Renault vu par Yves Dubreil*, Renault Histoire, Boulogne Billancourt, 2009.

FREYSSENET M. *(dir.)*, *The Second Automobile Revolution. Trajectories of the World Carmakers in the 21ˢᵗ Century*, Palgrave/Macmillan, Basingstoke/New York, 2009.

FROUD J., *Haslam C., Johal S.*, Jullien B., Williams K., "Les dépenses de motorisation comme facteur d'accentuation des inégalités et comme frein au développement des entreprises automobiles : une comparaison franco-anglaise", in G. Dupuy and F. Bost, *L'Automobile et son monde*, Paris, Editions de l'Aube, 2000, pp. 75-96.

FLIGSTEIN, N., *The Architecture of Markets: An Economic Sociology of Twenty First Century Capitalist Societies*, Princeton/Oxford, Princeton University Press, 2001.

HATCHUEL A., *Le Masson P.*, "Innovation répétée et croissance de la firme : microéconomie et gestion des fonctions de conception", *Cahier du CGS*, No. 18, 2001.

JETIN B., *Freyssenet M.*, *"Conséquence* de la crise financière ou crise d'une forme de capitalisme : la faillite des Big Three", *Revue de la Régulation*, No. 9, 2011.

JOLIVET F., *Navarre C.*, *"Grands* projets, auto-organisation, méta-règles : vers de nouvelles formes de management des grands projets", 1992, Paris, ronéoté.

JULLIEN B., *"Relativiser le statut* de la rupture dans la théorie évolutionniste", in Baslé M., Delorme R., Lemoigne J.L., Paulré B., *Approches évolutionnistes de la firme et de l'industrie*, Paris, L'Harmattan, 1999, pp. 207-228.

JULLIEN B., *"La seconde révolution* automobile et ses contours", *Sociétal*, No. 70, 2010, pp. 54-61.

JULLIEN B., *Pardi T.*, *"In* the name of consumer: the social construction of innovation in the European automobile industry and its political consequences", *European Review of Industrial Economics and Policy*, No. 3, 2011.

JULLIEN B., *Lung Y.*, *L'Automobile à la croisée des chemins*, Paris, La Documentation Française, 2011.

LANCASTER K., *"Socially Optimal Product* Differentiation", *The American Economic Review*, Vol. 65, No. 4, 1975, pp. 567-585.

LAYAN J.B., *"L'innovation péricentrale dans* l'industrie automobile : une gestion territoriale du risque de résistance au changement", *Flux*, No. 63-64, 2006, pp. 49-53.

LE MASSON P., *Weil B.*, Hatchuel A., *Strategic management of Design and Innovation*, Cambridge University Press.

LIPIETZ A., *La Société en sablier*, Paris, La Découverte, 1995.

LOUBET J.L., *Citroën, Peugeot, Renault et les autres. Soixante ans de stratégies*, Paris, Le Monde-Éditions, 1995.

LOUBET J.L., *"Logan : sur les* pas de la 2cv", *Gérer et Comprendre*, No. 85, 2006.

LUNG, Y., *"Repenser la dimension* géographique des trajectories d'innovation", in Christophe Bouneau and Yannick Lung (dir.), *Les trajectories de l'innovation : espaces et dynamiques de la complexité (XIXᵉ-XXIᵉ siècle)*, Peter Lang, Bern, Berlin, Bruxelles, Frankfurt am Main, New York, Oxford, Wien, 2012.

MARCH J.G., *"Exploration and exploitation* in organizational learning", *Organization Science*, Vol. 2, No. 1, 1991, pp. 71-96.

MAXTON G., *Wormald J.*, *Time for a Model Change: Re-engineering the Global Automotive Industry*, Cambridge, Cambridge University Press, 2004.

MIDLER C., *L'Auto qui n'existait pas : Management des projets et transformation de l'entreprise*, InterEditions, Paris, 1993.

MIDLER C., *"La révolution de* la Twingo", in *Séminaire Vie des Affaires de l'Ecole de Paris*, 1992.

MIDLER C., *"L'acteur projet, portrait* d'un rôle d'influence", *Revue Gestion 2000*, No. 2/93, Louvain-la-Neuve (Belgium).

MIDLER C. *"Projectification of the* Firm: the Renault case", *Scandinavian Management Journal*, Vol. 11, No. 4, pp. 363-375, 1995.

MIDLER C., Beaume R., *"Project-based* Learning Patterns for Dominant Design Renewal: The Case of Electric Vehicle", *International Journal of Project Management*, No. 28, 2010, pp. 142–150

MIDLER C., Maniak R., Beaume R., *Réenchanter l'industrie par l'innovation : stratégie et management de l'innovation dans l'industrie automobile*, Paris, Dunod, 2012.

MOORE G.A., *Crossing the Chasm*, New York, Harper Business, 1991.

NORMAND J.M., *"Les Allemands aiment* leurs berlines", *Le Monde*, 3 March 2012.

PÉLATA P., *"L'avenir de l'auto* se construit dans la crise", *Sociétal*, No. 70, 2010, p. 39-47.

PRAHALAD C.K., *"Strategies for the* Bottom of the Economic Pyramid: India as a Source of Innovation", *Reflections*, Vol. 3, No. 4, 2002, pp. 6-14.

SEGRESTIN B., *"Towards new governance* structure for merging organizations? Lessons derived from the Renault-Nissan Alliance", *International Journal of Automotive Technology and Management*, Vol. 6, No. 2, 2006.

VERDEVOYE A.-G., *"Citroën veut ressusciter* la 2CV", *La Tribune*, 8 March 2011.

58996 – (I) – (0.4) – OSB 90° – ARC - CDD

Dépôt légal : février 2013
Achevé d'imprimer par Dupli-Print
N° d'impression : 221135
www.dupli-print.fr

Imprimé en France